Radio Amateurs' Examination Manual

incorporating *How to Pass the RAE*

SIXTEENTH EDITION

John Case, GW4HWR

and

Hilary Claytonsmith, G4JKS

Radio Society of Great Britain

Published by the Radio Society of Great Britain, Cranborne Road, Potters Bar, Herts EN6 3JE.

Sixteenth edition 1998

ISBN 1 872309 45 3

Publisher's note

The opinions expressed in this book are those of the authors and contributors, and not necessarily those of the RSGB. While the information presented is believed to be correct, the authors, contributors, publisher and their agents cannot accept responsibility for consequences arising from any inaccuracies or omissions.

Cover design: Jennifer Crocker.

Illustrations: Derek Cole and Bob Ryan (Radio Society of Great Britain), and Ray Eckersley.

Design and typography: Ray Eckersley, Seven Stars Publishing.

Production: Mike Dennison.

Printed in Great Britain by The Nuffield Press, Abingdon.

Contents

Preface

THE changes to the Radio Amateurs' Examination, outlined in the Introduction, have necessitated a new edition of this book, and the opportunity has been taken to make several major improvements.

- The chapters have been re-ordered to follow the syllabus more closely.
- Material which is helpful in understanding the syllabus material but which is not strictly part of it is marked as such.
- Sample questions (including many based on those in the book *How to Pass the RAE*) are presented at the end of each chapter.
- The guide to the licensing conditions originally published in the booklet *A Closer Look at the Amateur Radio Licence* has been included.
- A complete sample paper provided by City & Guilds is included to familiarise the candidate with the real examination format.

In preparing this edition, we have built on the solid foundation of the previous editions written by George Benbow, G3HB. To us, he will always remain "Mr RAE".

Thanks are also due to all others who have contributed to the manual, for this 16th edition and previous ones, especially:

> Bob Heath, G3UJV
> Richard Horton, G3XWH
> Dave Lauder, G0SNO
> Robin Page-Jones, G3JWI
> Clive Smith, G4FZH

Input from readers is also much appreciated. Some of the ideas provided by Jeff Black, G0UKA, generated for the benefit of his daughter, have been incorporated.

Thanks to my nephew, Allen, who meticulously checked the index.

Acknowledgements are also due to the Radiocommunications Agency and the City and Guilds of London Institute for permission to use material from their publications, in particular the complete sample paper reproduced in Appendix 2.

John Case, GW4HWR
Hilary Claytonsmith, G4JKS

Introduction

HOW TO USE THIS MANUAL

This book can be used in one of two ways: by instructors in a classroom situation or by individuals who wish to teach themselves at home. It is not complete in itself and reference to other material is essential. The Radiocommunications Agency (RA) booklet BR68 – *Amateur Radio Licence (A) or (B) Terms, Provisions and Limitations* is part of the licence and must be studied carefully. It is a legal document and as such may be a little difficult to understand. The Radio Society of Great Britain (RSGB) has produced a booklet entitled *A Closer Look at the Amateur Radio Licence* which puts some of the information in simpler terms – it is included in Chapter 1 of this book. The RA also produces another publication – *How to Become a Radio Amateur* (RA190). One other document is crucial – the syllabus of the Radio Amateurs' Examination, a scheme pamphlet, which must be obtained from the City and Guilds. The addresses from which these publications can be obtained appear at the end of this introduction.

Some text covers topics not directly required by the syllabus but it is often helpful in understanding the syllabus material.

▶In order to make it easier to recognise, this subsidiary text is presented in the same manner as this paragraph.◀

The chapters have been arranged in the same order as they appear in the syllabus and have the same headings.

At the end of each chapter there are a number of revision questions to enable students to test themselves on the content of the preceding pages. The questions have the same format as those in the examination but are not necessarily of the same degree of difficulty. A specimen paper prepared by the C&G, and reproduced with their permission, appears in Appendix 2 and will give a better idea of the examination standard. The questions will enable candidates to make an assessment of their progress but they should not be lulled into a sense of complacency just because all are answered correctly.

Remember that a Radio Amateur Licence is a privilege. The degree of difficulty in obtaining a licence is such that anyone who is prepared to study long and hard can pass the examination.

LICENSING REQUIREMENTS

Before an amateur radio station can be established and used, it is necessary to obtain a licence from the Radiocommunications Agency (RA) of the Department of Trade and Industry which is the UK licensing authority. Full details are given in the Radiocommunications Agency publication *How to Become a Radio Amateur* (RA190). This is available free of charge from: Document Distribution Centre, Radio Communications Agency (address at end of this introduction).

Types of amateur licence

Entry into amateur radio can be made at two levels – there are two Novice Licences, Classes A and B, and two full licences, also Classes A and B. The two groups require different entry examinations. The Novice Licence is an incentive licence allowing operation on limited bands and power. The Class A licence permits operation on both HF and VHF/UHF while the Class B licence holder is restricted to frequencies above 30MHz (VHF and UHF).

A full Class A Licence allows the holder to transmit on any amateur band including the HF bands (below 30MHz) where worldwide communication is possible. In order to obtain a Class A licence, it is necessary to pass the Radio Amateurs' Examination (RAE) and the Radio Society of Great Britain (RSGB) 12 words per minute Morse test (at the time of going to press). A Class B licence only allows the holder to transmit on amateur bands above 30MHz and does not require a Morse test.

Requirements of the Amateur Licence

Citizens of any overseas country who are resident in the UK may take the RAE and obtain a UK licence.

Amateur Licence A
1. Applicants must be over 14 years of age (see also RA190 for special circumstances). A full licence can be obtained by anyone between the ages of 10–14 years if an RAE pass has been obtained and a Novice Licence held for one year.
2. Applicants must have passed the RAE.
3. Applicants must have passed the Morse Test.
4. The appropriate fee must be paid before the licence is issued and each year on the anniversary of the date of issue. No fee is payable by applicants under the age of 21.

Amateur Licence B
1. Applicants must be over 14 years of age (see RA190 for special circumstances).
2. Applicants must have passed the RAE.
3. The appropriate fee must be paid before the licence is issued and each year subsequently on the anniversary of the date of issue. No fee is payable by applicants under the age of 21.

The Radio Amateurs' Examination

The RAE is administered by the City and Guilds (C&G) on behalf of the licensing authority. The examinations are held in May and December at local colleges and examination centres throughout the country. A list of RAE centres is available for a nominal charge from the C&G.

Changes to the RAE took effect as from May 1998 and are as follows.

1. There is one examination divided into Parts A and B; a pass in Part A is obligatory.
2. The examination comprises 80 multiple choice questions.
3. The examination is of 2 hours 15 minutes duration.
4. The cost was reduced by about one third.
5. There is a speedier release of results to centres.

Applications to sit the examination should be made to centres well in advance (at least two months). A check should be made on the exact examination dates and the closing date for applications to the centre. Candidates should obtain a copy of the *Regulations, Objectives and Syllabus for the 7650-001 Radio Amateur Examination* which is available for a small charge from the C&G.

Format of the examination

The examination consists of one paper containing 80 multiple choice questions which are to be answered in 2 hours 15 minutes. It is divided into Sections A and B as shown below. Candidates must pass Section A in order to pass the examination as a whole. The questions are contained in a booklet with separate answer sheets, one for Section A and one for Section B. *Care should be taken not to put all 80 answers on the same answer sheet.*

Assessment pattern

Questions are allocated to the syllabus sections as indicated below.

Syllabus	Number of questions
Section A	
1. Licensing conditions	18
2. Operating procedures and practices	7
Section B	
3. Electronic principles and practice	6
4. Receivers, transmitters and transceivers	8
5. Transmitter interference	14
6. Electromagnetic compatibility	14
7. Propagation and antennas	7
8. Measurements	6
	80

RAE courses

Details of colleges and organisations which offer courses leading to the RAE are given in *Radio Communication*, the journal of the RSGB, and other radio magazines, usually in July, August and September each year. Such information may also be available from local amateur radio clubs, some of which may run their own RAE courses.

Tuition fees for RAE courses are set by the college or organisation which runs the course. Neither the C&G nor the RSGB have any control over tuition fees. Centres which offer the examination normally charge a 'local fee' in addition to the C&G entry fee.

The Amateur Radio Morse Test (12 WPM)

This is in two parts, receiving and sending, and is conducted by the RSGB on behalf of the licensing authority.

The test is in the format of a typical contact between two amateurs. Candidates therefore have to be familiar with some of the abbreviations, Q-codes and other Morse characters which are used, and must be able to send and receive mixed letters and figures. UK amateurs will be able to communicate by radio telegraphy before they receive their licence and should be confident in the use of this new language in which they can communicate worldwide.

The receiving test is a message of 120 letters and 75 figures sent on a manual key in approximately three minutes.

The sending test is a message of 75 letters and five figures to be sent on a manual key in approximately one minute and 30 seconds.

Full details of the test, an application form and a list of test centres may be obtained from the RSGB's Amateur Radio Department.

Those learning Morse will find much useful information and advice in *The Morse Code for Radio Amateurs*. This is also published by the RSGB.

The RAE and the Morse Test can be taken in any order, and passes in them are regarded as valid for life. They may be taken by nationals of other countries who have a permanent address in the UK and who are thus able to acquire a UK licence.

The Amateur Radio Certificate (ARC)

The Amateur Radio Certificate is no longer issued but this does not affect the validity of those certificates which previously have been issued.

The holder of an ARC should quote the number of the certificate when applying for the Amateur Licence (A).

A previously held licence may be re-issued to the legitimate holder (even when the original qualifications were not based upon the current C&G RAE syllabus). Details of the procedure for the issue of lapsed licences can be obtained from the Aeronautical, Maritime, Amateur and CB Radio Services (AMACB) Department of the Radiocommunications Agency.

Reciprocal licences

There are agreements between the UK and certain foreign countries whereby citizens of those countries who hold a transmitting licence issued by their own government may obtain a UK licence and vice versa.

Details of such licences are outside the scope of this book and applicants intending to apply for reciprocal licences should seek guidance from the Radio Society of Great Britain.

Temporary permission

The UK licence now permits holders to operate as temporary visitors in countries which have implemented the CEPT recommendation T/R 61-01.

PREPARING FOR THE RAE AND BEYOND
Acquiring the knowledge

There are many ways to study for the Radio Amateurs Examination (RAE).

1. *Evening classes.* Most people tend to go to local colleges and take part-time evening courses which vary in duration. Usually the courses begin in September, preparing candidates for the May examination, although some run express courses for the December examination. Colleges

may have different rules and regulations depending on the local authority. There may be a minimum number requirement before courses can be provided. There may also be an age restriction, with colleges not accepting students below the age of 16. The courses are usually conducted by radio amateurs and may include practical demonstrations, although this is not mandatory. The Amateur Radio Department of the Radio Society of Great Britain (RSGB) can provide a list of courses known to be available on receipt of an SAE. Many of the colleges, schools and radio clubs which are registered as C&G RAE Centres offer courses leading to the examination, so it may also be beneficial to obtain a list of these centres from the C&G.

2. *Radio clubs.* Many radio clubs offer RAE tuition as a service to their membership. This obviously varies from club to club. Locating and becoming involved in your local radio club can have many benefits for the beginner. Club members often prove useful in reinforcing theoretical concepts. They will also know where the local examination centres are and be able to give practical advice on enrolment etc. Details of your nearest radio club can be found in the local library or Citizens' Advice Bureau. A list of radio clubs throughout the UK can be found in the *RSGB Yearbook.*

3. *Self-tuition.* A large number of people, especially those with an electronic or scientific background, study at home or with a friend. As long as this manual is followed and its contents absorbed, and BR68 is 'digested' well, there should be no problem in feeling confident about entering the examination. The reinforcement questions at the end of each chapter and the specimen examination paper included in this book should give an indication as to whether you are ready to sit the examination or not. It is advisable to go out and meet other radio amateurs if you are studying in isolation, so that advice can be obtained if a problem has arisen which needs clarification. It is also beneficial to do as much background reading as is practical. The RSGB produces a wide variety of books and leaflets. A book list can be supplied on receipt of an SAE.

4. *Correspondence courses.* A number of such courses exist, but this does on the whole tend to be a more expensive way of acquiring the required knowledge. Before embarking on a correspondence course, it is worthwhile checking that the course does in fact cover the full syllabus and that it is suitable for your needs. The Amateur Radio Department of RSGB can provide details of such independent courses.

Finding an examination centre

It is advisable to identify the examination centre nearest you that will be able to offer the RAE as soon as possible. Some centres may not take external candidates. The City and Guilds of London Institute is the examination body responsible for the RAE and therefore all enquiries about availability of centres should be made directly to them. They produce a list of examination centres which includes colleges, some radio clubs and schools. Schools which offer the NRAE (Novice Examination) can also provide facilities to sit the RAE. A list of RAE centres can also be found in the *RSGB Yearbook*, obtainable from RSGB Headquarters. The City and Guilds has

CITY AND GUILDS RADIO AMATEURS' EXAMINATION EXAMINING CANDIDATES WITH SPECIAL NEEDS

City and Guilds has for many years made arrangements for candidates with a wide range of special needs who would have difficulties in taking the RAE under normal conditions. Essentially those who are house bound, blind or handicapped in some other way, may be examined at home. Moreover, if the candidate is unable to complete a written paper, it is possible for an examination to be conducted orally. (This provision makes radio amateurs unique – it is the only one of C&G schemes which can be examined in this way.)

Candidates who wish to take advantage of these special arrangements will be required to provide some official notification which confirms the reason they have given for requesting home examination. Examples of acceptable documentation include a doctor's certificate or a DHSS letter. In all cases however, the final decision concerning acceptance (or otherwise) rests with the C&G.

Application forms are available from Assessment Services, The City and Guilds of London Institute. Please note that completed application forms must be received at C&G by 25 October (for the exam in December) or 14 March (for the May examination).

Candidates must also be prepared to make themselves available for examination in the 10 days following the date of the regular examination. *(City and Guilds of London Institute)*

no control over how these centres operate. They vary from local authority to local authority.

The RAE can be taken abroad or through the forces. In these cases, you should contact the examinations department of the C&G for guidance. Allow extra time for registration in these cases. Individual arrangements can also be made for those with special needs (see panel above).

Registering for the RAE

Having taken the time to study and prepare for the RAE, make sure you do not miss the final date for registration! For May, this would mean registering by mid-March, and for the December examination, you would need to register by the end of October. The correct documentation required by the colleges will have to be filled in and the appropriate fee paid.

The day of the examination

Check that you have the following with you before you leave for the examination:

- Two HB pencils (not H or B).
- A battery- or solar-powered calculator.
- Ruler.
- Eraser.
- Reading glasses, if you need them!

You will also have been asked to bring along some form of identification, including a photograph. It is also best to take all paperwork previously received from the college, which will contain your candidate number. You will not be allowed to take any scrap paper, books or other material into the examination room with you.

Try to get to the examination centre 10 minutes before the examination starts, so that you are not rushed and have got yourself into the right frame of mind.

The multiple-choice examination

The RAE changed from essay style questions to two papers consisting of multiple choice questions in 1979. In May 1998 the examination was streamlined into one paper to bring it in line with most other countries (see earlier).

The exam questions book, usually comprising 15 pages, has specific instructions (the rubric) on the front cover which must be read carefully. This is especially true if you have not taken a multiple-choice style examination before (see sample paper in Appendix 2). The TWO answer sheets must be filled in correctly. One will have provision for answers to Section A (answer boxes numbered 1 to 25) and the other for Section B (answer boxes numbered 26 to 80). There is adequate warning about this in the examination question book. The schedule is incorporated into the question book and can be referred to in order to answer any of the questions. Any rough work you may need to do should be done on the question book and not on the answer sheets. The question book cannot be taken out of the examination room. On completion of the examination all question books have to be returned to the City and Guilds by the invigilator.

Before starting to answer any questions, read the whole examination paper through from beginning to end slowly – you have plenty of time to complete the examination.

Read through again, this time answering all questions you can do without too much thought. Make sure that your answers are put in the correct space on the answer sheet (use your ruler to help). A second reading will highlight those questions you can answer with a little thought. This will build up your confidence and help in the relaxation process, in preparation for the remaining few which will require virtually all your remaining time. Make sure you leave 10 minutes at the end to check your work thoroughly. Do not leave any gaps. If you cannot answer a question, make an educated guess; there are no penalties for wrong answers!

Results

The worst part of taking examinations is waiting for the results. From May 1998 there is a single grade of success (pass). If you take the examination in May you can expect that the results will be with the examination centres towards the end of June. The results for the December examination should be available at the end of January. The results will be sent to the examination centres for forwarding to you. The centre will make arrangements for you to collect your results or they will post them on to you. Candidates will receive a certificate on passing the examination. These will be issued though the examination centre.

What next?

The licence

If you are successful in your examination you may want to apply for your Class B licence. You will need to complete the appropriate forms from Subscription Services Limited (SSL) and to enclose your C&G RAE Pass Certificate as well as the appropriate licence fee. If you want to operate on the HF bands as well, you will need to take a 12 WPM Morse test (at the time of publication) conducted by the RSGB to obtain your Class A licence. Your Morse test pass slip will then need to be added to the items previously mentioned to be sent to SSL for the Class A licence.

The equipment

Amateur radio is a diverse hobby and covers many aspects of operating, from packet radio to moonbounce, from HF contesting to working through satellites and many other things in between. Do not expect to do everything at once. Once you have decided on your area of interest you may want to go to exhibitions or rallies or specialist meetings to look at and try out the various types of equipment and antennas available. Equipment varies in price from cheap simple kits to the expensive Japanese 'black box'. Antenna systems range from the effective simple dipole to the complicated stacked, phased arrays on a crank-up mast.

It is advisable to visit amateur radio shops, read reviews or visit other amateurs before deciding on your final piece of equipment. Some manufacturers have user groups which are a useful source of information.

The RSGB has published a book for newly licensed amateurs, entitled *Your First Amateur Station,* which gives helpful advice on choosing equipment and setting up a station.

The Radio Society of Great Britain

Every reader of this manual is advised to become, if not already so, a member of the Radio Society of Great Britain (RSGB).

The RSGB is the national society for radio amateurs in the UK. The majority of its members hold amateur transmitting licences: the others either hope to do so later or are interested primarily in the receiving side of amateur radio.

The Society acts as the spokesman for radio amateurs and amateur radio in the UK, and is one of the founder members of the International Amateur Radio Union, the worldwide association of the various national societies.

The Society was founded as the London Wireless Club in 1913 but soon attracted members throughout the country. The name 'Radio Society of Great Britain' was formally adopted in 1922. For many years its activities have been devoted almost entirely to the many aspects of amateur radio, that is, the transmission and reception of radio signals as a hobby pursued for the pleasure to be derived from an interest in radio techniques and construction and for the ensuing friendships with like-minded persons throughout the world.

The Society is recognised as the representative of the amateur radio movement in all negotiations with the Radiocommunications Agency (RA) of the Department of Trade and Industry on matters affecting the issue of amateur transmitting licences.

The Society maintains close liaison with the RA on all matters affecting licence facilities and the frequencies assigned to amateur radio, and sends official representatives to the important World Radio Conferences of the International Telecommunication Union and other conferences where decisions vital to the future of amateur radio are taken.

The Society helps amateur radio in many ways. Of particular importance is the provision of information on technical matters and on the various activities and events of concern to amateurs. Since 1925 it has published a monthly journal, *Radio Communication,* the oldest and largest magazine in this country devoted to amateur radio. All members receive this magazine by post, without payment other than their annual membership subscriptions.

The Society exists for the benefit of its members and,

USEFUL ADDRESSES

The City and Guilds of London Insitute
1 Giltspur Street,
London,
EC1A 9DD.

Telephone 0171 294 2468
Facsimile 0171 294 2400

Radiocommunications Agency *(temporary address)*
Aeronautical, Maritime, Amateur and CB Radio
   Services (AMACB),
New Kings' Beam House,
22 Upper Ground,
London,
SE1 9SA.

Telephone 0171 211 0211

The Radio Licensing Centre
SSL,
PO Box 885,
Bristol,
BS99 5LG.

Telephone 0117 925 8333

The Radio Society of Great Britain,
Lambda House,
Cranborne Road,
Potters Bar,
Herts,
EN6 3JE.

Telephone 01707 659015
Facsimile 01707 645105

through its elected officers and over 2000 volunteers, provides a mine of information and assistance to them. The larger the membership, the stronger is the Society's position when negotiating to protect the amateur radio bands from commercial pressures.

Membership of the RSGB is open to any person interested in amateur radio – there is no need to hold an amateur radio licence in order to join. Members receive *Radio Communication* (the Society's 100-page colour magazine) post free each month, free QSL sorting and delivery and a discount off Society publications and products. Further information about membership can be obtained by contacting the Society at the telephone number shown above, or from our pages on the Internet (www.rsgb.org).

1 Licensing conditions

AN Amateur Radio Licence is issued under the authority of the Secretary of State for Trade and Industry for the purpose of self-training in the science of radio communication and to allow technical investigation of that science. Any other activities in which radio amateurs may be involved, such as contesting, radio direction finding and DXing are just a means to the above end.

As has already been mentioned in the Introduction, there are two types of full licence, Class A and Class B, and in order to obtain either of these licences the necessary qualifications must be obtained. These include a pass in the RAE, the attainment of the minimum age (14 years, except where a Novice Licence has been held for one year and the candidate is over 10 years) and for those over 21 years the provision of the necessary fee. In addition, those requiring a Class A licence must have passed a 12 word per minute Morse test.

The terms, provisions and limitations have been set out in the booklet BR68 which can be obtained, together with *How to Become a Radio Amateur* (RA190), from the Radiocommunications Agency (address at the end of the Introduction). Questions will be asked in the RAE on the contents of BR68 (including the notes) so that it is essential that all candidates for the examination should have their own personal copies of these booklets.

BR68 contains the Schedule which sets out the bands and frequencies which may be used by radio amateurs, together with information relating to the type of transmission (mode), the maximum power permitted and the status of the bands (are they shared with other users?). A copy of the Schedule will be on the examination paper so that the entire content does not have to be remembered but a good knowledge of the location of certain material within the Schedule is essential.

The following text is taken directly from the RSGB information booklet *A Closer Look at the Amateur Radio Licence* and as such has no legal force. You will notice that there are references in the left-hand margin which refer to the legal document BR68. This chapter should therefore be read in conjunction with BR68.

AMATEUR RADIO LICENCE
Purpose of the Licence

1(1)   1. The licence is issued under the authority of the Secretary of State for Trade and Industry to allow you to train yourself in the art of radio communication, and to conduct technical investigations. This is – and always has been – its primary purpose; such popular activities as DXing, collecting QSL cards, contesting, and participating in 'field days', are of value as means to these ends. However, amateurs have always been ready to put their skills and experience at the service of the community; this additional function is officially recognised by provisions in the licence to use certain frequency bands for passing messages to assist the emergency services listed in paragraph 12(1)(o) of the licence.

1(2)
1(3)
2(8)
12(1)(o)

Operation

1(4)   2. You may transmit only to other licensed amateurs, and then only on technical and personal matters. If, in the course of a contact, you become aware that the other party is unlicensed you must break off communication.

1(7)   3. Normally you may communicate only with one other amateur at a time. Exceptions are:

1(7)(a)   (a) when making an initial (CQ) call,

1(7)(b)   (b) when sending to a group of amateurs after
1(7)(c)   you have first made individual contact with at least one of them (this is known as *net working*),

1(7)(d)   (c) when sending messages by RTTY or data transmission via a 'mailbox' or 'bulletin board' for reception by any licensed amateurs who have facilities for sending and receiving by this means.

1(9)   4. You may not use your station for playing music, making speeches or broadcasting to the public.

3(3)   5. You may not use it for conducting business, advertising or propaganda except on behalf of a non-profit-making organisation connected with amateur radio.

Note (d)   6. Sending messages containing obscene or grossly offensive matter in any form is a criminal offence. So is the sending of false or misleading messages which might adversely affect the work of the emergency and rescue services.

Note (i)

2(2)(b)   7. This licence allows you to receive signals from
2(3)   other amateurs, including those operating on frequencies not covered by paragraph 11 below; however, you will not normally be able to return their calls on those frequencies (but see paragraph 13 below).

1(13)   8. You may also use your equipment to receive signals from transmitters in the Standard

Frequency Service, which provide transmissions of high precision for testing purposes.

Note (h)
Note (c)
9. You are not licensed to listen to other transmissions (except, of course, those of public broadcasting stations) and if you do accidentally pick up a message not covered by these rules you must not disclose it to anyone except an authorised government official or a competent legal tribunal; nor may you copy it or let anyone else copy it.

Note (q)
10. This licence is personal to you and may not be transferred to anyone else. Your equipment must only be used by:

2(8)(a)
(a) you personally,

(b) in your presence and under your supervision by:

2(8)(b)(i)
1. another amateur who has a current UK licence,

2(8)(b)(iii)
2. a licensed amateur from another country,

2(8)(b)(ii)

2(9)
3. a person who has a Radio Amateur Examination Certificate of the City of Guilds of London Institute or an Amateur Radio Certificate issued by the DTI, and is not to your knowledge "disqualified",

2(8)(b)(iv)
4. a representative of one of the User Services (a full list of these is in paragraph 12(1)(o) of the Licence).

Note (p)
Whoever is operating, *you* remain responsible for compliance with the law.

Frequencies and modes of transmission

2(1)(a)
2(2)
11. You may transmit only on frequencies in the bands listed in the Schedule, and – if this is a Class B licence – not on frequencies below 30MHz.

2(1)(b)
12. You must not transmit with more power than is listed in the Schedule for each band. (See note (e) to the Schedule for details).

Note (f)
13. However, if you are operating under the supervision of another amateur who has a Class A licence you may transmit on any frequency band, by any mode, and with any power that he is allowed to use, provided that he gives you his permission to do so (and see paragraph 26 below).

1(5)
14. You may use Morse code (CW), telephony (AM, FM or SSB), radio teletype (RTTY), data transmissions (including AMTOR), facsimile, slow scan television (SSTV), and, on some bands, fast scan television (FSTV); check the Schedule to see which you may use on any particular band.

2(7)
15. You may use Pulse transmission only on frequency bands above 1000MHz – and then only with a peak power not exceeding 400 watts.

4(2)

4(5)
16. You should not send on a frequency that someone else is using – listen before sending! (This is particularly important on those frequency bands where other – non-amateur – services have priority and amateurs have only secondary status.) You must not transmit on a frequency – or by a mode of transmission – that you cannot also receive.

Codes and abbreviations

1(6)
1(4)(b)
17. You may use recognised abbreviations and codes (such as the Q-code) but not secret codes.

Interference

4(2)
Note (n)
18. You must not transmit in a way that causes undue interference to other radio users. In particular you must make sure that:

4(1)(a)

Note (o)
(a) your transmitted frequency is as stable as possible (this also makes it easier for your contacts to receive), and that the bandwidth occupied by your transmission is no more than is necessary for the mode you are using,

2(1)(a)
(b) your transmitted frequency (and any sidebands produced by the modulation) are within the permitted amateur bands, and

4(1)(b)
(c) you have suppressed harmonics and other spurious emissions outside the band you are using to the point where they account for less than 1% of the mean power radiated.

4(4)
4(3)
19. You must carry out checks from time to time to ensure that you are complying with these conditions – and take action to put things right if you are not.

4(2)
4(3)
Note (l)
20. You should avoid causing interference to your neighbours' wireless apparatus – TV, radio, cordless phones etc. For this reason you should erect your antenna well away from existing TV or other receiving antennas and from places where it could cause induced RF currents in the electricity mains – this applies particularly to indoor or loft antennas. In densely populated urban areas this may not always be possible. If all other remedies have failed you may need to modify your operating practice to avoid causing undue interference. You will not normally

Note (n)
have to take this to the point where you are deprived of making reasonable use of your station.

Antenna safety

Note (j)
21. You should not erect an antenna near an overhead power line if it can be avoided. If you do, it must meet the safety requirements of the local electricity company.

Note (j)
22. If your station is within one kilometre of the boundary of an aerodrome you must not put up antennas or masts more than 15 metres high.

Identification

7(1)(a)
23. When transmitting you must send your callsign:
    (a) when you make your first call (eg a test transmission or a CQ call),

7(1)(b)
7(1A)
    (b) when you contact another amateur (or group of amateurs, if you are operating in a 'net') at the start and end of the period of communication, and – if it's a long one – every 15 minutes,

7(1)(c)
    (c) whenever you change frequency.

7(1)(d)
7(1)(e)
Note (x)
7(1)(f)
24. You must send your callsign on the same carrier frequency and by the same mode of transmission as you are using for communication. If you are using some mode other than Morse code or speech you must also send your callsign in Morse or speech every half-hour during transmission.

Note (u)
25. When using telephony you may confirm the letters of your callsign by using words from the phonetic alphabet listed in Note (u).

7(2)
26. If you are operating another amateur's station under his supervision (see paragraph 13 above) you must use his callsign for identification instead of yours. (However, there is no objection to mentioning your own callsign during the exchange of signals to let your contact know who is operating.)

7(2)
27. Similarly, if another person is operating your station under your supervision in accordance with paragraph 10(b) he must use your callsign for identification instead of his.

Location

1(10)
1(11)(a)
1(12)
Note (a)
28. You will normally transmit from the place shown on the Validation Document as the 'Main Station Address'. If you change this you must notify the Radio Licensing Centre in writing (using the back page of your Validation Document) before you start using the new address for transmitting.

1(11)(b)
29. You may also transmit from any other fixed spot. (This is known as a *Temporary Location*.) If you want to do this you must either:

7(3)(b)
    (a) give advance notice in writing to the manager of the Radio Investigation Service* in the area where you intend to operate (you can get his address from the Radio Licensing Centre) or

7(3)(a)
    (b) add '/P' to your callsign and give your position every half-hour while you are transmitting. (Ways of describing your position are given in Note (v).)

1(11)(c)
2(14)
Note (k)
12(1)(g
12(1)(d)
7(4)
30. You may also transmit when you are on the move; this is known as *Mobile* operation and applies when you are on foot, in a vehicle (but not in an aeroplane, glider or balloon), in a boat on a lake, canal or river (but not in tidal waters or at sea). In all these cases you must add '/M' to your callsign.

1(11)(d)
12(1)(d)
7(4)
31. You may also transmit from a boat that is in tidal waters or at sea, but in this case you must add '/MM' to your callsign. This is known as *Maritime Mobile* operation.

2(12)(a)
2(12)(b)
8(3)
Note (k)
32. You may transmit in a boat (whether 'Mobile' or 'Maritime Mobile') only with the permission of the Master of the vessel, and must cease operation if he tells you to do so.

7(5)
Note (w)
33. Whenever you are operating away from your Main Station Address remember to put the local country letter in your callsign. For instance if your 'home' callsign is GW6ABC you change this to G6ABC/P if you are operating from a temporary location in England, to GM6ABC/M if you are operating from a boat on Loch Lomond, to GD6ABC/MM if you are sending from your yacht coming into Douglas in the Isle of Man, and so on. For the callsigns to use when you are operating abroad see paragraphs 51 and 52.

Logbook

6(1)
6(3)(a)
34. You must keep a proper logbook (not a loose-leaf binder) and make an entry whenever you transmit (with one exception – see paragraph 35 below), leaving no gaps between entries. You must enter:

6(1)(a)
    (a) the date,

6(1)(c)
    (b) which frequency band you are using,

6(1)(d)
    (c) what mode of transmission (codes for describing these are at Note (t)),

6(1)(e)
    (d) what power you are using,

6(1)(b)
    (e) the time in UTC (Greenwich Mean Time – see Note (a))
    when:

6(1)(b)(i)
        1. you start transmission,

6(1)(b)(ii)
        2. you change to a different frequency band,

6(1)(b)(ii)
        3. you change to a different mode of transmission,

6(1)(b)(ii)
        4. you change the power output,

6(1)(b)(i)
        5. you cease transmission.

6(1)(g)
    (f) the callsign of any other amateur you contact,

6(1)(f)
6(1)(h)
    (g) any test transmissions and any CQ calls you make – even if they get no response,

6(1)(i)
    (h) when operating from a Temporary Location you must make a note in the logbook of where you are, using one of the methods listed in Note (v) of the licence.

6(5)
    (i) you must also log any extra items of information that an authorised person (eg an Inspector from the Radio Investigation Service*) has instructed you to log for a specified period.

Most logbooks have spaces for recording the name and location of each person you contact, the strength and readability of his signals, his reception of your signals, what equipment and antennas he was using etc – but these are not compulsory items.

Note (r) 35. You do not need to keep a log when operating 'Mobile' or 'Maritime Mobile'.

6(2)
6(3)(b) 36. You may keep your log on a magnetic tape or on a computer disk instead of in a book, but the tape or disk must be used solely for the log. See also paragraph 53.

6(4) 37. In whatever form you have your log, you must keep it available for inspection by the authorities for at least six months after the date of the last entry in it – even if your licence has expired or been cancelled in the meantime.

Recorded and retransmitted messages

5(2) 38. If an amateur sends you a message to pass on to another amateur you may do so.

39. You may record a message sent to you by another amateur and:

5(1)(a) (a) send it back to him (eg if he wants to hear what his signals sound like) or

5(1)(b)
Note (e) (b) pass it on, at his request, to another amateur, but see Note (e).

5(3) 40. If what you are transmitting includes his callsign you must make it clear who sent it originally and who is retransmitting it (ie you).

5(4) 41. If you are retransmitting a digital communication which you haven't read you are not responsible for seeing that it doesn't breach the rules in paragraphs 5 and 6 above.

5(5) 42. This licence does not allow you to run a packet 'mailbox' or 'bulletin board' or a telephony repeater. For these you need special authority.

Unattended operation

2(4) 43. The only occasions when you may operate your transmitter when you are not present are:

2(4)(a)(ii)
2(5) (a) if you are operating the hidden transmitter for a direction finding competition. See paragraph 2(4)(a)(ii) of your licence for the conditions of operation and the frequencies you may use.

2(4)(a)(ii) (b) if you are using a low-power device to operate the transmitter at the Main Station Address by remote control. The device must have under 10 milliwatts RF output and a range limited to your own premises.

2(4)(b) (c) if you are operating a beacon on one of the frequencies listed in paragraph 2(4)(a)(i) of the licence.

2(4)(c) (d) if you are running a packet station at the Main Station or a Temporary Location.

In cases (c) and (d) you must give seven days notice, in writing, to the manager of the local branch of the Radio Investigation Service before starting up. Paragraph 2(5) of the licence lists the information he will require.

2(6) 44. You do not have to log the transmissions of the low-power device but you must still log the periods of transmission of the main transmitter (including, when operating an unattended packet station, any periods when it is switched on ready to transmit automatically in response to incoming signals). You must also make arrangements for sending your callsign at half-hourly intervals in speech or Morse
7(1)(f) code. If sent in Morse it should be no faster than 20 WPM.

Operating abroad

11(2)
11(1)(a)
Note (y) 45. Provided that this is not a temporary licence, it allows you to operate in certain countries abroad as a temporary, non-resident visitor. Your Validation Document has a list of these – but in a coded form; the decode is in Note (y).

46. You may operate:

11(1)(b)(i) (a) a mobile station,

11(1)(b)(i) (b) a station powered from the electricity mains of the place where you are staying temporarily,

11(1)(b)(ii) (c) the station of a local licensed amateur – with his permission.

11(1)(c)
11(1)(d) 47. You must comply with the licence conditions of your host country as well as those of your own licence, but if there is any conflict between them the former will prevail. However, you may not use frequencies or modes which you are not licensed to use in the UK – even if they are allowed to amateurs in the host country with a licence equivalent to yours. It is for you to find out what your host country rules are.

2(13) 48. If you are operating Maritime Mobile in international waters and have gone into a different ITU region you may not use frequency bands which have not been allocated to the Amateur Service in that region.

11(1)(f) 49. If this is a Class B licence you may use only frequencies above 144MHz, and then only the ones allowed by the rules of your host country.

11(1)(e) 50. You must take your licence with you and be prepared to produce it for inspection by the authorities in your host country if they ask to see it.

11(1)(g) 51. You will normally use your 'home' callsign (including your home country letter, if any) preceded by the host country prefix (eg F/GW6ABC/P if you are in a cottage in France, SM/GW6ABC/M if you are on the move in Sweden, LA/GW6ABC/MM if you are in a boat in Norwegian coastal waters etc). But if you are operating the station of a local amateur under his supervision you should first check whether there is a local requirement similar to that in paragraph 7(2) of your licence (see paragraph 27 above) which may require you to use his callsign.

52. If you are operating outside the territorial waters of any country (eg in mid-Atlantic) you should use your home callsign – of course with '/MM' added.

Inspection

8(1)

12(1)(h)

53. You must allow a properly authorised person acting on behalf of the Secretary of State (this usually means someone from the Radio Investigation Service*) to examine your licence and your logbook, and to inspect and test your equipment, at any reasonable time. (You may also be asked to demonstrate how you carry out the checking described in paragraph 19 above.) If your logbook is on tape or computer disk you must have equipment at your Main Station Address which enables the entries to be viewed on screen and a print-out made for him to take away.

54. The most likely occasion for such a visit is when someone has complained of interference from your transmitter. (This is why keeping an accurate log is so important.) If the Inspector thinks you have been at fault he may ask you to restrict your operations or even close down. You can suggest ways of dealing with the problem – eg by fitting extra filters, moving the antenna etc – but if he insists that you close down you must do so. You will be given a full explanation of the reasons in writing and will have an opportunity to appeal. However, if you are found to have committed a serious breach of the conditions of your licence it may be cancelled (and your equipment could be confiscated; you could even be prosecuted). If your licence is revoked you must surrender the Validation Document to the DTI at once.

8(2)
4(3)

Note (m)

9(4)

Renewal

9(1)
9(2)
9(3)

55. Each year the Radio Licensing Centre will send you a reminder to renew your licence and pay the annual fee. Renewal requests should be dealt with promptly to avoid the risk of the licence expiring and being cancelled.

Finally

56. Amateur Radio is an officially recognised service; it is invaluable in forming friendships between people all over the world as well as in learning about electronics and radio communication. If you have any difficulties your local amateur radio society or local RSGB

---

* The Radio Investigation Service offices are now known as 'Local District Offices of the Radiocommunications Agency'.

Liaison Officer will be glad to help. You can get their addresses by writing to the address for the RSGB given in the Introduction and enclosing a stamped addressed envelope for reply.

Remember that the examination will include 18 questions from this part of the syllabus and a pass in this section is mandatory.

PRACTICE QUESTIONS FOR CHAPTER 1

Note: reference to the schedule in BR68 may be made when answering these questions.

1.   If for any reason the licence is revoked it shall be
     (a) destroyed within seven days
     (b) returned to the Licensing Authority
     (c) returned to any Post Office
     (d) returned to the RSGB.

2.   The Class B licence does not authorise the use of frequencies for transmitting
     (a) above 144MHz
     (b) above 430MHz
     (c) in the microwave range
     (d) below 30MHz.

3.   Providing the licence fee is paid annually the licence is valid
     (a) for five years
     (b) for 10 years
     (c) for 20 years
     (d) until revoked.

4.   The callsign GI4XXX is issued to an amateur living in
     (a) Guernsey
     (b) Wales
     (c) Northern Ireland
     (d) Jersey.

5.   Which one of the following is allowed to be used as a log?
     (a) An A4 sheet of paper
     (b) A loose-leaf notebook.
     (c) A writing pad.
     (d) A stapled exercise book.

6.   Slow-scan and high-definition television using frequency modulation is
     (a) A3F
     (b) C3F
     (c) F3E
     (d) F3F.

7.   The minimum age for taking the RAE is
     (a) not specified
     (b) 14 years
     (c) 18 years
     (d) 21 years.

8.   A station is located 0.3km from the boundary of an airfield. The height of the antenna system must not exceed
     (a) 10 metres
     (b) 15 metres
     (c) 20 metres
     (d) 50 metres.

9. When operating a transceiver in a car which one of the following suffixes should be used?
    (a) /P.
    (b) /C.
    (c) /M.
    (d) /A.

10. Times entered in the log must be in
    (a) UTC
    (b) local time
    (c) ETA
    (d) BST.

11. CQ calls must
    (a) always be in CW at 12 WPM
    (b) not be entered in the log
    (c) always be entered in the log
    (d) only be entered if responded to.

12. The nationality requirement for holding an amateur licence in the UK is
    (a) British
    (b) English
    (c) European
    (d) not specified.

13. Which one of the following frequency allocations is not available within a 100km radius of Charing Cross, London
    (a) 430.000–431.000MHz
    (b) 430.100–430.200MHz
    (c) 431.000–432.000MHz
    (d) 435.000–438.000MHz.

14. The 24MHz amateur allocation in the UK lies between
    (a) 24.590–24.690MHz
    (b) 24.890–24.990MHz
    (c) 24.990–24.999MHz
    (d) 24.999–25.000MHz.

15. Terms of the Amateur Licence can be varied by a general notice in which one of the following?
    (a) London, Glasgow and Cardiff Gazettes.
    (b) Glasgow, Cardiff and Belfast Gazettes.
    (c) Edinburgh, Belfast and London Gazettes.
    (d) Cardiff, Edinburgh and Manchester Gazettes.

16. Tests to ensure that no undue interference is being caused by the station should be carried out
    (a) from time to time
    (b) only every three months
    (c) before licence renewal
    (d) only when an officer of the RIS is present.

17. The initial period for an amateur radio licence is
    (a) one year
    (b) six months
    (c) five years
    (d) for life.

18. The prefix used by a station in Guernsey is
    (a) GJ
    (b) GG
    (c) GC
    (d) GU.

19. Fast-scan transmissions can be used on
    (a) all amateur bands
    (b) 14MHz only
    (c) 73kHz only
    (d) certain specified amateur bands.

20. Which one of the following bands is used by amateurs in the UK on a primary basis?
    (a) 10.100MHz–10.150MHz.
    (b) 144.000MHz–146.000MHz.
    (c) 435.000MHz–438.000MHz.
    (d) 1240.000MHz–1260.000MHz.

21. Entries in the log may not be made in
    (a) type
    (b) ballpoint
    (c) ink
    (d) pencil.

22. As well as amateur frequency transmissions the licence allows reception of
    (a) Foreign Office messages
    (b) standard frequency transmissions
    (c) mobile phones
    (d) police transmissions.

23. It is forbidden to send messages containing which one of the following
    (a) ASCII
    (b) International No 2 Code
    (c) secret cipher
    (d) Baudot code.

24. The suffix when operating a hand-held transmitter while riding a bicycle is
    (a) /B
    (b) /P
    (c) /M
    (d) /C.

25. Frequency modulation using speech is termed
    (a) F3M
    (b) F3C
    (c) F2A
    (d) F3E.

26. The maximum carrier power level PEP permitted in the 1.830 to 1.850MHz band is
    (a) 9dBW
    (b) 15dBW
    (c) 20dBW
    (d) 26dBW.

27. A Class B licence allows operation above
    (a) 30MHz
    (b) 50MHz
    (c) 70MHz
    (d) 144MHz.

28. The purpose of the amateur radio licence is
    (a) to enable cheap overseas communications
    (b) to provide a communications network in the UK
    (c) for the purpose of self-training in Wireless Telegraphy
    (d) to provide a National Radio Relay Service.

29. The amateur station can be inspected
    (a) only during RIS office hours
    (b) Saturdays and Sundays only
    (c) at any and all reasonable times
    (d) between 1800 and 2100 on weekdays.

30. In which of the following bands is it permissible to use fast-scan TV?
    (a) 28.000MHz–29.700MHz.
    (b) 70.025MHz–70.500MHz.
    (c) 144MHz–146MHz.
    (d) 432MHz–440MHz.

31. Providing prior written notice has been given to the appropriate authority for operation from a different address in the UK, the suffix is
    (a) /A
    (b) /M
    (c) /P
    (d) not required.

32. The amateur licence can be revoked through a broadcast by the
    (a) BBC
    (b) IBA
    (c) RSGB
    (d) DTI.

33. Details of transmissions made when operating /M
    (a) must be entered in the main log
    (b) must be entered in a mobile log
    (c) need not be recorded in a log
    (d) must be recorded at a later date.

34. In the symbols 'J3E' the 'E' indicates
    (a) facsimile
    (b) telegraphy
    (c) television
    (d) telephony.

35. Which one of the following bands is used by amateurs in the UK on a secondary basis?
    (a) 1.810MHz–1.830MHz.
    (b) 10.100MHz–10.150MHz.
    (c) 21.000MHz–21.450MHz.
    (d) 144.000MHz–146.000MHz.

36. Messages which are permitted to be sent by radio amateurs are those of
    (a) a personal nature
    (b) an obscene nature
    (c) a misleading nature
    (d) a religious nature.

37. Items that can be inspected by a person acting under the authority of the Secretary of State are
    (a) apparatus comprising the station
    (b) the logbook of the station
    (c) the station and the logbook
    (d) the licence, log and apparatus of the station.

38. The licence requires that the receiver(s) at an amateur station must be capable of receiving
    (a) all amateur bands
    (b) one mode of emission
    (c) SSB transmissions only
    (d) any mode on which the station can transmit.

39. Using standard symbols, the designation 'F3E' stands for
    (a) telegraphy by frequency shift keying
    (b) telegraphy by on-off keying of a modulating audio frequency
    (c) frequency modulation by telephony
    (d) facsimile transmission.

40. A pass in which one of the following is necessary for obtaining an amateur licence A?
    (a) RAE and the 12 WPM Morse test.
    (b) RAE only.
    (c) 12 WPM Morse test only.
    (d) 5 WPM Morse test only.

41. An amateur has a 13m high tower, on top of which he wants to put a vertical antenna: he lives within 0.5km of the boundary of an airfield. The maximum height antenna he can use is
    (a) 0.5m
    (b) 1.25m
    (c) 2m
    (d) 15m.

42. Fast-scan TV transmissions are permitted on which one of the following bands?
    (a) 1.8MHz.
    (b) 21MHz.
    (c) 144MHz.
    (d) 10GHz.

43. The amateur licence also allows transmissions on behalf of the
    (a) head of the Radiocommunications Agency
    (b) National Broadcasting Corporation
    (c) public transport system
    (d) County Emergency Planning Officer.

44. A station can be closed down at any time by a demand from a person acting under the authority of the
    (a) local council
    (b) planning authority
    (c) Secretary of State
    (d) British Telecom.

45. When in communication with another station, the callsign should be sent for identification purpose at least every
    (a) five minutes
    (b) 15 minutes
    (c) half hour
    (d) hour.

46. What is the peak envelope power allowed on the 432–440MHz band?
    (a) 15dBW.
    (b) 26dBW.
    (c) 28dBW.
    (d) 40dBW.

47. In which one of the following bands can fast-scan television not be used?
    (a) 70.0–70.5MHz.
    (b) 430.0–431.0MHz.
    (c) 1240–1260MHz.
    (d) 5820–5830MHz.

48. J3E is the designation for
    (a) frequency modulated emission
    (b) SSB with suppressed carrier
    (c) SSB with reduced carrier
    (d) SSB with no carrier at all.

49. Which of the following bands is not for amateur use only?
    (a) 3.500–3.800MHz.
    (b) 7.000–7.1000MHz.
    (c) 14.000–14.350MHz.
    (d) 21.000–21.450MHz.

50. The emissions to be used by an amateur are
    (a) J3E and F3E only
    (b) not specified in the licence schedule
    (c) those specified in the licence schedule
    (d) as laid down by the IBA.

51. The licence conditions state that the licence
    (a) is not transferable
    (b) is transferable
    (c) can never be revoked
    (d) gives a waiver over copyright.

52. Under the terms of the licence it is an offence to send by wireless telegraphy
    (a) misleading messages
    (b) severe weather warnings
    (c) test transmissions
    (d) ASCII code.

53. If Glxxx is on holiday in Scotland and operating hand-held equipment from the top of Ben Nevis, the callsign used is
    (a) G1xxx/GM/P
    (b) G1xxx/M
    (c) GM1xxx/P
    (d) GM1xxx/M.

54. In which part of the 430–440MHz band is power limited to 16dBW ERP?
    (a) 431.0–432.0MHz.
    (b) 432.0–434.0MHz.
    (c) 434.0–437.0MHz.
    (d) 437.0–440.0MHz.

55. The callsign issued to an amateur living in the Isle of Wight is
    (a) GW7xxx
    (b) G7xxx
    (c) GIW7xxx
    (d) GI7xxx.

56. The station log can be kept
    (a) on a computer printout
    (b) in a loose-leaf binder
    (c) on a magnetic disc
    (d) in pencil.

57. Who is not eligible to operate an amateur radio station under the supervision of a Class A licensee?
    (a) A Class B licence holder.
    (b) A member of the armed forces.
    (c) Another Class A licence holder.
    (d) The holder of an RAE Certificate.

58. No part of a message in an amateur transmission must be
    (a) in plain language
    (b) in a language other than the mother tongue
    (c) sent in morse at 50 WPM
    (d) sent in secret code or cypher.

59. The maximum power level in PEP allowed on the 144MHz band is
    (a) 10dBW
    (b) 15dBW
    (c) 20dBW
    (d) 26dBW.

60. The 10m band lies between
    (a) 28.0–28.7MHz
    (b) 28.7–29.0MHz
    (c) 28.0–29.0MHz
    (d) 28.0–29.7MHz.

61. When using phonetics in telephony these should be
    (a) of an obscene nature
    (b) recognisable words
    (c) of a misleading nature
    (d) of a scientific nature.

62. Tests for harmonics and spurious emissions shall be
    (a) recorded for reference
    (b) put in a loose-leaf logbook
    (c) recorded in the station logbook
    (d) made each transmission.

63. A station is being operating from a private sailing boat on the Norfolk Broads. Which suffix should be added to the callsign?
    (a) /M.
    (b) /P.
    (c) /MM.
    (d) /A.

64. Pulse emissions must
    (a) not be used at anytime
    (b) be on frequency bands above 1000MHz
    (c) be on frequency bands below 1000MHz
    (d) only be used from time to time.

65. Single sideband, suppressed carrier transmission is denoted by the symbol
    - (a) A3E
    - (b) F3E
    - (c) R3E
    - (d) J3E.

66. If an urgent request for medical drugs is received from anywhere, this should be passed to the
    - (a) local St John's Ambulance Brigade
    - (b) local Red Cross branch office
    - (c) local doctor
    - (d) duly authorised officer of Her Majesty's Government.

67. If the licence is revoked, the Validation Document shall be
    - (a) destroyed
    - (b) surrendered to the Secretary of State
    - (c) returned to the local post office
    - (d) returned to the RSGB.

68. The Class B licence does not authorise the use of frequencies for transmitting
    - (a) above 144MHz
    - (b) above 430MHz
    - (c) in the microwave range
    - (d) below 30MHz.

69. The callsign GW4xxx is issued to a
    - (a) Class A licensee living in Wales
    - (b) Class B licensee living in Wales
    - (c) Class A licensee living in Winchester
    - (d) Class A licensee living in Scotland.

70. A UK amateur licence also authorises the licensee to operate in any country
    - (a) in the world
    - (b) within the Commonwealth
    - (c) which has implemented the appropriate CEPT recommendation
    - (d) in Europe.

71. Which of the following represents a valid log?
    - (a) Loose-leaf book.
    - (b) Non-loose-leaf book.
    - (c) Magnetic disc containing propagation and RTTY programs.
    - (d) Magnetic tape which also includes games programs.

72. Providing the licence fee is paid, an amateur licence is
    - (a) in force from year to year unless revoked
    - (b) valid for six months
    - (c) valid for five years
    - (d) valid for life.

73. Operation from which one of the following is not permissible under the terms of the licence?
    - (a) Private yacht on Loch Lomond.
    - (b) Private yacht between Liverpool and Northern Ireland.
    - (c) Helicopter above the Channel Isles.
    - (d) The inter-island ferry in the Orkney Islands.

74. Using voice modulation, the nomenclature J3E corresponds to
    - (a) SSB with full carrier
    - (b) SSB with suppressed carrier
    - (c) FM using voice modulation
    - (d) a CW transmission.

75. When using a UK amateur radio licence it is an offence to send by wireless telegraphy
    - (a) messages offering articles for sale
    - (b) severe weather warnings
    - (c) test transmissions
    - (d) ASCII code.

76. Which one of the following bands is shared with other services?
    - (a) 3.5–3.8MHz.
    - (b) 7.0–7.1MHz.
    - (c) 14.0–14.35MHz.
    - (d) 21.0–21.45MHz.

77. If a station is located within 1km of the boundary of an airfield, the height of the antenna system above ground level must not exceed
    - (a) 10 metres
    - (b) 15 metres
    - (c) 20 metres
    - (d) 50 metres.

78. What is the peak envelope power allowed on the 432–440MHz band?
    - (a) 15dBW.
    - (b) 26dBW.
    - (c) 28dBW.
    - (d) 40dBW.

79. Which of the following is not defined as a user service?
    - (a) Fire brigade.
    - (b) British Telecom.
    - (c) County Emergency Planning Officer.
    - (d) St John Ambulance Service.

80. An Amateur Licence A requires
    - (a) a pass in the RAE and the Morse test
    - (b) a pass in the RAE only
    - (c) a pass in the Morse test only
    - (d) to have held a Class B licence previously.

81. As well as amateur frequency transmissions, the licence allows reception of
    - (a) diplomatic messages
    - (b) standard frequency transmissions
    - (c) news agency transmissions
    - (d) Police transmissions.

82. Which one of the following occurrences need not be entered into the station log?
    - (a) Tests for interference made from time to time.
    - (b) Station used by licensed operator other than licensee.
    - (c) Station operated at temporary location
    - (d) Station temporarily dismantled.

83. The callsign prefix GD should always be used whenever the station is being operated from
    (a) Scotland
    (b) Isle of Man
    (c) Isle of Dogs
    (d) Guernsey.

84. The 10 metre band lies between
    (a) 28.0–28.7MHz
    (b) 27.4–30.0MHz
    (c) 28.5–30.0MHz
    (d) 28.0–29.7MHz.

85. In the UK, a licensee may receive messages from an overseas amateur on a frequency band not specified in the first column of the schedule as long as the licensee
    (a) transmits only in a band specified in the schedule
    (b) obtains a permit from the Licensing Authority
    (c) holds a reciprocal licence from that country
    (d) informs the RSGB.

86. Time in the log book must always be in
    (a) local time
    (b) UTC
    (c) BST
    (d) Local time of the station worked.

87. When the station is used from a temporary location and the Radio Investigation Service is not informed, the location must be given
    (a) at least every five minutes
    (b) in CW only
    (c) within 0.5km
    (d) within 5km.

Check your answers using the key in Appendix 4.

2 Operating procedures and practices

GENERAL PRINCIPLES OF OPERATING

Listening on the short wave bands is an excellent way of getting to appreciate how to operate effectively. Not only do you learn what constitutes good, and in some cases bad, operating but also what radio propagation conditions prevail on the amateur bands at different times of the day and night, and at different times of the year.

It is advisable to listen on the amateur bands on which you are going to operate before attempting to call 'CQ' (a general invitation for amateurs to respond), or working a specific station – ie someone who you have just heard calling CQ. By listening, you will discover how active the band is and also get an idea of propagation conditions. It is always good to remember when operating on the bands that you may not be able to hear both sides of a conversation, and what may appear to be a quiet spot may be just where someone is listening intently to a signal you cannot hear. ALWAYS ask if a frequency is in use before calling CQ; this applies to telegraphy as well as telephony operation.

Once having established contact, it is usual on the first transmission (or *over*) to give a signal report, your name and your location. The signal report should be realistic, as this will give the person you are contacting a good idea of the conditions which prevail between you and may determine how often information is repeated. Honest reports should always be given. Do not give a report of RS(T) 59(9) to a station merely because he has just given you 59(9) or because you want his QSL card! S-meter readings should be taken with a pinch of salt, since different equipment might give different values for the same signal. Your location is also important, as the person with whom you are in contact may need to turn his beam towards you to peak up your signal.

Often you may hear a station calling CQ DX (or CQ USA, CQ Africa, etc). This means they only want to be called by DX stations (from long distance, or stations from USA, Africa etc). It would be bad practice for you to answer if you were not regarded as DX or were not from the specific areas requested.

If you answer a CQ call remember that when the contact is finished it is usual for you to move off that frequency, unless the person whom you have just contacted indicates otherwise.

The long-distance (DX) bands, particularly 14, 21 and 28MHz, should not be used for purely local contacts when these bands are open for long-distance working.

It is not good practice to call a station (to *break in*) while the operator is in contact with someone else, unless, of course, you know the other station well. The conditions of your licence should be borne in mind at all times when operating on the amateur bands. Don't forget there could be many people out there listening to you. Although there is freedom to talk about virtually anything on the air, your licence conditions do not allow you to talk about religion or politics, nor to engage in any discussions of a commercial nature.

Before using any band for the first time, you should familiarise yourself with specific frequencies which are allocated to data modes, SSTV, satellite links, QRP (low power) calling channels, etc – in other words, the band plan (see later).

OPERATING PROCEDURES USING TELEGRAPHY

Telegraphy is now looked on as being rather outdated as a mode of communication. However, it will always have a part to play in amateur radio. This is because it is an effective method of passing information and takes up far less bandwidth than, say, single sideband. Equipment for operation using Morse code can be easier and cheaper to build than a sideband transceiver, for example.

Morse code, with its use of worldwide abbreviations and Q-codes (see later) helps to break down barriers in language.

The most common procedural and punctuation signals are shown in Table 2.1. Reports on readability and signal strength (and tone in the case of telegraphic signals) are given in terms of the RST code (see Table 2.2).

Speed of sending

The golden rule is "Never send faster than you are able to receive". The speed of sending should depend to a large extent on circumstances: when conditions are poor with low signal strengths or in heavy interference it is sensible to send more slowly. It is a good principle to send at the same speed as the operator at the other end.

Table 2.1. Punctuation/procedure signals

Punctuation

Question mark	di-di-dah-dah-di-dit
Full stop	di-dah-di-dah-di-dah
Comma*	dah-dah-di-di-dah-dah

* Sometimes used to indicate exclamation mark.

Procedure signals

Stroke (/)	dah-di-di-dah-dit
Break sign (=)	dah-di-di-di-dah
End of message (AR)§	di-dah-di-dah-dit
End of work (VA)§	di-di-di-dah-di-dah
Wait (AS)§	di-dah-di-di-dit
Error	di-di-di-di-di-di-di-dit
Invitation to transmit (general) (K)	dah-di-dah
Invitation to transmit (specific station) (KN)§	dah-di-dah-dah-dit

§ AR, VA, AS and KN are sent as one character.

Table 2.2. The RST code

Readability

R1	Unreadable
R2	Barely readable, occasional words distinguishable
R3	Readable with considerable difficulty
R4	Readable with practically no difficulty
R5	Perfectly readable

Signal strength

S1	Faint, signals barely perceptible
S2	Very weak signals
S3	Weak signals
S4	Fair signals
S5	Fairly good signals
S6	Good signals
S7	Moderately strong signals
S8	Strong signals
S9	Extremely strong signals

Tone

T1	Extremely rough hissing note
T2	Very rough AC note, no trace of musicality
T3	Rough, low-pitched AC note, slightly musical
T4	Rather rough AC note, moderately musical
T5	Musically modulated note
T6	Modulated note, slight trace of whistle
T7	Near DC note, smooth ripple
T8	Good DC note, just a trace of ripple
T9	Purest DC note

If the note appears to be crystal-controlled add X after the appropriate number. Where there is a chirp add C, drift add D, clicks add K.

Table 2.3. Amateur abbreviations (CW)

AA	All after...(used after a question mark to request a reception)
AB	All before...(see AA)
BK	Signal used to interrupt a transmission in progress
CFM	Confirm (or I confirm)
NIL	I have nothing to send you
NW	Now
OK	We agree (or it is correct)
QSLL	If you send a QSL, I will do likewise
RPT	Repeat (or I repeat)
TFC	Traffic
W	Word(s)
WA	Word after (see AA)
WB	Word before

The good CW operator is the one whose copy is easy to read and who does not send faster than he is capable of doing properly. Badly sent 20 words per minute Morse may well be almost unreadable but Morse sent properly at 25 WPM should be considerably easier to read.

Establishing communication

The first step is to spend a short time listening on the band it is proposed to use, in order to check:

(a) if conditions are good or bad;
(b) who is working who and what signal reports are being exchanged.

The propagation forecasts published each month in *Radio Communication* are invaluable as an indication of the part of the world likely to be heard at a particular time.

There are two main ways of establishing contact:

(a) by calling a specific station;
(b) by transmitting a 'CQ' (general invitation to reply) call.

On most bands you will hear stations calling 'CQ' so it is usually preferable to answer such a call rather than to initiate another, particularly if you are still a relative novice. However, a CQ call made when a band appears 'dead', especially on 21 or 28MHz, sometimes results in an unexpected contact.

Calling procedures

Calling a specific station

First of all, *net* on to the frequency of the station which you are going to call, ie adjust transmitter frequency to the signal being received. On most modern transceivers, turning the tuning dial to adjust the tone of the incoming signal to be the same as the sidetone of your rig when the key is depressed

will result in you being on the right frequency. However, you should check this rule applies to your equipment, and conduct tests to prove it. It is very important to be exactly on the same frequency, not only to reduce the amount of the band being used for the contact, but also because many operators use very narrow filters on their receivers, and if you are a few hundred hertz off-frequency, you may not be heard at all.

The basic call (assuming your station callsign to be G4QME, and the station you are attempting to contact G2MAB) would be:

G2MAB G2MAB G2MAB DE G4QME G4QME
G4QME $\overline{KN}$

'DE' here means 'from'. Note that '$\overline{KN}$' is an invitation to the specific station, G2MAB, and no other, to reply. A line above two letters, in this case $\overline{KN}$, indicates that when sent, the letters are run together. This basic call can be varied, depending on signal strengths etc. In poor conditions or where there is heavy interference it would be sensible to send your callsign (G4QME) more times. In good conditions, there is no need to send his callsign (G2MAB in this example) several times, as it is presumed he knows his own callsign already! However, both callsigns should be sent at least once.

Making a CQ call

The first step is to choose a frequency where no other station is operating – this is often very difficult, especially under crowded band conditions. Before calling CQ, the signal QRL? is often sent two or three times; this means "Is this frequency in use?" If so, then you may hear QRL coming back which means "I am using this frequency" or sometimes YES or PSE QSY meaning "Please change frequency." The action is then obvious – you should find another space!

The basic call is:

CQ CQ CQ DE G4QME G4QME G4QME K

Note here that 'K' is a general invitation to any station to reply.

Basic calls may be repeated up to five or six times – this depends on conditions and activity on the band. Never send a long series of CQ signals without interspersing the station call.

A CQ call may be made specific, eg if you looking for long-distance contacts:

CQ DX CQ DX CQ DX DE G4QME G4QME G4QME K

or directional, eg if you are looking for stations in Australia:

Table 2.4. Informal amateur abbreviations (CW)

ABT	about	INPT	input
ADR	Address	LID	poor operator
AF	africa	MNI	many
AGN	again	MOD	modulation
ANI	any	MSG	message
ANT	antenna	MTR	meter (or
BCNU	be seeing you		metres)
BD	bad	NA	North America
BFO	beat frequency	NBFM	narrow band
	oscillator		frequency
BK	break-in		modulation
BLV	believe	NR	number
BUG	semi-automatic	OB	old boy
	key	OM	old man
CK	check	OP	operator
CLD	called	OT	old timer
CONDX	conditions	PSE	please
CRD	card	PWR	power
CUD	could	RPRT	report
CUAGN	see you again	RX	receiver
CUL	see you later	SA	South America
CW	continuous	SED	said
	wave	SIG	signal
DR	dear	SKED	schedule
DX	long distance	SN	soon
ELBUG	electronic key	SRI	sorry
ENUF	enough	SSB	single sideband
ES	and	STN	station
FB	fine business	SUM	some
FM	frequency	SWL	short-wave
	modulation		listener
FER	for	TKS	thanks
FONE	telephony	TMW	tomorrow
FREQ	frequency	TNX	thanks
GA	go ahead, or	TRX	transceiver
	good afternoon	TVI	television
GB	goodbye		interference
GD	good day	TX	transmitter
GE	good evening	U	you
GLD	glad	UR	your
GM	good morning	VY	very
GN	good night	W	watts
GND	ground (earth)	WID	with
GUD	good	WKD	worked
HAM	amateur	WKG	working
	transmitter	WL	will or well
HI	laughter	WUD	would
HPE	hope	WX	weather
HR	hear or here	XMTR	transmitter
HRD	heard	XYL	wife
HV	have	YL	young lady
HVY	heavy	73	best regards
HW	how		

CQ VK CQ VK CQ VK DE G4QME G4QME G4QME K

If your CQ call goes unanswered, spend some time listening since there may be a very weak station in the noise.

If you miss part of the callsign, you should send QRZ? ("Who is calling me?"), eg:

QRZ? QRZ? DE G4QME G4QME G4QME K

Note that QRZ? is not an alternative to CQ.

Conducting the contact

Once you have established contact after a CQ call, the format of a typical contact (QSO) using CW (Morse code) is likely to be as follows (assuming your station callsign to be G4QME,

and the station you have contacted is ZS6AOG in South Africa):

ZS6AOG DE G4QME = GM OM ES MNI TNX FER CALL = UR RST 579 579 = MY QTH IS HARTFORD HARTFORD ES NAME IS MARY MARY SO HW? AR ZS6AOG DE G4QME KN

These transmissions are known as *overs*. The following should be noted:

(a) Report, QTH and name are generally sent twice (but may be sent more times, depending on conditions).
(b) Each sentence is separated by the break sign = (dah-di-di-di-dah) See Table 2.1.
(c) After contact has been established, each callsign need only be sent once at the beginning and end – there is no point in sending them more than once.
(d) 'SO HW?' means "So how do you receive me?"
(e) 'AR' signifies "End of message".
(f) 'KN' means specific station (ZS6AOG) to reply.

The contact may then continue thus:

G4QME DE ZS6AOG R ES VY GM MARY = MNI TNX FER RPRT = UR RST 599 599 = QTH IS JOBURG JOBURG ES NAME IS TONY TONY = HR RIG IS TS930 WID 100 WATTS = ANT IS BEAM AT 24M = WX SUNNY ES 30 C OK? AR G4QME DE ZS6AOG KN

The following should be noted:

(a) 'R' signifies "Received all sent", which is obviously preferable to such phrases as "solid cpy hr" etc.
(b) Refer to Table 2.4 for such abbreviations as ES, GM, VY etc.

The contact then goes on:

ZS6AOG DE G4QME = R FB TONY ES OK UR FB STATION = HR RIG IS TS50 PWR 10W 10W TO DIPOLE AT 25 FEET = WX COLD = TONY PSE UR QSL CARD = NW QRU SO 73 AR ZS6AOG DE G4QME KN

G4QME DE ZS6AOG = R ES TNX FER INFO = MNI TNX FB QSO ES HPE CUAGN SN = QSL OK VIA BURO = VY 73 ES 88 MARY = AR G4QME DE ZS6AOG VA

This is the last transmission from ZS6AOG since he has sent VA ("End of transmission").

ZS6AOG DE G4QME 73 VA

The above describes a fairly basic contact but in practice CW contacts range from just an exchange of RST/QTH/name to a chat lasting an hour or more.

Remember the following important indicators when tuning across a band:

'K' is an invitation for any station to reply.
'KN' is an invitation for a specific station to reply.
'VA' means "I have finished this contact."
'CL' means "I am closing down and am unlikely to answer any further calls."

Abbreviations used in amateur telegraphy are generally

understood throughout the world. A great deal of information can be transmitted in a short time using Morse code if full use is made of the standard amateur abbreviations (see Table 2.4) and Q-codes (see later).

OPERATING PROCEDURES USING TELEPHONY

When using speech (SSB, FM etc), because it is the most natural of modes, we tend to forget that (unless VOX is being used) the other station cannot reply until the transmission is passed over. It is good practice, therefore, to keep the 'overs' relatively short, so that the conversation is more interactive. You should speak clearly and at a reasonable pace, especially when in conversation with someone whose first language is not English.

The phonetic alphabet should be used when it is necessary to clarify a callsign or the spelling of a word, especially when conditions are poor (see later). Plain language should be used at all times – there is no need to make use of the abbreviations used in Morse code. So often you hear amateurs using SSB saying "73 to your family" instead of "Best wishes to your family" or worse still saying "Best 73s" which translates as "Best best wisheses!" Q-codes should also be avoided, unless there is a problem with the language.

Occasionally under poor conditions, it might be necessary to increase the audio gain. However, it is very important that the final amplifier stage is not overdriven, as this may cause deterioration of the signal quality as well as interference to other users of the band. Speech processing is often used to enhance speech quality. However, over-processing the signal can have the opposite effect. Make sure you read the operating manual of your transmitter to check on these areas.

Conversation

The use of CW abbreviations (including "HI") and the Q-code should normally be avoided. The Q-code should only be used on telephony when there is a language difficulty.

Plain language should be used, and clichés and jargon should be kept to a minimum. In particular, avoid the use of "we" when "I" is meant and "handle" when "name" is meant. Other bad habits include saying "that's a roger" instead of "that's correct", and "affirmative" instead of "yes". You will no doubt have heard many more – just don't feel you have to copy them.

Procedure

As noted earlier, when calling a specific station it is good practice to keep calls short and to use the callsign of the station called once or twice only, followed by one's own callsign pronounced carefully and clearly at least twice using the phonetic alphabet, for example:

"WD9ZZZ. This is Golf Four Quebec Mike Echo calling, and Golf Four Quebec Mike Echo is standing by."

Emphasis should be placed on your own callsign and not on that of the station being called. If there is no response, your callsign may be repeated once more after a brief listen.

As in CW operation, CQ calls should also be kept short and repeated as often as desired. An example would be:

"CQ, CQ, CQ. This is Golf Four Quebec Mike Echo, Golf Four Quebec Mike Echo, Golf Four Quebec Mike Echo calling CQ and standing by."

There is no need to say which band is being used, and certainly no need to add "for any possible calls, dah-di-dah!" or "K someone please" etc!

When replying to a call, both callsigns should be given clearly, so that the calling station can check its callsign has been received correctly. From then on it is not necessary to use the phonetic alphabet for callsigns until the final transmissions. An example would be:

"Whiskey Delta Nine Zulu Zulu Zulu. This is Golf Four Quebec Mike Echo."

Once contact is established it is only necessary to give your callsign at the intervals required by the licence. This way, a two-way conversation can be enjoyed more naturally. If necessary the words "break" or "over" may be added at the end of a transmission to signal the wish for a reply from the other station. In good conditions this will not normally be found necessary. When FM is in use it is self-evident when the other station has stopped transmitting and is listening, because the carrier drops.

The situation is more complex where three or more stations are involved, and it is a good idea to give one's own callsign briefly before each transmission, for example:

"From G4QME . . ."

At the end of the transmission the callsign should again be given, together with an indication of whose turn to speak it is next, for example:

". . . WD9ZZZ to transmit. G4QME and the group."

It is not necessary to run through a list of who is in the group, and who has signed off (and who may possibly be listening) after each transmission, although it may be useful to do this occasionally.

Signal reports on telephony are usually given as a single two-digit number, in a similar fashion to the three-digit CW RST code.

It is good practice to send both callsigns in the final transmission using the phonetic alphabet so that listening stations can check that they have them correct before calling, for example:

". . . This is Golf Four Quebec Mike Echo signing clear with Whiskey Delta Nine Zulu Zulu Zulu and Golf Four Quebec Mike Echo is now standing by for a call."

Note that some indication to listening stations is useful to indicate what you intend to do next, for example:

"Golf Four Quebec Mike Echo
. . . is closing down.
. . . is moving to eighty metres.
. . . is tuning the band."

The restrictions imposed by the UK licence conditions are particularly relevant in telephony operation. It should be made a golden rule never to discuss politics, religion or any other matter which may be offensive to those listening.

DIGITAL COMMUNICATIONS
Packet radio
One of the most popular form of digital communication used by radio amateurs is packet radio. It first emerged onto the amateur radio scene in Canada in 1978 and was introduced into the United Kingdom in the 'eighties. Many people have a computer in their shack and by linking this to their amateur radio equipment, messages can be passed to other amateurs in the UK and around the world. The packet radio network is continually being enhanced as more use is made of the mode. For UK licence requirements see BR68 relating to unattended operation.

Operating a packet radio station
A text message is typed into the computer and is passed to a special radio modem called a *TNC* (terminal node controller) which assembles the message into *packets* which are chunks of data each with their own identity and callsign address. This data is then converted into audio tones suitable for feeding into an ordinary VHF/UHF type transceiver. There are various ways of passing messages by packet radio:

1. *To a station within range.* The amateur addresses the message with the destination station's callsign directly and 'connects' to the far station, who must have a similar setup. The far station automatically confirms connection and messages can be sent back and forth.

2. *To a station out of range, via another, or a number of other stations.* In order to contact the distant station, the packet message is passed in short hops via intermediate stations. These stations act as repeaters and are known as *digipeaters*. Most normal packet stations can also be used as digipeaters. For this system to work, the TNC must be made aware of the intermediate station's addresses (callsigns). Once connection is established, messages can be sent without further intervention, since the TNC handles all the protocol.

3. *Via mailboxes or BBSs (bulletin board systems).* Mailboxes are special packet stations (using the GB7 prefixes in the UK) which can accept your messages and forward them to the end destination, very much like e-mail in concept. The message may be routed via a number of other mailboxes, which are linked to form a national and international network. The amateur sending the message logs on to his local mailbox and sends a message by addressing it to his friend's callsign at that friend's local mailbox. The system handles everything else and his friend will be informed there is a message waiting the next time he logs on. The packet radio network handles all the routing, which may be by high-speed links on VHF, UHF, microwaves, or occasionally HF, or via undersea cable or satellite. The routing is coincidental and could vary from day to day, though the message will get through eventually. Most contacts made by packet radio are not in real time, because of delays, but the system is very powerful for message handling.

4. *Through special interest groups – DX cluster.* The DX cluster network is similar to mailbox operation except that you can stay logged on to it for as long as you wish to receive the information available. The network is a real-time disseminator of DX information. It indicates *spots* – which DX stations are on the air, on which bands, at any time.

This is done by amateurs who have heard or worked DX stations entering the details (callsign and frequency etc) into the system. This is then passed around the network almost instantaneously and all people who are logged on can benefit from the shared information, selecting which bits they want. Many amateurs use computers to control their whole station and can automatically tune to the DX cluster posted frequency, as and when they choose, to enable a contact to be made. This is a shortcut to successful DX working, but relies on all stations contributing to the information. Specific DX information can also be requested at any time, since the system holds historical information, as well as a mass of information useful for DX operators. For example, you could see all instances of a rare station appearing and see perhaps that he usually comes through at dusk on 14.012MHz. The next day you could be ready and waiting!

Other modes
The area of digital communication is by its very nature experimental and enhancements are being developed all the time. RTTY (radio teletype) was one of the earliest of the digital communication modes. Since converting from early mechanical devices to all-electronic ones, developments and enhancements have been made to RTTY. Now amateurs use AMTOR and PACTOR, both designed to operate under noisy band conditions and incorporate error checking, with corrupted messages being repeated until they are received correctly.

LOG KEEPING
Apart from the fact that keeping a log is a licence requirement, a well-kept logbook provides a record of contacts and friendships made, reports, conditions and other information on which applications for operating awards can be made.

The basic requirements of the Radiocommunications Agency with regard to log keeping are as follows:

1. A permanent record must be kept in a book (not loose leaf) with no gaps between entries. The only exception to this is when you are operating /M or /MM when there is no requirement to keep a log. If you wish, you can keep a log on a magnetic tape or computer disk, but the tape or disk must be used solely for the purpose of the log. In whatever form you keep your log, it must be available for inspection by the authorities at any time, and for at least six months after the date of the last entry, even if your licence has expired or been cancelled in the meantime.

2. The following data MUST be recorded in the log:

    - Date of transmission.
    - Time of commencement of operation in UTC.
    - Frequency band of transmission.
    - Class of emission.
    - Transmitter power or power level in dBW.
    - Unsuccessful CQ calls or unsuccessful calls to specific stations should be logged.
    - Callsigns of stations called and with whom communication is established.
    - Time of establishing communication with each station and time of closing station.
    - Tests carried out from time-to-time (eg for EMC).

AMATEUR RADIO STATION LOG

DATE	TIME (UTC) start	finish	FREQUENCY (MHz)	MODE	POWER (dBW)	STATION called/worked	REPORT sent	received	QSL sent	rcvd	REMARKS
2 Nov '88	0800	0810	3	J3E	20	GM5ABC	59+10	59+5			Bert
"	0811	0820	145	F3E	16	G7XYZ	57	56			Terry first G7
"	0825	0830	14	J3E	20	CQ					No reply
"	1725	1735	145	F2D	16	GB7XYZ					Local packet mailbox
"	1740	Station closed down									
4 Nov '88	1030	/P	from 73 Antenna Lane, Squelch-on-Sea								
"	1031	1036	50	J3E	10	G1ØXYZ	55	56			Jim, Bridgetown
"	1036	1045	50	J3E	10	G7XYL	58	58			Anne, Nr Squelch-on-Sea. QRM
"	1205	1215	433	F3E	13	G2XYZ	46	47			
"	1220	Station closed down									
5 Nov '88	0945	/P	from 73 Antenna Lane, Squelch-on-Sea								
"	0950	1005	144	J3E	16	GB2GUY	56	56	✓		Catherine Fawkesville
"	1010	1015	144	A1A	16	GD5ZZZ	542	541	✓		QSB! QSL via WF9XYZ
"	1526	1530	144	A1A	16	G7CW	579	589			Good keying!
"	1535	Station closed down and dismantled									
7 Nov '88	1810	1902	435	C3F	10	G7ZZZ	P3	P3			Ted, First ATV contact!
"	1930	1945	21	J2B	16	VK2ABC	559	569	✓		RTTY, Sid at Bandedge
"	1946	2005	21	J2B	16	ZL3ZZZ	569	559	✓		1st ZL on RTTY
"	2010	Test for TVI/Harmonic Radiation - Nothing noted									
"	2020	Station closed down									
8 Nov '88	1735	1737	7	J3E	20	CQ					
"	1738	1805	7	J3E	20	G1ØZZZ	58	58			Nobby - chatted about G5RV ant
"	1930	1945	51	F3E	10	GØSIX	55	55			Allen, wanted WIAB ref.
"	1950	Station closed down.									

NOTES

Fig 2.1. Typical log entries

The detailed requirements for log keeping will be found in the *Amateur Radio Licence (A) or (B) Terms, Provisions and Limitations* booklet BR68 which is available from the Radiocommunications Agency. This booklet should be read thoroughly before taking the RAE.

Fig 2.1 illustrates a number of typical log entries which satisfy the basic licence requirements.

REPEATERS AND SATELLITES

VHF and UHF contacts are usually line-of-sight. To extend the range, various techniques are employed. Two of these, repeaters and satellites, will now be considered.

Repeaters

Repeaters are usually built by amateurs and maintained by a local repeater group. The users are encouraged to join repeater groups and contribute to the upkeep and administration. Repeaters are normally to be found on high ground; they are unmanned and, to the user, fully automatic. They are designed to help extend the coverage of mobile and portable stations.

▶**How repeaters work**
The repeater's receiver continually monitors the input frequency. All repeaters need a 1750Hz initial access tone-burst. This tone must be between 300 and 500 milliseconds long. Some may additionally need a few seconds of speech or a certain strength of signal to operate successfully. The repeater receiver's squelch tells the repeater if it has a signal to relay. If the repeater sends a 'T' or 'K' in Morse code, it indicates that a person can proceed to use the repeater. Most repeaters automatically time the length of overs which are typically two minutes for VHF and five minutes for UHF. If the over lasts longer than this, the repeater will *time out* which means it will stop relaying the input. All repeaters identify themselves in Morse code by sending a callsign at least every 15 minutes. The callsign is typically GB3 plus two letters. The difference in frequency between input and output on 432MHz is 1.6MHz and on 145MHz is 600kHz.◀

Operating through repeaters
The procedure for working through repeaters is slightly different to that employed on the simplex frequencies. To put out a general call, you would use your callsign and also that of the repeater, eg "G4QME listening through GB3PI" is usually sufficient. If you are calling someone specifically through a repeater, put their call first – eg "G2XYZ from G4QME, are you about, John?" At the beginning and end of each over, you need only give your own callsign, eg ". . . this is G4QME" or ". . . from G4QME". Keep your overs short because of the time-out feature and also because, if mobile, you could be moving out of the repeater service area. Repeaters are not designed for long chats between local fixed stations, or for DX operation. An up-to-date list of all UK repeaters can be obtained from the RSGB.

Satellites

Artificial satellites used by radio amateurs

▶OSCAR satellites (orbital satellites carrying amateur radio) have been part of the amateur radio scene since the first launch in 1961. This is an area of the hobby in which radio amateurs have played a significant part in the development of technology which has then been translated into commercial use. Much of the research into the designing and building of low-cost LEO (low earth orbit) satellites has been undertaken at Surrey University under the direction of Professor Martin Sweeting, OBE, G3YJO.◀

Amateur satellites have many different modes of operation and use, some of which are as follows:

1. As 'flying repeaters' they transpond signals between various amateur bands, eg 2m to 70cm, 2m to 10m etc. It is vital to consult the band plans to be familiar with the uplink and downlink frequencies.
2. They enable the use of VHF/UHF to relay signals over much greater intercontinental distances than otherwise would be possible under 'flat band' conditions. This also lets the Class B licence holder have access to communication distances usually only available on bands below 30MHz.
3. Phone, CW, packet and data modes are available, depending on the satellite in use.
4. Some take pictures of the Earth from space for use by amateurs.
5. Beacon transmissions relay telemetry data about the satellite's operating parameters eg temperatures, state of battery charge etc.
6. Propagation studies may be undertaken by monitoring signals as the satellites pass below the horizon.

▶In addition, both the American Space Shuttle programme and the Russian Mir Space Station have active educational amateur radio operations called 'SAREX' for the Shuttle and 'MIREX' for Mir. On selected Shuttle missions, SAREX contacts are made with groups of schools to encourage active participation in the space programme. These SAREX QSOs are scheduled by the ARRL who should be contacted for further details. Space Station Mir has also been activated on phone and packet by Russian cosmonauts as well as visiting international astronauts (including Helen Sharman contacting UK schools as GB1MIR in 1991). As a semi-permanent station, non-scheduled Mir contacts can be made by amateurs on phone and packet with more chance of success than for the Space Shuttle, but the competition for such QSOs over Europe is quite fierce as many amateurs greatly value a contact with space!◀

Operating through satellites

Accessing a satellite does not require an access tone as the satellite monitors incoming signals continuously and its transmitter is permanently operational.

Obviously the satellite will only receive sufficient signal when it is in direct line-of-sight to the transmitter. This happens periodically when the satellite, which is rotating round the Earth, appears over the horizon.

The power required to use the Oscar series transponders is 80–100W ERP. This power level is usually achieved with a low-power transmitter (10–15W output) followed by an antenna with a gain of 10dB. The antenna must be pointed in the direction of the satellite to achieve this gain and so it must move in both azimuth and elevation in order to track the satellite properly. This can lead to complex antenna systems if best results are desired, although simple fixed antennas are capable of satisfactory operation if correctly designed. Information on the current amateur radio satellite scene can be obtained from AMSAT-UK which is the national arm of AMSAT, the international amateur radio organisation which co-ordinates the collection of funds and the construction of such satellites for use by radio amateurs. Their details can be obtained from the RSGB.

Comparison of operating through repeaters and satellites

A brief comparison of the modes of operation of repeaters and satellites may be useful:

- A repeater accepts FM signals at a single frequency and re-transmits them in the same band. An access tone (1750Hz) is often required (sometimes only for the initial transmission of a contact) and the input signal must be of the correct frequency and deviation.
- A satellite transponds a band of frequencies from one amateur band to another and will accept any form of modulation (CW, SSB and RTTY are preferred).
- A repeater extends the user's range by a relatively small factor and the final range is still essentially local under most conditions. However, a satellite permits coverage of very long distances on VHF and UHF.

Q-CODES AND ABBREVIATIONS

Q-codes are used when sending Morse code. They enable information to be shortened for speed of sending. CW would be rather laborious if everything had to be sent in full.

The international Q-code is sometimes rather like a series of questions and answers, and the Q-signals in Table 2.5, which are taken from the official list, are commonly used in the Amateur Service. For example, QRS? means "Shall I send more slowly?", which might be answered by QRS ("Send more slowly"). You might also send PSE QRS, which would be understood to mean "Please send more slowly". Amateurs use many of the Q-signals as nouns as well as in question-and-answer form (see Table 2.6).

▶After Samuel Morse had sent his first line telegraph message in May, 1844, and after the setting up of coast-to-coast telegraph lines in the USA, messages were being sent and received across the country. To speed up the flow of traffic, it was realised that short codes could be sent to replace simple sentences and phrases and these could be decoded when received. The first conference held to try and establish some common standards on this issue was held in the USA in April 1857. This resulted in the production of the *National Telegraphic Review and Operator's Guide*. This is where the meaning of '73' was first recorded (at that time it meant "love and kisses" – it now means "best wishes"). Two years later the Western Union brought out the Standard 92 Code. Each number from 1 to 92 equated to a sentence or phrase. The receiving station had a list of numbers and their meanings and, once received, the numbers were turned back into plain language for the recipient. The telegraph and railway companies all had their own, different, codes, with resulting confusion. In 1908 the British Post Office issued its own list of two-letter abbreviations for use between coastal stations and ships. These ranged from RA to RZ and SA to SF. At an international Telegraphic Convention held in London in 1912, the Post Office abbreviations were adopted and extended by the addition of a 'Q' as prefix to the already existing codes. Hence, the Q-code was born. It became accepted as the standard international code for military and civil telegraphy. There have been some changes and refinements over the years, resulting in the present-day code.◀

PHONETIC ALPHABET

The phonetic alphabet is used mainly in telephony operation to avoid ambiguity. It is particularly used when sending information such as callsign, name and town, especially when conditions between the stations are difficult. Very often letters can sound the same over the air, eg 'S' and 'F', 'T' and 'D', whereas 'Sierra' and 'Foxtrot', 'Tango' and 'Delta' could never be confused. See Table 2.7.

▶Necessity is the mother of invention and during the First World War the first official alphabet was being used by the forces to avoid misunderstandings when passing vital messages.

Table 2.5. International Q-code (extract)

QRG	Will you tell me my exact frequency? Your exact frequency is ....kHz
QRH	Does my frequency vary? Your frequency varies.
QRI	What is the tone of my transmission? The tone of your transmission is ....(amateur T1–T9)
QRK	What is the readability of my signals? The readability of your signals is......(amateur R1–R5).
QRL	Are you busy? I am busy. Please do not interfere.
QRM	Are you being interfered with? I am being interfered with.
QRN	Are you troubled by static? I am troubled by static.
QRO	Shall I increase power? Increase power.
QRP	Shall I decrease power? Decrease power.
QRQ	Shall I send faster? Send faster.
QRS	Shall I send more slowly? Send more slowly.
QRT	Shall I stop sending? Stop sending.
QRU	Have you anything for me? I have nothing for you.
QRV	Are you ready? I am ready.
QRX	When will you call me again? I will call you again at ....hours.
QRZ	Who is calling me: You are being called by .... (on kHz).
QSA	What is the strength of my signals? The strength of your signals is..........(amateur S1–S9).
QSB	Are my signals fading? Your signals are fading.
QSD	Is my keying defective? Your keying is defective.
QSL	Can you give me acknowledgement of receipt? I give you acknowledgement of receipt.
QSO	Can you communicate with ....direct or by relay? I can communicate with ....direct (or by relay through..........).
QSP	Will you relay to........? I will relay to ....
QSV	Shall I send a series of VVVs? Send a series of VVVs.
QSY	Shall I change to another frequency? Change to transmission on another frequency (or on .....kHz).
QSZ	Shall I send each word more than once? Send each word twice?
QTH	What is your location? My location is..........
QTR	What is the correct time? The time is ....hours.

Table 2.6. Use of Q-signals as nouns

QRA	Address	QRP	Low power
QRG	Frequency	QRT	Close down
QRI	Bad note	QRX	Stand by
QRK	Signal strength	QSB	Fading
QRM	Interference from other stations	QSD	Bad sending
		QSL	Verification card
QRN	Interference from atmospherics or local electrical apparatus	QSO	Radio contact
		QSP	Relay message
		QSY	Change of frequency
QRO	High power	QTH	Location

In 1945, another phonetic alphabet had emerged, beginning 'Able', 'Baker', 'Charlie', 'Dog'. With the growing popularity of flight, there was a need for an agreed international alphabet for air traffic control purposes. This developed into the NATO phonetic alphabet we have today. It is interesting to note that the only phonetic which has remained constant through all the variations is 'Charlie' ◀.

Table 2.7. Recommended phonetic alphabet

A	Alpha	J	Juliett	S	Sierra
B	Bravo	K	Kilo	T	Tango
C	Charlie	L	Lima	U	Uniform
D	Delta	M	Mike	V	Victor
E	Echo	N	November	W	Whiskey
F	Foxtrot	O	Oscar	X	X-ray
G	Golf	P	Papa	Y	Yankee
H	Hotel	Q	Quebec	Z	Zulu
I	India	R	Romeo		

BAND PLANNING

So that all forms and modes of communication can co-exist on the crowded wavebands, a form of order has to be maintained. Apart from restrictions laid down within the licence, this is achieved by agreed band plans, which designate certain areas of the bands for specific modes of operation, thus helping to provide the best utilisation of the amateur spectrum. In the UK, the band plans are not mandatory but the vast majority of amateurs observe these voluntary regulations because they are, in the end, of benefit to all. These band plans should not be confused with conventions, such as the use of lower sideband (LSB) below 10MHz and upper sideband (USB) above 10MHz. Because band plans are not fixed, and may be changed following International Amateur Radio Union (IARU) Conferences, it is advisable to check on the latest position which can be found in current RSGB publications.

Example of band planning

The lower end of the 10m band (28.000MHz–28.150MHz) is set aside for CW and digital modes. Both these modes are relatively narrow in bandwidth. If SSB signals were allowed in that segment, the CW and digital modes would be swamped by the wider SSB signals. A section of the 28MHz band is set aside for beacons, which give a real-time indication of propagation paths. In general these can be found between about 28.200MHz and 28.300MHz. Even if you might not be able to hear any signals, your transmissions would not be appreciated by the many stations who monitor the frequencies continuously or for the automatic stations logging propagation. Also on 28MHz, the section between 29.300MHz and 29.500MHz is reserved exclusively for satellite down-links. As can be seen, it is beneficial to know your bands!

SAFETY
Safety precautions in the amateur station

The main unseen danger lurking in the amateur shack is that of high voltage. While much amateur equipment uses transistors operating from a 13.5V supply, many high-power HF, VHF and UHF linear amplifiers with valves operating at voltages over 2000V are in use.

It is not possible to define a voltage which is 'safe to touch' – no voltage source should ever be touched deliberately. The effects of an electric shock of a particular voltage depend on various factors, from the source of the voltage to the state of health of the person receiving the shock.

It is therefore best to consider any voltage above 30V as dangerous and to act accordingly. Probably the three most important precautions are:

1. Ensure that all equipment is satisfactorily earthed and that the earthing system is checked periodically.
2. Switch off and disconnect all equipment from the mains supply before attempting inspection or repair.
3. Capacitors of high value, particularly if the dielectric is paper, will hold their charge for long periods (days/weeks) and may be lethal. Bleed resistor chains should therefore be connected across high-voltage smoothing capacitors in order to dissipate this charge within a few seconds. Bleed resistor chains should be conservatively rated as regards dissipation and ideally should consist of two separate chains in parallel. In spite of the presence of bleed resistor chains, high-voltage smoothing capacitors should be shorted as recommended in paragraph 5 of the RSGB Safety Recommendations given below before any servicing of a power supply is carried out.

Using a low-voltage power supply can still create dangers, though these may not be at first apparent. The mains voltage of 240V will still be present in the unit which can be fatal if accessible. The high current capability of many power supplies may be sufficient to generate molten metal if the supply is accidentally shorted to earth by, say, a ring on one's finger. Similar problems can exist with nicads and some other batteries, including car batteries.

The electromagnetic compatibility aspects of the protective multiple earthing (PME) system of house wiring are dealt with at the end of this chapter. The installation of PME systems in the UK started in the mid-'seventies. It would seem likely therefore that the majority of houses in UK do not use PME. Before modifying any RF grounding or safety grounding in your station, it is essential to find out whether your property uses PME. If you are at all unsure, contact your Regional Electricity Supply company (REC) for advice.

RSGB Safety Recommendations for the Amateur Radio Station
1. All equipment should be controlled by one master switch, the position of which should be well known to others in the house or club.
2. All equipment should be properly connected to a good and permanent earth. (Note A and PME Section)
3. Wiring should be insulated to easily withstand the voltage in use especially if this is 500V or more. Also, terminals should be suitably protected.
4. Transformers operating at more than 100V RMS should be fitted with an earthed screen between the primary and secondary windings.
5. Capacitors of more than 0.01μF capacitance operating in power packs, modulators etc (other than for RF bypass or coupling) should have a bleeder resistor connected directly across their terminals. The value of the bleeder resistor should be low enough to ensure rapid discharge. A value of $1/C$ megohms (where C is in microfarads) is recommended. The use of earthed probe leads for discharging capacitors in case the bleeder resistor is defective is also recommended. (Note B). Low-leakage capacitors, such as paper and oil-filled types, should be stored with their terminals short-circuited to prevent static charging.
6. Indicator lamps should be installed showing that the equipment is live. These should be clearly visible at the operating and test position. Faulty indicator lamps should be replaced immediately. Gas-filled (neon) lamps are more reliable than filament types.
7. Double-pole switches should be used for breaking mains circuits on equipment. Fuses of correct rating should be connected to the equipment side of each switch. (Note C). Always switch off before changing a fuse. The use of AC/DC equipment should be avoided.
8. When using metal-enclosed equipment, install primary circuit breakers such as micro-switches (which operate when the door or lid is opened). Check their operation frequently.
9. Test probes and test lamps should be suitably insulated.
10. A rubber mat should be used when the equipment is installed on a floor that is likely to become damp.
11. Switch off before making any adjustments. If adjustments must be made while the equipment is live, use one hand only and keep the other in your pocket to prevent an electrical path through your body should you touch high voltage by mistake. Never attempt two-handed work without switching off first. Use good-quality insulated tools for adjustments.
12. Do not wear headphones while making internal adjustments on equipment connected to the mains supply.
13. Ensure that the metal cases of microphones, Morse keys etc are properly connected to the earthed chassis.
14. Do not use meters with metal zero-adjusting screws in high-voltage circuits. Beware of live shafts projecting through panels, particularly when metal grub screws are used in control knobs.
15. Antennas should not, under any circumstances, be connected through a capacitor which may have HT on the other side; a low-resistance DC path to earth should be provided (RF choke).

Note A – Owing to the common use of plastic water main and sections of plastic pipe in effecting repairs, it is no longer safe to assume that a mains water pipe is effectively connected to earth. Steps must be taken, therefore, to ensure that the earth connection is of sufficiently low resistance to provide safety in the event of a fault. Checks should be made whenever repairs are made to the mains water system in the building.

Note B – A 'wandering earth lead' is an insulated lead permanently connected at one end to the chassis of the equipment; at the other end a low-value resistor (1.0kΩ is suitable) for touching the high-potential terminals to be discharged. The resistor is necessary to prevent an 'explosive' spark when high-capacitance capacitors are discharged, which could cause injury to the operator or damage to the capacitor.

Note C – Where necessary, surge-proof fuses can be used.

RSGB Mobile Safety Recommendations
1. All equipment should be constructed and installed so that, in the event of accident or sudden braking, it cannot become dislodged and injure the occupants of the vehicle.
2. Mobile antennas should be soundly constructed, taking into account flexing at speed and possible danger to other vehicles or pedestrians. The maximum height should not exceed 14ft above ground.
3. Wiring should not constitute a hazard, either electrical or mechanical, to driver or passengers.

4. All equipment should be adequately fused and a battery isolation switch is desirable.

5. The transmit/receive switch should be within easy access of the operator and one changeover switch should perform all functions.

6. The microphone when attached to the vehicle should not impair the vision or movement of the driver.

7. When the driver is operating he should not use a hand microphone or headphones covering both ears.

8. All major adjustments, for example a band change, should be carried out while the vehicle is stationary.

9. Essential equipment controls should be adequately illuminated during the hours of darkness.

10. All equipment must be switched off when (a) fuelling, (b) in close proximity to petrol tanks and (c) near quarries where charges are detonated electrically.

11. A suitable fire extinguisher should be carried and be readily accessible.

RF and microwave hazards

A great deal of research has been done on the effects of exposure to radio frequencies. It is generally agreed by Western scientists that the only biologically significant property of RF energy is heating of cells and that this is only a hazard if the heat is not removed quickly by the body's temperature regulating mechanisms. This is the principle of the microwave oven and medical diathermy. RF radiation is therefore totally different in its properties to ionising radiations such as gamma rays and X-rays. The maximum level for continuous exposure to RF has been set at a power density of $10mW/cm^2$.

Close proximity to a source of RF energy must be avoided. Measurements of power density made in the vicinity of various 300–400W output amateur stations operating on 28MHz and 144MHz and their antennas have given values of less than $1mW/cm^2$. Calculation shows that standing 20cm from a vertical quarter-wave antenna fed with 140W at 28MHz is equivalent to being in a $10mW/cm^2$ field. This is not, however, a normal situation to be in!

Microwave radiation itself is not more hazardous, but the smaller area over which microwaves are likely to radiate results in a greater power density. Any exposure to RF which results in a sensation of heat is far in excess of $10mW/cm^2$ and is therefore very dangerous. The eyes are particularly susceptible to damage in this way.

Situations to be avoided:

1. Do not look down a waveguide unless you know that there is no RF present.

2. Do not work on high-power RF equipment with the covers off. (There is probably high voltage present as well!)

3. Do not use an unscreened dummy load or a small antenna in the shack for test purposes.

4. Do not adjust antennas using full power; use low power only.

5. Do not use a hand-held set without a thick insulating cap on the end of the antenna.

6. Hold the hand-held set so that the antenna is as far as possible from the face.

PME

The protective multiple earthing system is where the mains earth of the house wiring is bonded to the neutral where the electricity supply enters the building. Some houses, particularly those built or wired since the mid-'seventies in the UK use this system. Under certain rare fault conditions it is possible for the earth and neutral conductors all over the house to rise to a voltage which is significantly above that of true earth. In extreme cases the earth/neutral voltage could reach full mains voltage above true earth. It is therefore not advisable to connect any radio earths to any metalwork inside the house. All metallic surfaces within a house on the PME system, ie gas/water pipes, central heating system etc are bonded together at the consumer unit. This gives a highly reliable earth of low impedance.

If you are not sure whether your house is on PME, check with your local Regional Electricity Company (REC). If you would like more information on PME, write to the RSGB enclosing an SAE for a PME leaflet in relation to amateur radio.

PRACTICE QUESTIONS FOR CHAPTER 2

1. Initially a transmitter should always be tuned to
   (a) an SWR meter
   (b) a Yagi antenna
   (c) a dummy load
   (d) a half-wave dipole.

2. COIL spelt using the International Phonetic Alphabet would be
   (a) Charlie, Ocean, Italy, Lima
   (b) Charlie, Oscar, India, Lima
   (c) Coil, Oscar, Inductance, London
   (d) Charlie, Oscar, India, London.

3. The band plans should be observed because they
   (a) are mandatory
   (b) are governed by international regulations
   (c) aid good operating
   (d) are only for novices.

4. The Q-code for changing frequency is
   (a) QSF
   (b) QSY
   (c) QRF
   (d) QCF.

5. The difference in frequency between input and output of a 432MHz repeater in the UK is
   (a) 600kHz
   (b) 1.6MHz
   (c) 2.4MHz
   (d) 4.5MHz.

6. In a CW call the abbreviation $\overline{\text{KN}}$ indicates
   (a) any station can reply to the call
   (b) this is the end of a test transmission
   (c) the reply is expected immediately
   (d) reply only expected from the station called.

7. A readability report of R4 indicates
   (a) unreadable
   (b) readable with considerable difficulty
   (c) readable with practically no difficulty
   (d) perfectly readable.

8. When using a repeater, priority should be given to
   (a) stations operating /M
   (b) DX stations in Europe
   (c) members of the local repeater group
   (d) stations operating from the home base.

9. In a CW contact 'WX' refers to
   (a) working conditions
   (b) weather
   (c) wife
   (d) type of antenna.

10. Which of the following uses the International Phonetic Alphabet?
    (a) Alpha, Norway, Delta.
    (b) Charlie, Alpha, Tosca.
    (c) Denmark, Oscar, Gordon.
    (d) Bravo, Uniform, Golf.

11. The Q-code used by amateurs to mean fading is
    (a) QSB
    (b) QRG
    (c) QRF
    (d) QSY.

12. For reasons of safety which one of the following should be used across a high-value capacitor?
    (a) An inductor.
    (b) A bleed resistor.
    (c) A short-circuit.
    (d) An open-circuit.

13. When replying to a CQ call on telegraphy it is advisable to reply
    (a) at a speed you can receive
    (b) at a faster CW speed
    (c) by changing to telephony
    (d) with QRZ.

14. The band plans in the UK are
    (a) to be observed for good operating practice
    (b) applicable only to contacts outside the UK
    (c) enforceable by the RA
    (d) applicable only to inter-UK contacts.

15. The tone required for repeater access is
    (a) 1725Hz
    (b) 1750Hz
    (c) 1775Hz
    (d) 1800Hz.

16. When making a CQ call it is good practice to
    (a) use a frequency occupied by a weak station
    (b) always use CW well in from the band edge
    (c) only call DX stations using high power
    (d) ask if the frequency is clear before starting.

17. In the RST code, which of the following represents a perfectly readable signal?
    (a) R1
    (b) R5
    (c) S5
    (d) S9.

18. In order to activate a UK repeater, it is necessary to
    (a) obtain a special licence
    (b) be a member of the local repeater group
    (c) use a toneburst
    (d) send K or T in CW.

19. The Q-code for 'stand by' is
    (a) QRN
    (b) QRM
    (c) QRS
    (d) QRX.

20. In a telephony contact it is advisable to
    (a) speak as fast as possible in order to clear the frequency
    (b) speak very slowly using phonetics as often as possible
    (c) use Q-codes as often as possible
    (d) speak clearly and not too quickly.

21. The recommended phonetic spelling of VALE is
    (a) Volt, Alpha, Lima, Echo
    (b) Victor, Alpha, London, Echo
    (c) Victor, America, Lima, Echo
    (d) Victor, Alpha, Lima, Echo.

22. The only general call allowed from an amateur station is
    (a) a news bulletin
    (b) a CQ call
    (c) a third party call
    (d) on VHF.

23. Directional CQ calls should
    (a) not be made
    (b) be ignored
    (c) only be made in CW
    (d) be respected.

24. When working through a satellite
    (a) only use sufficient power to maintain reliable communication
    (b) it is necessary to have special permission from the Licensing Authority
    (c) one must be a member of AMSAT UK
    (d) high power must be used at all times.

25. In the UK, a 2m repeater is accessed by a tone of
    (a) 1650Hz
    (b) 1700Hz
    (c) 1750Hz
    (d) 1800Hz.

26. Having established contact with another station on a calling frequency, one should
    (a) continue the QSO on that frequency
    (b) move to another frequency, having first checked it is clear
    (c) move to an agreed frequency, even if it is already in use
    (d) remain on the calling frequency.

27. Using Morse telegraphy, 'QTH' is used to denote
    (a) "How do you copy?"
    (b) location
    (c) "How many watts?"
    (d) "Will you repeat?"

28. The purpose of a terrestrial repeater is to
    (a) increase satellite coverage
    (b) increase the range of mobile stations
    (c) increase the range of fixed stations
    (d) minimise contacts of pedestrian stations.

29. Using the International Phonetic Alphabet, RADIO would be
    (a) Romeo, Alpha, Delta, India, Oscar
    (b) Radio, Alpha, Delta, India, Oscar
    (c) Romeo, Alpha, Denmark, India, Oscar
    (d) Radio, Alpha, Delta, Italy, Oscar.

30. When calling a station, it is good practice to
    (a) put your callsign before the station being called
    (b) use your callsign only when in contact
    (c) put the callsign of the station being called first
    (d) use the callsign of the other station only.

31. In the RST code, 'T' stands for
    (a) temperature
    (b) tone
    (c) time
    (d) transmitter.

32. Using the Q-code, interference from other stations on the band is known as
    (a) QRI
    (b) QRM
    (c) QRN
    (d) QRO.

33. If a signal report of R5 is received it is
    (a) almost unreadable
    (b) readable with considerable difficulty
    (c) readable with practically no difficulty
    (d) perfectly readable.

34. When using CW, the invitation for a specific station to transmit is
    (a) $\overline{BT}$
    (b) K
    (c) $\overline{KN}$
    (d) $\overline{VA}$

35. Using the International Phonetic Alphabet DIAL would be
    (a) Delta, India, Alpha, Lima
    (b) Denver, India, Able, Log
    (c) Delta, Italy, Able, Lima
    (d) Diode, India, Alpha, Logo.

36. To be able to operate through a satellite, one must
    (a) use an access tone
    (b) get permission from AMSAT
    (c) call the satellite with its number
    (d) just transmit in the correct frequency range.

37. The Q-code for "Who is calling me?" is
    (a) QRW?
    (b) QRZ?
    (c) QRQ?
    (d) QRX?

38. For safety the integrity of the earthing system should be checked
    (a) every decade
    (b) when you move house
    (c) periodically
    (d) in the spring.

39. When testing on live equipment it is good practice to
    (a) keep one hand in a pocket
    (b) use uninsulated probes
    (c) have both hands in the equipment
    (d) use a soldering iron.

40. The main purpose of a repeater is to
    (a) improve communication between mobile stations
    (b) provide a convenient frequency for local nets
    (c) aid DX working during lift conditions
    (d) aid propagation studies.

41. When using telephony, it is good practice to
    (a) use the phonetic alphabet as much as possible
    (b) always use Q-codes
    (c) speak clearly and not too quickly
    (d) make long transmissions before allowing the other station to reply.

42. The letter 'C' after an RST report indicates
    (a) aurora
    (b) clicks
    (c) chirp
    (d) drift.

43. The 'golden rule' in Morse telegraphy is
    (a) never send faster than one can receive
    (b) send as fast as the transmitting station
    (c) send slower than one can receive
    (d) keep to 20 WPM.

44. The Q-code for closing down is
    (a) QRT
    (b) QRC
    (c) QRZ
    (d) QRX.

45. Using the International Phonetic Alphabet, HENRY would be
    (a) Hotel, Enrica, Norway, Romeo, Yankee
    (b) Hotel, Echo, Nancy, Romeo, Yokohama
    (c) Hotel, Echo, November, Romeo, Yankee
    (d) Hotel, Echo, November, Radio, Yankee.

46. The duration of an access tone for a UK repeater should be at least
    (a) 100ms
    (b) 300ms
    (c) 1 second
    (d) 5 seconds.

47. The use of repeaters by base stations
    (a) should be encouraged
    (b) is allowed by the RA
    (c) will damage the repeater
    (d) should not be encouraged.

48. Which one of the following represents a fairly good signal strength using the RST code?
    (a) R5.
    (b) S2.
    (c) S5.
    (d) S8.

49. Band plans should be
    (a) ignored at all times
    (b) observed because they are mandatory
    (c) used only by new operators
    (d) observed because they are an aid to operating.

50. The Q-code for interference caused by static bursts would be
    (a) QSL
    (b) QRM
    (c) QRZ
    (d) QRN.

51. When calling CQ in Morse, the transmission should be terminated by
    (a) $\overline{K}$
    (b) $\overline{KN}$
    (c) $\overline{AR}$
    (d) $\overline{CT}$.

52. It is good practice for
    (a) plastic piping to be used as an earth
    (b) all metal cases to be unearthed
    (c) there to be no master switch
    (d) all power to be supplied via a master switch.

53. When working through a satellite use
    (a) as much power as possible
    (b) CW at 100 wpm
    (c) sufficient power to maintain reliable communication
    (d) FM only.

54. If a readability report of R1 is given, this would indicate
    (a) an unreadable signal
    (b) readable with considerable difficulty
    (c) readable with practically no difficulty
    (d) perfectly readable.

55. To obtain an indication if a particular international path is open on HF
    (a) call CQ to the country required on any HF band
    (b) look at the propagation forecasts
    (c) telephone the licensing authority
    (d) examine the weather forecasts.

56. When operating through a repeater
    (a) only use CW at 12 WPM
    (b) give priority to mobile stations
    (c) do not give any breaks between overs
    (d) give priority to base station nets.

57. To access a repeater in the UK one must
    (a) send the callsign of the repeater in ASCII
    (b) send a 1750Hz tone burst
    (c) send an 1850Hz tone burst
    (d) speak the callsign of the repeater.

58. The abbreviation using the Q-code for high power is
    (a) QRH
    (b) QRP
    (c) QRX
    (d) QRO.

59. When wearing headphones it is not safe to
    (a) be calling CQ
    (b) be switching off
    (c) have one's hands inside live equipment
    (d) have rubber gloves on.

60. An RF choke is commonly connected between the antenna and earth. The purpose of the choke is to
    (a) help tune the system
    (b) reject some interference
    (c) provide a DC path to prevent high-voltage static build-up
    (d) prevent excessive power being radiated.

61. When using voice transmissions, it is wise to
    (a) use jargon continuously
    (b) use plain language
    (c) use Q-codes as much as possible
    (d) speak as fast as possible.

62. It is good practice to
    (a) leave pauses between overs on a repeater
    (b) leave no pauses between overs on a repeater
    (c) let base stations have priority on a repeater
    (d) test a repeater with a tone burst three times before using it.

63. If a K is sent after the report in a CW contact this means
    (a) a crystal-controlled signal
    (b) key clicks on the signal
    (c) carrier on the signal
    (d) cross-modulation on the signal.

64. For safety reasons all exposed metalwork in an amateur station should be
    (a) connected to the live
    (b) free of the earth
    (c) left floating
    (d) connected to earth.

65. A satellite will
    (a) relay only a single band of frequencies
    (b) relay any band of frequencies
    (c) need a toneburst for access
    (d) only be operated by a personal code.

66. If a station requests "please QSY" this means
    (a) there is fading
    (b) change frequency
    (c) stop transmitting
    (d) reply in Morse.

67. In the International Phonetic Alphabet, ZEBRA is
    (a) Zulu, Echo, Bravo, Romeo, America
    (b) Zebra, Elephant, Bravo, Romeo, Alpha
    (c) ZuIu, Echo, Bravo, Romeo, Alpha
    (d) Zanzibar, Echo, Bravo, Romeo, America.

68. Using the RST code, a barely readable signal with only occasional words distinguishable is
    (a) R1
    (b) R2
    (c) R3
    (d) R4.

Check your answers using the key in Appendix 4.

3 Electronic principles and practice

MOLECULES, ATOMS, AND ELECTRONS

All matter is comprised of *molecules*; the molecule is the smallest quantity of a substance which can exist and still display all the physical and chemical properties of that substance.

Molecules are made up of smaller particles called *atoms*, of which there are over 100 different types. All molecules consist of various combinations of these atoms, for example, two atoms of hydrogen and one of oxygen form one molecule of water, and sulphuric acid is made up of two atoms of hydrogen, one of sulphur and four of oxygen.

Atoms are so small that they cannot be seen under the most powerful optical microscope but their structure is most important in electrical and communication engineering.

Atoms consist of a relatively heavy, positively charged core or nucleus, around which a number of much lighter negatively charged electrons move in one or more orbits. A 'normal' atom will have equal numbers of electrons and protons.

One type of atom differs from another in the number of positive and neutral particles known as *protons* and *neutrons* which make up the nucleus and the number and arrangement of the negative *electrons* which are continually orbiting round the nucleus. Some atoms are extremely complex, having a large number of electrons in several orbits, and others are quite simple as with the hydrogen and helium atoms.

Under some circumstances it is possible to detach an electron from an atom, particularly when its outer orbit contains only one electron. In other atoms it is virtually impossible to detach an electron.

CONDUCTORS AND INSULATORS

The ease with which electrons can be detached from their parent atoms varies from substance to substance. In some materials there is a continual movement of electrons in a random manner from one atom to another, and the application of a voltage (for example from a battery) to the two ends of a piece of wire made of such a substance will cause a drift of electrons along the wire – this is an *electric current*. It should be noted that if an electron enters the wire from the battery at one end it will be a different electron which immediately leaves the other end of the wire.

By convention, the direction of current flow is said to be from positive to negative – this is the reason for the term *conventional current*. Materials which conduct electricity are called *conductors*. All metals belong to this class. Materials which do not conduct electricity are called *insulators*. See Table 3.1.

The use of electricity in all branches of electrical engineering depends on the existence of a conductor to carry the electric current and insulators to oppose flow of the current so that it stays in the conductor.

Table 3.1. Materials commonly used as conductors and insulators	
Conductors	**Insulators**
Silver	Mica
Copper	Ceramics
Aluminium	Plastics

In practice, the conductor is almost universally a single or stranded wire of copper, generally tinned for ease of soldering. For some applications the copper may be silver plated (silver is a slightly better conductor than copper).

Many different insulators are in common use, from mica and glazed ceramic to synthetic materials such as PVC, polythene, polystyrene and PTFE, the last three of which have good insulating properties at very high frequencies.

ELECTRICAL UNITS

Current

The unit of current flow is called the *ampere* (symbol 'A') and the strength of a current is said to be '*x* amperes'. Currents are indicated in formulae by the variable I. The currents used in radio are often very small fractions of an ampere and for convenience the two small units *milliampere* (10^{-3}A) and *microampere* (10^{-6}A) are used. A current of 0.003 ampere is written as '3 milliamperes' or '3mA' for short. See Table 3.2 for abbreviations.

Voltage

In order to make a current flow through a circuit, it is necessary to have some device which can produce a continuous supply of electrons. This may be a battery, in which the supply of electrons is produced by chemical action, or a dynamo or generator in which mechanical energy is converted into electrical energy. The battery or generator produces an *electromotive force* (EMF, symbol E) which may be used to force a current through a circuit. The unit of electric potential is the *volt* (abbreviated to 'V'), and voltages are usually denoted in formulae by the variable V.

Resistance

The ease with which an electric current flows through a wire depends on the dimensions of the wire and the material from which it is made. The opposition of a circuit to the flow of current is called the *resistance* of the circuit. The resistance of a circuit is measured in *ohms* (symbol Ω). For convenience, because the resistances used in radio equipment may be up to $10,000,000\Omega$, two larger units called the *kilohm* (1000Ω) and the *megohm* ($1,000,000\Omega$) are used. The kilohm is usually abbreviated to 'k' and the megohm to 'M', eg

Table 3.2. Units and symbols

Quantity	Symbol used in formulae	Unit	Abbreviation
Current	I	ampere	A
EMF	E	volt	V
Electric potential	V	volt	V
Time	t	second	s
Resistance	R	ohm	W
Capacitance	C	farad	F
Inductance	L	henry	H
Mutual inductance	M	henry	H
Power	W	watt	W
Frequency	f	hertz (one cycle per second)	Hz
Wavelength	λ	metre	m

Abbreviations for multiples and sub-multiples

T	tera	10^{12}
G	giga	10^{9}
M	mega	10^{6}
k	kilo	10^{3}
c	centi	10^{-2}
m	milli	10^{-3}
μ	micro	10^{-6}
n	nano	10^{-9}
p	pico	10^{-12}

$47,000\Omega$ would be written '47kΩ'. Resistance is normally denoted by R in formulae.

THE DIRECT CURRENT CIRCUIT

Fig 3.1(a) is the simplest possible circuit where a current from a battery flows through R. The ratio of the voltage across the circuit to the current which flows though it is a constant:

$$R = \frac{V}{I}$$

which is known as the *resistance* (R), and is the opposition to the flow of the electric current, while the relationship is known as *Ohm's Law*. V is measured in volts and I in amperes (amps); R is then in ohms.

It should be noted that in this circuit the current I also flows through the battery, which has an internal resistance r. Thus the EMF of the battery is the total voltage available to drive the current I through a total resistance of $(R + r)$. Therefore the EMF is equal to $(IR + Ir)$. Some voltage is inevitably lost in driving the current through the battery itself. That which is left to do useful work is known as the *potential difference*

between the points a and b. The best battery is one with the lowest internal resistance.

By simple manipulation two other formulae can be formed: $V = I \times R$ (which shows that the voltage across a resistor is equal to the value of the resistor, multiplied by the current flowing through it) and $I = V/R$ (indicating that the current through any resistor can be found by dividing the voltage across it by the value of the resistor). The definition of 'resistor' appears later in the section with that heading.

An easy aid to remembering the three formulae is shown in Fig 3.1(b). Simply remember this picture and then by covering the quantity required its value in terms of the other two will be revealed.

Power in the DC circuit

An electric current flowing through a resistance causes heat to be dissipated in the resistance. Electrical energy is converted into heat energy.

The power dissipated in the resistance is:

power (watts) = voltage (volts) × current (amps)

$$W = V \times I$$

By the use of Ohm's Law, the power dissipated in the resistance may be expressed in two other forms:

$$W = V^2/R \quad \text{and} \quad W = I^2 \times R$$

All materials have the property of resistance. In the case of metals suitable for use as conductors of electricity, eg copper (silver is better but is of course much more expensive), it is very low. Special alloys intended for heating elements are made with a very high resistance. Nichrome, for example, has a resistance which is about 60 times that of copper. Insulators are materials which have an extremely high resistance and therefore for all practical purposes do not conduct electricity. Some materials, such as germanium and silicon, have a resistance which is higher than that of conductors but is lower than insulators. These are known as *semiconductors*.

The resistance of a conductor is proportional to its length and inversely proportional to its cross-sectional area. It also depends upon the material from which the conductor is made.

The *resistivity* of a material is the resistance measured between the opposite faces of a 1cm cube of the material.

RESISTORS
In series

A discrete component having the property of resistance is called a *resistor*. A number of these can be connected as shown in Fig 3.2(a). This is the *series* connection and the effective resistance R is:

$$R = R_1 + R_2 + R_3 + \ldots$$

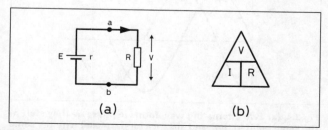

(a)   (b)

Fig 3.1. (a) A simple DC circuit. (b) Triangle diagram to help you remember Ohm's Law

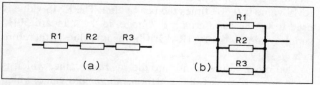

(a)   (b)

Fig 3.2. Resistors (a) in series and (b) in parallel

In parallel

The *parallel* connection is shown in Fig 3.2(b). The effective resistance in this case is:

$$\frac{1}{R} = \frac{1}{R_1} + \frac{1}{R_2} + \frac{1}{R_3} + \ldots$$

or

$$R = \frac{1}{\dfrac{1}{R_1} + \dfrac{1}{R_2} + \dfrac{1}{R_3} + \ldots}$$

The effective resistance of only two resistors in parallel is:

$$R = \frac{R_1 \times R_2}{R_1 + R_2} \quad \text{ie} \quad \frac{\text{Product}}{\text{Sum}}$$

The commonest forms of resistor are:

(a) carbon (in the form of a rod);
(b) spiral carbon or metal oxide track (on glass or ceramic former);
(c) wire wound (with high-resistance wire).

They are graded according to their *dissipation*, ie the amount of heat they can dissipate safely for a given temperature rise.

A connection may be taken from the junction of two resistors in series. This combination is known as a *fixed potentiometer* or *potential divider* because when it is connected across a source of voltage it enables any required proportion of the voltage to be obtained according to the values of the two resistors. These are generally fairly high in value to avoid putting too heavy a load on the source.

The two resistors are often replaced by a single resistor in which the position of the 'tap' is varied by a sliding contact (a *variable potentiometer*).

The main application of the resistor in electronic circuits is to create a given voltage drop across it for a particular purpose as a result of a known current flowing through the resistor (by Ohm's Law). A fairly high value of resistor may often be employed to provide a leakage path to earth from a particular part of the circuit. Resistors are also used as the load across which the output of an amplifier stage is developed, or in which the output of a transmitter is dissipated.

THE ALTERNATING CURRENT CIRCUIT

In the AC circuit the voltage and current are not constant with time as in the DC circuit; the value of each alternates between positive and negative states.

The AC waveform is shown in Fig 3.3 and is a *sine wave* or *sinusoidal* waveform. There are two values of the amplitude of this waveform which are relevant:

(a) the peak value;
(b) the RMS value.

The *peak* value is clear from Fig 3.3 and the *root mean square* (RMS) value is that value which is equivalent in heating effect to a DC supply of the same value. For a sine wave, the RMS value is 0.707 times the peak value. The RMS value is used to define an alternating voltage, ie the standard 50Hz supply mains is 240V (RMS) (the peak value is therefore nearly 340V).

Two other values of use are the *average* value, which is 0.636 times the peak value, and the *instantaneous* value, which is the value of the current (or voltage) at a particular instant

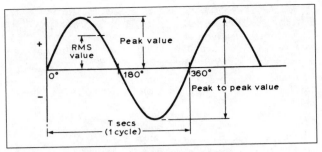

Fig 3.3. An alternating (sinusoidal) waveform

in an alternating cycle. It is usually denoted by small letters, ie *i* (or *v*).

The time occupied by one complete cycle is the *period T* and the number of cycles per second (hertz) is the *frequency f*.

$$f = \frac{1}{T} \quad \text{and} \quad T = \frac{1}{f}$$

Phase difference between waveforms

'Phase' in this context means 'time' or time difference between two waveforms. For convenience, this time difference or phase difference is measured in degrees; one complete cycle of the waveform is taken to be 360° and a half-cycle is 180° etc. The time difference between two alternating waveforms can be defined by the phase angle between them.

Two alternating waveforms are said to be *in phase* when they begin at the same point in time: see Fig 3.4(a). At any other point they are *out of phase*. The term *in phase opposition* is sometimes used to describe a phase difference of 180°. In this case, two waveforms of equal amplitude would cancel each other.

In Fig 3.4(b), A leads B by 90°, conversely B lags on A by 90°.

▶**Distortion of alternating waveforms**

Distortion of an alternating waveform is caused by the presence of other sinusoidal waveforms of frequencies which are related to the original frequency (known as the *fundamental*); if the fundamental

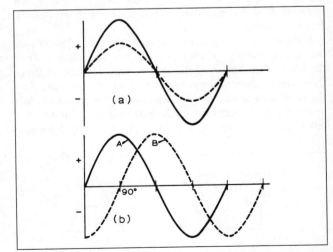

Fig 3.4. (a) Two alternating waveforms in phase, ie they start at the same point in time and increase (or decrease) with the same polarity. (b) Two alternating waveforms with a phase difference of 90°

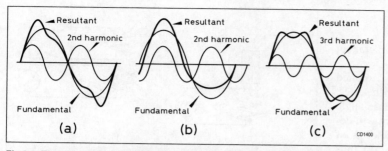

Fig 3.5. The distortion created by the addition of second harmonic (a) and (b) and third harmonic (c) to the fundamental

frequency is f, then $2f$ is the *second harmonic*, $3f$ is the *third harmonic* and so on.

Fig 3.5(a) shows the distortion resulting from the addition of 30% of second harmonic which starts in phase with the fundamental, Fig 3.5(b) 30% of second harmonic which starts 90° to the fundamental and Fig 3.5(c) the result of adding 20% third harmonic which starts in phase with the fundamental. Distortion increases as the number and amplitude of the harmonics present increases. A distorted waveform is often known as a *complex waveform*. Note that the resultant in Fig 3.5(a) is moving towards a sawtooth waveform and in Fig 3.5(c) is moving towards a square wave.

In practice it is the inability of the electronic circuit to provide an output having the same 'shape' as the input which causes distortion. If the output waveform has a shape which resembles that produced by adding a certain harmonic, eg second harmonic as shown in Fig 3.5(b) the distortion is said to be *second harmonic*. ◄

Inductance and capacitance in the AC circuit

Two new circuit elements are of great importance in the AC circuit. These are:

(a) the inductor which has inductance;
(b) the capacitor which has capacitance.

A circuit possesses inductance if it can store energy in the

form of a magnetic field. The unit of inductance is the *henry* (H) and the symbol for inductance is L.

► A circuit has an inductance of one henry if a current in it, changing at the rate of one ampere per second, induces an EMF of one volt. The energy stored in an inductor is $\frac{1}{2}LI^2$ joules, where L is in henrys and I is in amperes. ◄

A circuit possesses capacitance if it can store energy in the form of an electric field. The unit of capacitance is the farad (F); the symbol for capacitance is C.

►A circuit has a capacitance of one farad if a charge of one coulomb sets up a voltage of one volt across it. The energy stored in a capacitor is $\frac{1}{2}CV^2$ joules, where C is in farads and V is in volts.◄

The farad is an impracticably large unit and the practical unit is the *microfarad* or μF (0.000001 farad).

Note that no energy is stored in an inductor if there is no current flowing. In a capacitor, however, there need be no movement of charge and the energy stored is static. A good-quality capacitor can maintain a considerable, perhaps lethal, voltage across its terminals, long after being charged up.

If the effect of resistance is temporarily ignored, the opposition to the flow of an alternating current is the *reactance* (X).

Inductive reactance X_L is the reactance due to an inductance and:

$$X_L = 2\pi f L$$

(π is a mathematical constant which may be taken as 22/7 or 3.14 to two decimal places). X_L is in ohms when f is in hertz and L in henrys.

Similarly, capacitive reactance X_C is the reactance due to a capacitor and:

$$X_C = \frac{1}{2\pi f C}$$

X_C is in ohms when f is in hertz and C in farads. (Note that $2\pi f$ is often written as ω in mathematical formulae.)

Fig 3.6 shows the variation of reactance with frequency.

When an alternating voltage V is applied to a resistance R the current which flows is exactly in step with the voltage. The voltage and current are said to be *in phase*. The value of the current will be by Ohm's Law:

$$I = \frac{V}{R} \qquad \text{amps}$$

When an alternating voltage V is applied to an inductor L (Fig 3.7) the current which flows will lag behind the voltage, the phase difference being 90°. The current flowing is given by:

$$I_L = \frac{V}{X_L}$$

where X_L is the inductive reactance, $2\pi f L$ ohms.

When an alternating voltage V is applied to a capacitor C (Fig 3.8) the current leads the voltage by 90°. The current which flows is given by:

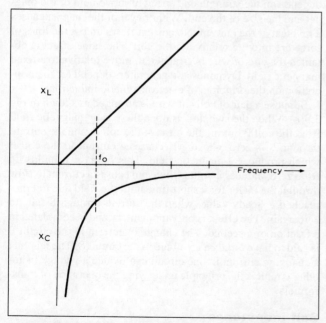

Fig 3.6. How the reactance of a capacitor and an inductor vary with frequency

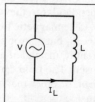

Fig 3.7. Alternating voltage applied to an inductor L

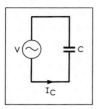

Fig 3.8. Alternating voltage applied to a capacitor C

$$I_C = \frac{V}{X_C}$$

where X_C is the capacitive reactance, $1/(2\pi f C)$ ohms.

When an alternating voltage is applied to an inductor and a capacitor in series, the current flowing and the phase angle between the voltage and current will depend upon the effective reactance X of the circuit, ie $(X_L - X_C)$ or $(X_C - X_L)$; thus the circuit will be inductive if X_L is greater than X_C or capacitive if X_C is greater than X_L.

If there is a resistor R in series with the inductor and capacitor, the total opposition to the flow of an alternating current is known as the *impedance (Z)*. This impedance is made up of resistance R and the effective reactance X. Both R and X are measured in ohms but they must not be added arithmetically. As a result of the 90° phase shift introduced by the inductance and capacitance, they must be added vectorially, ie by taking the square root of the sum of the squares of R and X:

$$Z = \sqrt{(R^2 + X^2)}$$

Ohm's Law can now be applied and so the current flowing is:

$$I = \frac{V}{Z}$$

The following relationships should be noted:

Capacitors in series: $\quad \dfrac{1}{C} = \dfrac{1}{C_1} + \dfrac{1}{C_2} + \dfrac{1}{C_3} + \ldots$

Capacitors in parallel: $\quad C = C_1 + C_2 + C_3 + \ldots$

Inductors in series: $\quad L = L_1 + L_2 + L_3 + \ldots$

Mutual inductance (which will be discussed later) is assumed to be zero.

MAGNETISM
Permanent magnets

The magnet and its properties of attracting a piece of iron by exerting a magnetic force on it or causing a compass needle to be deflected, are well known.

Magnets made from certain types of steel and alloys of aluminium, nickel and titanium etc retain their magnetism more or less permanently. Such magnets find many uses in radio equipment such as moving-coil meters, headphones and loudspeakers.

Electromagnets

An electric current flowing through a straight wire creates a magnetic field, the lines of force of which are in a plane perpendicular to the wire and concentric with the wire.

The magnetic field surrounding a straight wire is relatively weak, but a strong magnetic field can be produced by a current if, instead of a straight wire, a coil of wire or *solenoid* is used. The field can be greatly strengthened if a piece of soft iron or other magnetic material (known as a *core*) is placed inside the coil.

The magnetic field produced by a solenoid is similar to that produced by a bar magnet and it exhibits identical properties.

The extent by which the strength of the solenoid magnet is

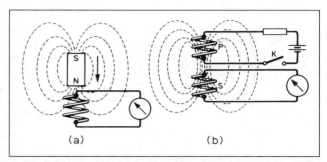

(a)   (b)

Fig 3.9. Electromagnetic induction. (a) Relative movement of magnet and coil causes a voltage to be induced in the coil; (b) when the current in one of a pair of coupled coils changes in value, a voltage is induced in the second coil

increased by the introduction of the core is called the *permeability* of the core material. Permeability is really the ratio of the number of lines of force (or *flux density*) in the magnetic core to the flux density in a vacuum (ie no magnetic core). The difference between a vacuum and an air core is so small that it is ignored. As it is a ratio, strictly it should be referred to as *relative permeability* (μ_r), but the word 'relative' is often omitted in common use.

The strength of a magnetic field produced by a current is directly proportional to the current. It also depends on the number of turns of wire, the area of the coil and the permeability of the core.

ELECTROMAGNETIC INDUCTION

If a bar magnet is moved into a solenoid, as indicated in Fig 3.9(a), the moving coil microammeter connected across the coil shows a deflection. The explanation of this phenomenon, known as *electromagnetic induction*, is that the movement of the magnet's lines of force past the turns of the coil causes a voltage to be induced in the coil which in turn causes a current to flow through the meter. The magnitude of the effect depends on the strength and speed of movement of the magnet and the size of the coil. Withdrawal of the magnet causes a reversal of the current. No current flows unless the lines of force are moving relative to the coil. The same effect is obtained if a coil of wire is arranged to move relative to a fixed magnetic field. Dynamos and generators depend for their operation on the principle of electromagnetic induction.

Suppose a pair of coils of wire is arranged as shown in Fig 3.9(b). When the switch K is open there is no magnetic field from the coil P linking the turns of the coil S, and the current through S is zero. Closing K causes a current in the coil P which produces a magnetic field. This field, as it builds up from zero, induces a voltage in S and causes a current to flow through the meter for a short time until the field due to P has reached a steady value, when the current through S falls to zero again. The effect is only momentary and is completed in a fraction of a second. The change in current in the circuit P is said to have *induced* a voltage in the circuit S. The fact that a changing current in one circuit can induce a voltage in another circuit is the principle underlying the operation of transformers.

Self-inductance

If a steady current is flowing through a coil, there is a steady magnetic field due to that current. A current change tends to alter the strength of the field, which in turn induces in the coil a voltage (*back EMF*) tending to oppose the change being made. A negative sign is generally used before a back EMF to indicate that it opposes the supply voltage. This process is called *self-induction*. A coil is said to have *self-inductance*, usually abbreviated to *inductance*. It has a value of one henry (H) if, when the current through the coil changes at a rate of one amp per second, the voltage appearing across its terminals is one volt. Inductance is usually denoted by the symbol *L* in formulae. As the inductance values used in radio equipment may be only a fraction of a henry, the units *millihenry* (mH) and *microhenry* (μH) (0.001 and 0.000001H respectively) are commonly used.

▶The inductance of a coil varies as the square of the number of turns, the cross-sectional area, and the permeability of the core, and inversely as the length of the magnetic path.

$$L \propto \frac{\mu_r A T^2}{l} \blacktriangleleft$$

Mutual inductance

A changing current in one circuit can induce a voltage in a second circuit (see Fig 3.9(b)). The strength of the voltage induced in the second circuit S depends on the closeness or *tightness* of the magnetic coupling between the circuits; for example, if both coils are wound together on an iron core, practically all the lines of force or magnetic flux from the first circuit link with the turns of the second circuit. Such coils are said to be *tightly coupled* but if the coils are both air-cored and spaced some distance apart they are *loosely coupled*.

▶The mutual inductance between two coils is measured in henrys, and two coils are said to have a *mutual inductance* of 1H if when the current in the primary coil changes at a rate of 1A/s the voltage across the secondary is 1V. Mutual inductance is denoted in formulae by the symbol *M*.

The mutual inductance between two coils may be measured by joining the coils in series, first so that the sense of their windings is the same, and then so that they are reversed. The total inductance is measured in each case.

If L_a and L_b are the total measured inductances, L_1 and L_2 are the separate inductances of the two coils and M is the mutual inductance, then:

$$L_a = L_1 + L_2 + 2M$$

$$L_b = L_1 + L_2 - 2M$$

$$L_a - L_b = 4M$$

$$M = \frac{L_a - L_b}{4}$$

Therefore the mutual inductance is equal to one quarter of the difference between the series-aiding and series-opposing readings.◀

INDUCTORS USED IN RADIO EQUIPMENT

An inductor consists of a number of turns of wire. However, within the framework of this simple definition there is an extremely wide range of inductance values and types of construction. For example, an inductor required as a tuning coil at VHF might have an inductance of 0.5μH; this would probably be one or two turns of 2mm wire and self-supporting. At the other extreme, a smoothing choke in a power unit would

have an inductance of, say, 30H and consist of between 1000 and 2000 turns wound on a paxolin bobbin with a laminated iron core. If this choke was designed to carry a current of 500mA, it might weigh about 6kg and occupy a 15cm cube in volume. Specialist low-frequency applications may require inductance values up to 500H.

The form of construction depends basically on the inductance value required. The number of turns of wire necessary to give the inductance depends on the permeability of its core. Air has a permeability of 1 but there are magnetic materials which have a very much higher permeability. To achieve a reasonably high inductance without having to wind many thousands of turns of wire on an 'air' core, fewer turns are wound on a magnetic core appropriate to the particular frequency involved.

The commonest magnetic core is made up of laminations, normally 0.3mm thick, of silicon iron. Laminations are available in many shapes and sizes and are insulated on one side so that when they are assembled in a core they are insulated from each other. This reduces the power loss due to *eddy currents* induced in the core. The commonest shape of lamination is a pair, one T-shaped and the other U-shaped, so that they fit together when assembled into the paxolin bobbin which carries the winding. This type of core is standard for low-frequency chokes and power transformers. Thinner laminations of different types of iron are available for use at frequencies in the audio range.

Radio-frequency coils are usually air-cored, either self-supporting or wound on low-loss plastic or ceramic formers. The number of turns involved is often quite small, with inductance values up to about 20μH.

Larger values of inductance up to 1 or 2mH at frequencies from about 100kHz upwards may be wound on dust iron or ferrite cores. A dust iron core is a core of very finely divided iron alloy moulded in an insulating medium. Being moulded, different shapes and sizes can be made cheaply. Often a brass-threaded rod is moulded into a small cylindrical core. This reduces the inductance. The position of the core within the coil can then be adjusted to vary the inductance value to tune the coil to a specific frequency. This is known as *slug tuning*.

Modern ferrite cores are non-ferrous materials of high resistivity, and therefore low eddy current loss.

Moulded cores are often in two similar halves as a *pot core*. The winding is put on a small plastic bobbin which goes inside the two halves and so is surrounded by the ferrite material. Ferrite materials are also moulded in the form of a ring or *toroid* (a *toroidal* core). Cores of this type ensure that the magnetic flux is nearly all contained within the windings, ie there is practically no stray field.

CAPACITORS USED IN RADIO EQUIPMENT

Capacitance may be defined as the ability of a conductor to store an electric charge. A device in which this effect is enhanced is called a *capacitor*. In its simplest form, the capacitor consists of two parallel plates as shown in Fig 3.10. The material between the plates is known as the *dielectric*; in this case the dielectric is air.

The capacitance of this type of capacitor is proportional to the area of the plates and inversely proportional to the distance between them. It also depends upon a property of the dielectric known as the *permittivity* (the *dielectric constant*). As in the

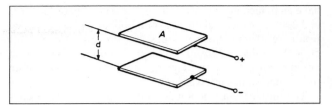

Fig 3.10. A parallel-plate capacitor. The capacitance is proportional area *A* and inversely proportional to the spacing *d*

case of permeability, referred to earlier, permittivity is a quantity referred to the vacuum (or air) state. Therefore it is a ratio or relative property.

Typical relative permittivities are:

Air	1
Paper	2 approx
Polythene, rubber etc	2–3 approx
Mica	5 approx
Ceramics	10 and upwards

The dielectric material determines the maximum frequency at which a capacitor may be used, eg paper up to 20MHz or so, some ceramics and plastics (polythene or polystyrene) up to 150 to 200MHz, and mica even higher.

The capacitor exists in many forms and is classified by the material used as the dielectric. The range of capacitance commonly available is from 1pF to at least 1,000,000µF = 1 farad. Capacitors have the property of being able to store a charge of electricity and must be capable of withstanding a voltage difference between the plates. The larger the plates and/or the smaller their separation, the greater is the charge that the capacitor holds for a given voltage across its plates. If the voltage between the plates becomes too high the capacitor will flash over or break down. The safe working voltage is therefore an important property of a capacitor. Capacitors are made with working voltages from 6V to many thousands of volts.

It is clear from its form of construction that a capacitor presents an open-circuit to a direct current but it appears to pass an alternating current because of the charge and discharge which takes place as the value of the alternating applied voltage changes.

Mica capacitors are normally made up to a value of 0.01µF and may be used up to very high frequencies (VHF). They consist of a stack of plates interleaved with layers of mica, which are clamped together, dipped in wax or potted in resin. In the silvered-mica type, the plates are made by spraying a very thin layer of silver on to the mica dielectric.

Synthetic dielectrics such as polystyrene, polytetrafluoroethylene (PTFE) and polycarbonate in the form of thin film have now generally replaced paper as their dielectric loss is lower. This means that they can be used at higher frequencies than the normal limit of about 20MHz for paper.

Ceramic capacitors are made by spraying silver plates on to both sides of a ceramic cup, disc or tube. The ceramic used has high permittivity so that a high capacitance is obtained in a small volume. They are made in relatively low working voltages and are most commonly used as bypass capacitors at VHF.

The feedthrough capacitor is a form of ceramic capacitor in which one plate is a threaded bush on the outside of a

ceramic tube (the 'dielectric'), and the other plate a stiff wire through the centre of the tube. This type is used for feeding through power supplies into a screened box; it combines a feedthrough insulator with a bypass capacitor.

Electrolytic capacitors have plates of aluminium or tantalum foil with a semi-liquid conducting compound, often in the form of impregnated paper, between them. The dielectric is a very thin insulating layer which is formed by electrolytic action on one of the foils when a DC polarising voltage is applied to the capacitor. As the dielectric is very thin and the permittivity is very high, extremely high values of capacitance can be put into a small space. The capacitance value can be 1,000,000µF or more.

▶Capacitors having a very high value such as 1F are often used to provide 'backup' in the place of a small battery in some computers.◀

There is a small leakage current through an electrolytic capacitor and it must be emphasised that generally they are polarised, ie one terminal is positive and the other is negative. Although electrolytic capacitors can withstand a small ripple (alternating) current, this polarity must be strictly observed otherwise the capacitor may explode.

The capacitor has many uses:

(a) as part of a tuned circuit;

(b) as a coupling capacitor between two stages in an RF or AF amplifier, it 'passes' AC but holds off the direct voltage supply to the first stage from the input to the following stage;

(c) a capacitor of the appropriate value provides a low-impedance path at a particular frequency or range of frequencies and is used to bypass to earth unwanted AF or RF voltages which may occur on the direct voltage supply line (this is known as *decoupling*). The smoothing capacitors in a power supply perform an identical function by bypassing harmonics of the supply frequency to earth. (In practice the charge in the capacitor maintains the supply while the capacitor is not being charged.) More information on this effect will be found in the section on power supplies.

THE DECIBEL NOTATION

The need to compare voltage levels or power levels at different points in a circuit or at different frequencies very often arises in radio engineering.

The most realistic way to do this is by means of the decibel notation which is based on logarithms as the following example shows.

Consider the statement "The power level has increased by 1W." What does this mean? Obviously an increase in power from 0.25W to 1.25W is vastly different from an increase from 10W to 11W or from 100W to 101W, yet in each case the power level has increased by 1W.

The effect of a 1W increase in power in each case may be compared with the use of the decibel notation. The difference between a power level W_1 and a power level W_2 when expressed in decibels is:

$$\text{Number of decibels} = 10 \log_{10} \frac{W_2}{W_1}$$

In the above examples

(a) 0.25W to 1.25W

Increase in decibels $= 10 \log_{10} \dfrac{1.25}{0.25} = 7\text{dB}$

(b) 10W to 11W

Increase in decibels $= 10 \log_{10} \dfrac{11}{10} = 0.4\text{dB}$

(c) 100W to 101W

Increase in decibels $= 10 \log_{10} \dfrac{101}{100} = 0.04\text{dB}$

The advantage of this notation is therefore obvious. Voltages may also be compared in this way, since:

$$W = \frac{V^2}{R}$$

$$\frac{W_2}{W_1} = \frac{V_2^2}{R_2} \div \frac{V_1^2}{R_1}$$

$$= \frac{V_2^2}{R_2} \times \frac{R_1}{V_1^2}$$

If, and only if, $R_1 = R_2$ then:

$$\frac{W_2}{W_1} = \frac{V_2^2}{V_1^2}$$

hence number of decibels $= 10 \log_{10} \dfrac{V_2^2}{V_1^2}$

$$= 20 \log_{10} \frac{V_2}{V_1}$$

Other ratios may be calculated easily from the above. If two decibel figures are added, the corresponding power or voltage ratios must be multiplied, eg

45dB = 40dB + 5dB = 100 × 1.78 (voltage ratios)
    = 178

A wide range of power and voltage ratios is given in Table 3.3.

The decibel notation is a way of expressing a ratio, therefore it can only be used to express a magnitude when a reference level is defined. This is often done as follows.

The unit 'dBW' specifies a power level which is so many decibels above one watt, ie the reference level. +20dBW is a power level which is 20dB above one watt, ie 100 watts. The + sign here is quite often omitted. (Note 0dBW is zero decibels above 1 watt, ie it is 1 watt!)

This is the method now used to express transmitter output power in the UK amateur radio licence.

Powers less than 1 watt are also expressed in this way, eg −20dBW means 20dB down on 1 watt, that is 10mW (the negative sign here is never omitted).

Similarly, 20dBmW is 20dB up on 1mW or 100mW. And −20dBmW is 20dB below 1mW, that is 10μW.

Other common examples of the use of the decibel are:

(a) The variation in gain of an audio amplifier at different frequencies may be expressed as so many decibels above or below the gain at, say, 1000Hz.

dB	Power ratio	Voltage ratio	dB	Power ratio	Voltage ratio
1	1.26	1.12	15	31.6	5.62
2	1.58	1.26	20	100	10
3	2.00	1.41	30	1000	31.6
4	2.51	1.58	40	10^4	10^2
5	3.16	1.78	50	10^5	316
6	3.98	2.00	60	10^6	10^3
7	5.01	2.24	70	10^7	3160
8	6.31	2.51	80	10^8	10^4
9	7.94	2.82	90	10^9	31600
10	10.00	3.16	100	10^{10}	10^5

Table 3.3. Ratios of power and voltage in terms of decibels

(b) The characteristic of a bandpass filter is specified by its shape factor which is the ratio of its bandwidths at −60dB and −6dB.
(c) The variation in level of the selectivity or response curve of a tuned circuit or receiver is expressed in decibels (see Fig 4.6).
(d) The AGC characteristic of a receiver is a graph of the variation in output of the receiver (in decibels) plotted against increasing signal input (also in decibels).

▶Other reference levels used are *dBV* and *dBmV* ('dBmW' is commonly abbreviated to 'dBm'). *dBd and dBi* are used to compare the gain of an antenna with reference to a dipole or an isotropic radiator respectively.◀

Acoustic power level (ie loudness) is also specified in decibels, a standard reference level being assumed.

TUNED CIRCUITS

The parallel and series connections of an inductor and a capacitor to form a tuned circuit are shown in Figs 3.11(a) and 3.11(b) respectively.

At one particular frequency, the numerical values of the reactance of the inductor and the reactance of the capacitor will be equal (see Fig 3.6), that is:

$$X_\mathrm{L} = X_\mathrm{C}$$

or

$$2\pi f_\mathrm{r} L = \frac{1}{2\pi f_\mathrm{r} C}$$

This can be simplified to give:

$$f_\mathrm{r} = \frac{1}{2\pi \sqrt{LC}}$$

(f_r is in hertz when L is henrys and C in farads). f_r is called the *resonant frequency* of the tuned circuit.

There are inevitably losses associated with all tuned circuits because neither the inductor nor the capacitor is perfect;

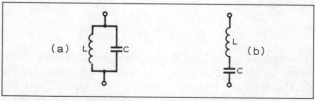

Fig 3.11. An arrangement of capacitor and inductor to form a tuned circuit; (a) parallel-tuned; (b) series-tuned

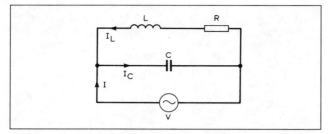

Fig 3.12. The relationship between voltage and current in a parallel-tuned circuit

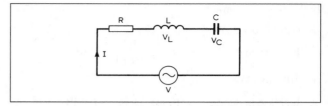

Fig 3.13. The relationship between current and voltage in a series-tuned circuit

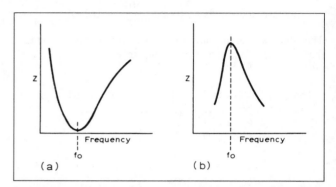

Fig 3.14. The impedance/frequency characteristics of (a) a series-tuned circuit and (b) a parallel-tuned circuit

these losses are always assumed to be resistive and are shown, when required, as a resistor R in series with the inductor.

Consider the circuit of Fig 3.12. It can be shown that the impedance at resonance of this circuit is L/CR ohms. By using Ohm's Law:

$$V = I \times \frac{L}{CR}$$

and

$$I_C = \frac{V}{X_C}$$

$$= I \times \frac{L}{CR} \times 2\pi fC$$

(It is convenient here to use ω rather than $2\pi f$.)

so that

$$I_C = I \times \frac{\omega L}{R}$$

Similarly it can be shown that the current which flows through the inductor is:

$$I_L = I \times \frac{\omega L}{R}$$

The currents flowing through the capacitor and the inductor I_C and I_L are both greater than the input current I by a factor of $\omega L/R$. This factor is called the *magnification factor* of the tuned circuit. It is generally just known as the 'Q' and may be quite large:

$$Q = \frac{\omega L}{R}$$

The current which flows through L and C is known as the *circulating current*. This, as shown above, can be quite large although the current I taken from the supply V may be small.

As a capacitor generally has quite low losses when correctly used, the Q of a tuned circuit is mainly determined by the inductor. The range of Q obtainable is roughly 100 to 400 depending on the type and form of the inductor. The Q may be reduced by the load placed upon the tuned circuit by the circuit which follows it.

The currents flowing through the inductor and capacitor vary with the frequency as they depend upon the term

$$\frac{\omega L}{R} \quad \left(\text{ie } \frac{2\pi fL}{R} \right)$$

If the ratio of I_L and I is plotted against frequencies above and below the resonant frequency, a curve similar in shape to Fig 3.15 is obtained. This curve is called a *response curve* because it indicates how the tuned circuit responds to different frequencies; it is also known as a *resonance curve*. The shape

of this curve is determined by the Q – the greater the Q, the higher and narrower the curve becomes.

The above discussion also applies to the series-tuned circuit (see Fig 3.13) in which the impedance is at a minimum at resonance and is equal to R. The voltages across the inductor and capacitor, not the current flowing in each, are calculated as before and the increase in the voltages is equal to Q. If in this case, the ratio V_L/V_C is plotted, a similar resonance curve is obtained.

The value of the impedance of the parallel-tuned circuit at resonance is known as the *dynamic resistance*. This is a fictitious resistance and exists for alternating currents at the resonant frequency. Its symbol is R_D.

The dynamic resistance can be expressed in terms of Q as follows:

$$R_D = \frac{L}{CR}, \quad \text{since } Q = \frac{\omega L}{R}, \quad R_D = \frac{Q}{\omega C}$$

A good-quality tuned circuit will have a R_D of about 50,000Ω. The DC resistance is usually very low.

The parallel-tuned circuit is by far the one most commonly used.

The series-tuned circuit, having minimum impedance at resonance, accepts maximum current at resonance and is sometimes known as an *acceptor circuit* (see Fig 3.14(a)).

In a parallel-tuned circuit, the impedance is at maximum at resonance. The parallel-tuned circuit is often called a *rejector circuit* because, having a high impedance at resonance, it rejects current at this frequency (see Fig 3.14(b)).

L/C RATIO

The resonant frequency of a tuned circuit is fixed by the product of inductance and capacitance, ie $L \times C$. There is an infinite number of values of L and C which will tune to a given frequency.

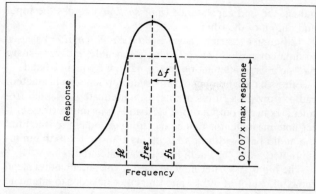

Fig 3.15. A resonance curve of a parallel-tuned circuit

The choice of the ratio of *L* and *C* is determined by practical considerations according to the particular use.

For instance, in receiver tuned circuits, in order to achieve a high value of dynamic resistance (required for high gain) the *L/C* ratio is high. The limitation here is that there is always a minimum value of capacitance inherent in any circuit (this is the *stray capacitance*).

In some applications, it may be required to swamp completely the stray circuit capacitance, in which case the *L/C* ratio is low.

The optimum choice of *L/C* ratio is sometimes difficult. As a compromise, it is convenient to assume that the value of *C* is 1.5pF per metre of wavelength; thus to tune to 30MHz (ie 10m) a capacitance of about 15pF would be reasonable.

RESONANCE CURVES AND SELECTIVITY

The ability of a tuned circuit to differentiate between a wanted frequency and an adjacent unwanted frequency is its *selectivity*. This depends upon its *Q*; good selectivity requires high *Q*.

Fig 3.15 is a typical response curve (or selectivity curve) of a tuned circuit. The width of this curve, ie $f_h - f_l$, is known as the *bandwidth* of the tuned circuit. Bandwidth can be defined at various levels, eg at the level where the response has fallen to $1/\sqrt{2}$ or 0.707 (70.7%) of the maximum response (this is also known as the *half-power point* or −3dB level). The ratio of the widths at −60dB and −6dB is known as the *shape factor*.

The relationship between bandwidth and *Q* is:

$$Q = \frac{f_r}{f_h - f_l} = \frac{f_r}{2\Delta f}$$

where f_r is the resonant frequency and $2\Delta f$ is $f_h - f_l$. From this it is seen that the lower *f* is, the lower Δf is, ie the bandwidth is less and selectivity is greater for a given value of *Q*. Similarly, the bandwidth is inversely proportional to *Q*; ie the higher the *Q*, the smaller the bandwidth.

The effect of several tuned circuits in cascade, eg in successive stages of an amplifier, is to reduce the overall bandwidth, ie increase the selectivity. This is particularly apparent in the region known as the *skirts* of the selectivity curve where the bandwidth is greatest. In the majority of cases, the aim is to increase the effective overall selectivity, but in some instances it is necessary to decrease the selectivity or increase the bandwidth. This is achieved by a *damping resistor*

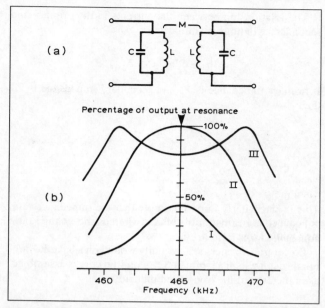

Fig 3.16. Inductively-coupled tuned circuits. Curves shown at (b) represent various frequency-response characteristics of the coupled circuit shown in (a) for different degrees of coupling

connected across the tuned circuit; the lower the resistor, the greater its effect.

▶ Coupled circuits

Pairs of coupled tuned circuits are often used in receivers and transmitters. The effect of varying the degree of coupling between two parallel tuned circuits resonant at the same frequency is shown in Fig 3.16.

When the coupling is loose, the response from one circuit to the other is as curve I. As the coupling is increased to what is known as *critical coupling*, the output at resonance increases to curve II; here the mutual coupling between the coils is 1/*Q* of the inductance of either coil. Further increase (tight coupling) results in the formation of the double-humped characteristic shown in curve III, where the output at resonance has decreased.

Two tuned circuits are often mounted in a screening can, the coils generally being wound the necessary distance apart on the same former to give the required coupling. The coupling is then said to be *fixed*. ◀

TRANSFORMERS

The principle of electromagnetic induction is illustrated in Fig 3.9(b). This is the basis of the transformer in which an alternating current flowing in the winding P creates an alternating magnetic field which cuts the turns of the winding S. It should be obvious that transformers can only operate on an alternating supply!

Transformers perform many vital functions in electrical and radio engineering; for example, the transfer of electrical energy from one circuit to another and, following from this, increasing or decreasing the alternating voltage.

If the number of turns on the primary and secondary are n_p and n_s respectively, n_p/n_s is the *turns ratio* and also the *voltage ratio*.

$$V_s = \frac{n_s}{n_p} \times V_p \quad \text{or} \quad \frac{V_s}{V_p} = \frac{n_s}{n_p}$$

These ratios can be greater or less than unity, ie *step up* or *step down*.

The relationship between the currents in the primary and secondary windings is similarly:

$$I_p = \frac{n_s}{n_p} \times I_s \quad \text{or} \quad \frac{I_p}{I_s} = \frac{n_s}{n_p}$$

If primary impedance is Z_p and secondary impedance is Z_s, then:

$$Z_p = \left(\frac{n_p}{n_s}\right)^2 Z_s$$

$$\text{or} \quad \frac{Z_p}{Z_s} = \left(\frac{n_p}{n_s}\right)^2$$

This is particularly important; note that the impedance ratio is equal to the turns ratio squared whereas the voltage ratio equals the turns ratio itself.

Power transformers are normally wound on a bakelite bobbin through which a laminated silicon iron core is assembled, as in the case of the iron-cored inductor.

FILTERS

Filters, or to give them their full name *wave filters*, are passive networks of capacitors and inductors which exhibit certain characteristics as the input frequency is varied. (A passive circuit is one which does not require any power supply other than the input signal.)

The filters of most interest in amateur radio are:

(a) *Low-pass filters.* A low-pass filter passes all frequencies below a specified frequency but attenuates frequencies above it.

(b) *High-pass filters.* A high-pass filter passes all frequencies above a specified frequency but attenuates frequencies below it.

The specified frequency referred to is the *cut-off frequency* (f_C). The configuration of the simplest form (*single section*) of each filter is shown in Fig 3.17 which also shows the general shape of the characteristics.

Two or three (or occasionally more) single-section filters may be connected in cascade to increase the rate of the fall-off of the response in the stop band. Further improvement may be achieved by connecting a series arrangement of

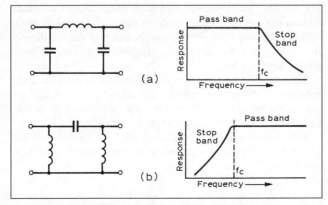

Fig 3.17. (a) A single section low-pass filter configuration together with its response curve. (b) A single-section high-pass filter configuration together with its response curve

inductance and capacitance (*half sections*) across the input and output of the filter.

Although not strictly a wave filter, a *T-notch filter* has uses in amateur radio. This provides a tuneable and very sharp *null*, ie a large attenuation over a narrow frequency band.

Filters have a number of important applications in amateur radio. Low-pass filters are used to attenuate unwanted frequencies in the output of the HF bands transmitter (transmitter-antenna matching unit connection). Another use is to limit the audio bandwidth of a telephony transmitter to the minimum necessary for intelligible communication.

The high-pass filter may be used in the antenna downlead (coaxial cable) of a television receiver in order to attenuate unwanted frequencies.

MIXING

The *mixing* or *heterodyne* process is one in which two signals are mixed to produce two new signals, one of which is equal in frequency to the sum of the original frequencies and the other equal to the difference between them. The undesired product and the two original frequencies are rejected by some form of filter which is generally a tuned circuit. This process is also called *frequency changing*, *frequency conversion* or *frequency translation* and is shown in Fig 3.18.

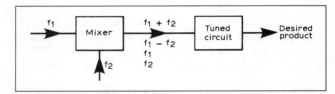

Fig 3.18. The process of frequency mixing

The mixer has many uses in communication engineering. In particular, it is the basis of the superheterodyne receiver and the single-sideband (SSB) transmitter.

Owing to various factors in the mixer element, spurious products harmonically related to the two original frequencies (f_1 and f_2) are often produced. The suppression of these is particularly important in an SSB transmitter. They may be reduced by careful mechanical layout of the circuit and the use of a push-pull, ie balanced, circuit. Further details will be found in Chapter 4.

TOLERANCE AND EFFECT OF TEMPERATURE ON COMPONENTS

These are important aspects of all electronic components, particularly resistors and capacitors.

Tolerance

The tolerance on the value of a component is a measure of how accurate its value is. For example, a resistor of nominal value $10,000\Omega$, and a tolerance of plus or minus 10% (written '±10%'), may have an actual resistance between 9000Ω (ie $10,000 - 10\%$) and $11,000\Omega$ (ie $10,000 + 10\%$).

The usual tolerances on the values of resistors and capacitors are ±20, 10, 5, 2 and 1%.

Temperature effects

Generally the value of a component increases as the temperature increases. A constant known as the *temperature*

Table 3.4. Preferred values

20% tolerance	10% tolerance	5% tolerance
10	10	10
–	–	11
–	12	12
–	–	13
15	15	15
–	–	16
–	18	18
–	–	20
22	22	22
–	–	24
–	27	27
–	–	30
33	33	33
–	–	36
–	39	39
–	–	43
47	47	47
–	–	51
–	56	56
–	–	62
68	68	68
–	–	75
–	82	82
–	–	91

coefficient is a measure of this increase, and (for most items) the temperature coefficient is positive.

There are a few exceptions, eg ceramic capacitors having a negative temperature coefficient can be made. Carbon and semiconductors have a negative coefficient.

PREFERRED VALUES

The three common ranges of basic *preferred values* for components are listed in Table 3.4. Resistors are made in multiples of basic values from 1Ω to $10^7\Omega$; capacitors from 1pF to about 1µF according to type and working voltage. Closer tolerance and high-stability types are made for special purposes.

QUARTZ CRYSTALS

▶A quartz crystal is a very thin slice of quartz which has been cut from a large, naturally occurring crystal of quartz. Quartz exhibits the *piezo-electric effect*, ie a mechanical strain applied to a suitably cut piece of quartz causes an electric stress to be set up between opposite faces of the piece. Conversely an electric stress applied between opposite faces of the piece causes a mechanical deformation. The frequency of resonance of this mechanical deformation depends upon the dimensions of the slice and the mode of vibration; other properties (eg temperature coefficient) depend upon the orientation of the slice with reference to an axis of the natural crystal. Fig 3.19 shows some of these properties.◀

Crystals can operate up to a frequency of about 22MHz in the fundamental mode, and up to about 200MHz in the *overtone* mode with the appropriate circuit. Overtone operation occurs at frequencies close to the odd multiples of the fundamental frequency.

Crystals for frequencies below about 1MHz are generally in the form of a bar rather than a thin slice; at 20kHz, for example, this bar is about 70mm long.

Connections to the modern crystal are made to electrodes of gold or silver which are deposited on opposite faces of the crystal. These connections also support the crystal, which is then hermetically sealed in an evacuated glass envelope or a small cold-welded metal container.

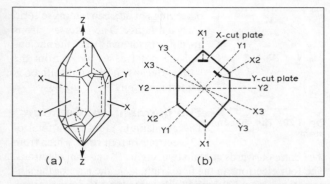

Fig 3.19. A natural quartz crystal indicating the relationship between X, Y and Z axes. The crystal usually has one pyramidal termination and a rough end where it has broken from the parent rock. (b) Various X and Y axes as viewed along a direction parallel to the Z axis and examples of the positions of the X-cut and Y-cut plates

The frequency of a crystal can be changed or *pulled* by a few kilohertz by variation of capacitance in parallel with it (a varactor diode or a variable capacitor).

The quartz crystal is equivalent to a very-high-Q tuned circuit and so can be substituted for the tuned circuit in an oscillator. Crystals are also used in pairs in band-pass filters.

SCREENING

It is often necessary to restrict the magnetic field around an inductor to prevent coupling between that inductor and another one close to. This is achieved by enclosing the inductor in an earthed metal can, this being known as *screening*. The can should be at least 1½ times the coil diameter from the coil, otherwise the Q of the latter will be degraded. Generally, it is not necessary to screen coils which are separated by at least three coil diameters or which are tuned to different frequencies.

It is often required to screen one part of a circuit from another, eg to prevent feedback from the output of a high-gain amplifier to its input, or to prevent an unwanted strong signal getting to the input of an amplifier.

Aluminium and preferably copper are satisfactory screening materials at radio frequencies, but a high-permeability alloy such as mu-metal is necessary at audio frequencies.

SOLID-STATE DEVICES

The majority of electronic circuits found in amateur equipment today use solid-state devices. These devices are based on *semiconductor* materials; these can be broadly defined as materials whose resistance lies between that of a conductor and an insulator. The most common materials in this category, silicon and germanium, are the basis of the majority of transistors and diodes.

The silicon (Si) atom

A simplified picture of a silicon atom is shown in Fig 3.20. Around the positive nucleus there are three rings (*orbits* or *shells*) containing negatively charged electrons. The sum of the negative charges balances the positive charge of the nucleus – so that the atom is electrically neutral. The first ring contains two electrons and cannot accept any more. The next ring contains eight electrons. However, the third ring contains only four electrons and these join with the four electrons in the

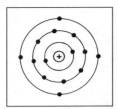

Fig 3.20. The silicon atom

outer rings of adjacent atoms to form a crystal lattice. The outer electrons are not very far away from the nucleus and are not free to move from the lattice. Because of this pure silicon is a good insulator.

The germanium (Ge) atom

The germanium atom has a total of 32 electrons in four rings which from the centre outwards contain two, eight, 18 and four electrons. The four electrons in the outer ring, as in the case of the silicon atom, join with those of adjacent atoms to form a crystal lattice. Because the electrons in the outer ring are further away from the nucleus, they can become detached more easily than in the silicon crystal. This means that germanium is not such a good insulator as silicon.

SEMICONDUCTOR MATERIALS

The manufacturing process of solid-state devices is complex: it requires the refinement of silicon and germanium to an extremely high purity and then the introduction of a very small but closely controlled amount of an impurity. It is this impurity that gives the base material (silicon or germanium) its semiconductor properties which provide transistor and diode action.

N-type material

In the manufacturing process, impurity atoms having an outer ring containing five electrons are introduced into the crystal lattice but, because only four electrons are needed to complete the crystal lattice, one electron from each impurity atom is released into the crystal. This electron is free to move and therefore provides a means of current flow. This process is known as *doping* and the resulting material is known as *N-type*. Typical impurities are phosphorus and arsenic.

P-type material

If the impurity added has only three electrons in its outer ring a gap is left in the lattice which could be filled by a free electron. Such a gap is called a *hole* and the resulting material is known as *P-type*. Typical impurities are boron and aluminium. The holes can also be moved around the crystal so allowing current to flow.

The doped material of both N- and P-types is electrically neutral because each one of the individual atoms present is itself electrically neutral.

THE PN JUNCTION

A diode consists of a small single piece of silicon or germanium in which one end has been made N-type and the other P-type. Because the two ends of the material have different characteristics as described above, there is a diffusion of holes in one direction and electrons in the other. This forms an area where electrons will have jumped into vacant holes and a boundary or junction formed, stopping any further migration of holes and electrons as shown diagrammatically in Fig 3.21. This area is known as the *depletion layer* and is typically 0.001mm in thickness.

The depletion layer has formed a region where work must be done to get further electron/hole movement, ie energy must

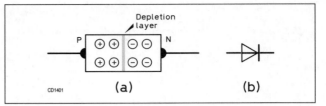

Fig 3.21. The junction diode

be provided externally. This can be provided in the form of a voltage from, say, a battery.

Consider the circuit of Fig 3.22 with the polarity of the battery as shown. The electrons from the N-region will be attracted by the positive plate of the battery and so will be assisted to cross the depletion layer. This will then leave holes in the N-region which are filled by electrons entering from the wire conductor and the rest of the circuit by a chain reaction. The electrons that enter the P-region will be pulled into the wire due to this chain reaction. Thus a conventional current flows (note that conventional current flow is in a direction opposite to that of electron flow). This condition is known as *forward bias*.

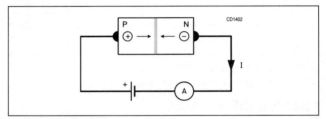

Fig 3.22. A forward-biased junction diode

If the polarity of the battery is reversed it is found that the electrons accumulate at the battery end of the N-region and similarly for the holes in the P-region.

The thickness of the depletion region has increased and negligible current flows. This is known as *reverse bias*. The device that has been formed is known as a *diode* (or *rectifier*). It allows current to flow in only one direction and this is determined by an externally applied voltage. In the forward bias condition no current flows until a certain voltage has been applied across the diode (called the *barrier potential*). With germanium this is about 0.3V and with silicon about 0.6V. This corresponds to the work that must be done in helping the electron to cross the depletion layer. The depletion layer becomes narrower with increased forward bias.

This property of the PN junction can be described by the graphs in Fig 3.23. A small current will flow under reverse bias conditions and increases with temperature. This is much more marked in germanium diodes than silicon diodes. This

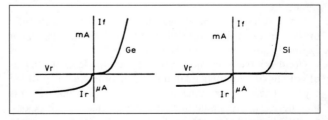

Fig 3.23. The characteristics of germanium and silicon diodes

current is known as *leakage current*. Please note the change in scale of the vertical axes.

This basic diode is used for the rectification of alternating voltages in power supplies, demodulating signals in radio receivers and certain logic functions. The type of diode for an application will depend on current, maximum reverse voltage to be expected and frequency.

By changes in the manufacturing process, diodes can be made to exhibit somewhat different characteristics. Two of these, the *zener diode* and the *variable-capacitance diode*, are examined next.

ZENER DIODE

In normal diodes only a small current will flow under reverse bias conditions until the voltage becomes so large that there is a catastrophic (sudden and absolute) breakdown of the diode and it is of no further use. With the zener diode the manu-

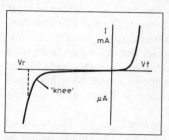

Fig 3.24. The characteristic of a zener diode

facture is such that only a small current flows up to a certain well-defined point, when there is a sudden increase in current and the voltage across the diode becomes virtually constant. Typical characteristics are shown in Fig 3.24.

There are technically two diodes, the zener and avalanche, depending on voltage, but by popular usage 'zener' is used to describe both types. These diodes are manufactured in various fixed values from less than 3V up to about 150V. They can be put in series for greater values. Zener diodes are useful in DC power supplies which need to provide a constant output voltage irrespective of loading and changes in input voltages.

VARIABLE-CAPACITANCE DIODE

This diode is also referred to as a *varactor diode* or more commonly as a *varicap diode*. It is used in the reverse bias mode and uses the width of the depletion layer to vary the capacitance. All diodes exhibit this effect to some extent but the doping of the semiconductor used can have a marked effect on the capacitance range available. The depletion layer can be likened to a parallel-plate capacitor – by widening the distance between the plates the capacitance drops and vice versa. As the reverse bias increases so the depletion layer widens and the capacitance decreases. This is depicted in Fig 3.25 for a BB110-type diode.

There are many different devices available with varying specifications covering the range from 2pF up to 600pF. Their use varies from tuning circuits to FM modulators and frequency multipliers.

NPN AND PNP TRANSISTORS

The word 'transistor' must be treated carefully. It is in fact a word describing a family of devices but is often used to refer to the NPN and PNP type only. The NPN and PNP transistors are *bipolar transistors*.

▶The transistor was invented in 1947 and entered production in 1951. Early types were made from germanium but silicon has

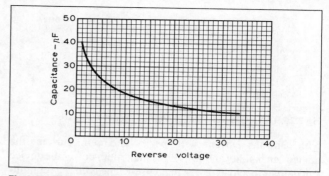

Fig 3.25. The variation in capacitance of a varactor diode

now surpassed them in most applications. It has also been fabricated in various forms, and names such as *junction*, *epitaxial*, *planar* etc are common in data sheets. The basic operation is, however, the same, the different methods of fabrication offering different characteristics.◀

The device is made from a single piece of silicon (or germanium). The various regions are created by heat treatment to

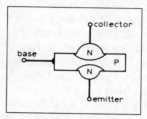

Fig 3.26. The NPN bipolar transistor

give an NPN or PNP structure (the NPN form being more common). It has three terminals known as *collector*, *base* and *emitter*. Fig 3.26 shows a typical NPN junction-type bipolar transistor. The device is *current controlled*, ie the base current controls the amount of current flowing between the collector and emitter. The higher the base current, the greater the current flow between collector and emitter.

To enable a bipolar transistor to function, the voltages of the collector, base and emitter must be correct with respect to one another – this is known as *biasing*. The following relates to a silicon device as these are more common. Also, the de-

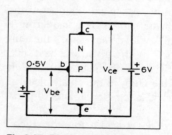

Fig 3.27. Biasing the transistor

scription is for an NPN device (all voltages and currents are reversed for a PNP type). Fig 3.27 shows a very basic method of biasing; in reality only one power supply source would be used.

From Fig 3.27 it can be seen that the base is 0.5V above the emitter, and this therefore forms a forward-biased PN junction. The collector voltage is higher than the base voltage and so this forms a reverse-biased PN junction. A set of measurements could be carried out for various values of collector voltage, collector current, base voltage and base current and a set of curves would be obtained as shown in Fig 3.28. These are known as the *characteristic curves*. They are the graphs shown in transistor data sheets.

There are various parameters available to describe a transistor. These can relate to voltage, current, power, gain, frequency and operating temperature; which of these are relevant depends on the application. The *voltage rating* gives an indication of the maximum voltages the transistor can

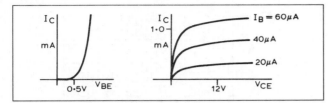

Fig 3.28. The characteristics of a small-signal transistor

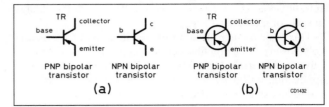

Fig 3.29. Bipolar transistor symbols. The optional envelope is shown at (b)

withstand; the *current* will specify maximum currents the device can handle; and *power*, the maximum power the device can deliver to a load or dissipate itself. The *gain* is a relationship between input and expected output, the *frequency* will specify the range the device is capable of working over and the *temperature* will specify how hot the device can run (this is also related to power). Transistors come in various shapes and sizes, usually depending on the current or power to be handled. Unfortunately there are subdivisions of the above which can make matters more complicated but some basic parameters are discussed below. The maximum collector voltage specifies, as the name suggests, the maximum voltage that can be safely applied between the collector and the emitter.

The *current gain* relates the change of collector current with change of base current. If the collector current changes from 1 to 2mA when the base current changes from 5 to 10mA, then the current gain is 1mA/5mA = 200. The symbol for current gain is h_{FE} or (mainly in older literature) β. Depending on transistor type, current gains from 2 to 800 are possible. Values for silicon devices are higher than those for germanium.

The *transition frequency* f_T is the frequency at which the current gain of the device has fallen to unity. Transistors are normally used up to a value of 10–15% of this figure. There are no hard and fast rules as this depends on the application.

The *power* the device will handle is dependent on several factors: how efficient the particular circuit arrangement is, the output power wanted, the ambient temperature and the cooling available (heat sink, air circulation etc). Always run as cool as possible for reliability. A typical example of the advantage of a heat sink can be shown by considering a BFY50. This will dissipate 0.8W with no heat sink if the temperature can be kept below 25°C. With a given size heat sink, this could be extended to 100°C and a dissipation of 2.8W. It is the actual temperature of the chip, ie the small piece of silicon on which the transistor is assembled, that is of paramount importance.

Germanium transistors were developed before the silicon transistor but they tend to be much more affected by operating temperatures. For example, the maximum safe working temperature for a germanium device is about 75°C while for a silicon device it is about 150°C. For this reason silicon devices are generally preferred.

The symbols for the two types of transistor are given in Fig 3.29. The arrow is always on the emitter.

FIELD-EFFECT TRANSISTOR (FET)

This is another member of the transistor family which is widely used and has advantages in certain applications. It comes in various forms: JFET, IGFET, MOSFET etc, but only the JFET (junction FET) will be described here. Both N- and P-types exist but the description of operation will be that of an

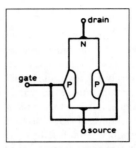

Fig 3.30. The field-effect transistor

N-channel type. Fig 3.30 shows the construction diagrammatically.

It consists essentially of a P-type region diffused into an N-type channel. The P-type region, or *gate*, creates a junction with the N-type bar and a depletion layer is formed. The main current flow is from drain to source, the voltage applied at the gate being used to control this current. The FET is a voltage-controlled device as opposed to the NPN/PNP transistor which is current controlled (ie base current controls collector-emitter current).

To operate, biasing is required (see Fig 3.31). This is shown with batteries but in reality only one DC supply would be used. This must make the gate negative with respect to the source and the PN junction becomes reverse-biased, causing it to have a high input resistance. The drain must be positive with respect to the source. By varying the voltage on the gate the depletion layer width can be varied – the more negative the voltage, the wider the depletion layer, and the less the drain-source current. The voltage required to reduce the drain current to zero is known as the *pinch-off voltage*.

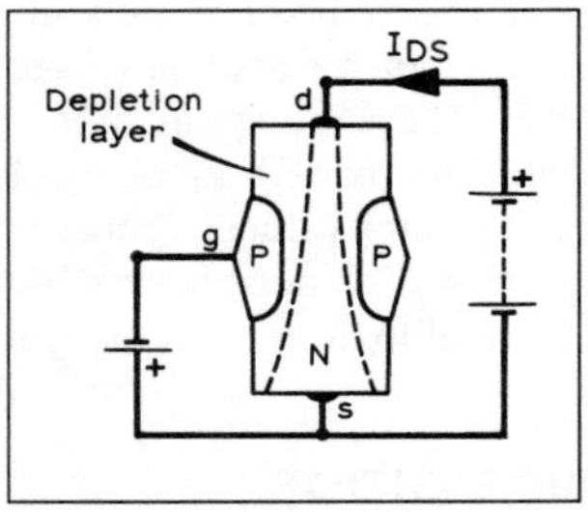

Fig 3.31. Configuration and operation of a FET

A typical set of characteristics for a 2N3823 JFET is shown in Fig 3.32.

The FET is a useful device as it always exhibits very high

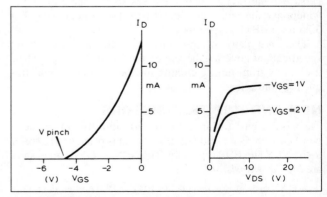

Fig 3.32. The characteristics of a 2N3823 FET

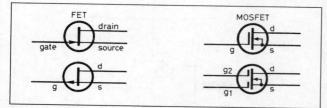

Fig 3.33. Symbols for various FETs (shown with optional envelopes)

input resistance. The symbols for the types of JFET and IGFET (insulated gate FET) are given in Fig 3.33.

APPLICATION OF SOLID-STATE DEVICES

The application of solid-state devices is almost endless. Individual devices such as the transistor and diode are called *discrete semiconductors*. The following gives a sample of the uses and typical circuit arrangements. These are sufficient for the examination. However, there are many other arrangements and these can be found in many of the amateur radio handbooks available. All semiconductor devices can easily be damaged by excessive power, voltage and/or current. Power devices should be mounted on heat sinks – that includes diodes as well as transistors. Never restrict the cooling path. If used within their design limits, semiconductors are very reliable.

The diode or rectifier

It is hard to define the difference between these two terms – usually *diode* is used for low-power applications and *rectifier* for higher-power mains applications. The silicon diode has now replaced the germanium diode for mains rectification. The germanium diode may still be found in signal-detection circuits where its low forward voltage drop is an advantage. The main use of the rectifier in power supplies is dealt with later in this chapter.

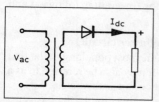

Fig 3.34. Use of a diode as a rectifier

Fig 3.34 shows a typical use as a rectifier. It will produce half-wave rectification as indicated. The circuit of Fig 3.35 shows the typical use of the diode as an AM demodulator, the tuned circuit being the output from the final IF stage. A similar arrangement can be used to generate AGC voltages. The diode can also be used in FM demodulation (see Chapter 4).

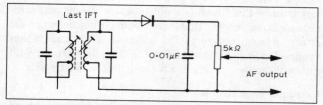

Fig 3.35. Use of the diode as a demodulator

Zener diode

The basic arrangement is shown in Fig 3.36. The resistor R_S is chosen so that when the load resistor R_L is carrying its normal current, the voltage drop across R_S will ensure that the diode is always operating beyond the knee of its characteristic (see Fig 3.24). If the output voltage tends to rise due to a reduction in load current, the zener diode will take more current from the supply and so keep the output voltage reasonably constant.

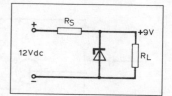

Fig 3.36. A simple zener diode circuit

The zener diode can also be used as a basis for more sophisticated power supplies (see later in this chapter).

Variable-capacitance diode

This is used when the frequency of a tuned circuit must be varied electronically. Its use is mainly at RF. The nominal operating point of a varicap diode is determined by its standing bias voltage, and this must keep it in reverse bias and near the midpoint of its characteristic so that equal changes in applied voltage cause equal changes in capacitance. Fig 3.37 shows a typical application.

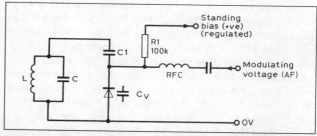

Fig 3.37. A typical application of a variable-capacitance diode

The resonant frequency of the tuned circuit is determined by C in parallel with C1 and C_V in series. A standing bias is applied via R1 and the capacitance of the whole circuit, and therefore the resonant frequency, is altered by the voltage applied via RFC. If an audio voltage is applied via RFC the resonant frequency will change in sympathy with this and, if the tuned circuit is part of an oscillator, frequency modulation will take place. The application of a DC voltage from a potentiometer instead of an audio input provides variable tuning. Further discussion will be found in Chapter 4. The varicap diode in a similar arrangement forms the heart of the frequency synthesiser. The varicap diode can also be used for frequency multiplication, eg 144MHz to 432MHz.

The transistor as a small-signal amplifier

Small-signal amplifiers get their name because their inputs are usually in the microvolt or millivolt range as opposed to large-signal amplifiers which have inputs of the order of volts. The latter are normally referred to as *power* amplifiers; these are dealt with later. Every type requires the base, emitter and collector of the transistor to be set to various DC voltages so that it will act as an amplifier. This setting up of DC conditions is known as *biasing* and, if incorrectly chosen, the amplifier may distort the signal. Amplifiers can be used for DC, AF, up to RF and microwaves. Only AF and RF types are considered.

Common-emitter amplifier

Fig 3.38 shows a typical common-emitter circuit which is the most widely used of the amplifiers. Capacitors C1 and C2

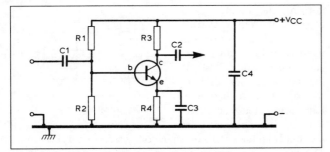

Fig 3.38. A common-emitter amplifier circuit

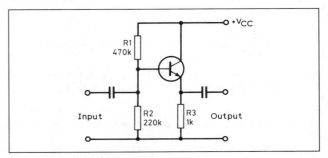

Fig 3.40. A typical emitter-follower circuit

provide AC coupling into and out of the circuit respectively. R1 and R2 provide biasing (note that this is not the only method of biasing but is the most stable). R3 is the collector load and R4 helps set up the DC bias conditions with C3 (the emitter bypass capacitor). With C3 acting as an AC short-circuit (ie its reactance is very small at the operating frequency), the emitter is effectively connected to the 0V line which is common to input and output signals. This gives the amplifier its name.

The values of C1, C2 and C3 are chosen so that they have very low reactance at the operating frequency. Their value will therefore vary according to the frequency being amplified; at audio they may be electrolytic capacitors, while at RF they may be in the 1000pF range or less. The biasing of the transistor has to be carefully chosen so that minimum distortion of the signal being amplified will occur. The voltage of the base must be about 0.6V above the emitter (assuming a silicon transistor). This allows a standing bias current through the transistor to be determined by R4 which sets the standing (or quiescent) voltage of the collector. Fig 3.39 shows the effect of too high and too low a voltage at the collector. In cases (a) and (b) distortion occurs which manifests itself as harmonics. (Compare the curves shown in Fig 3.39 with those in Fig 3.5(b).) Case (a) is when the input voltage cannot maintain the 0.6V differential between the base and emitter and has effectively caused zero collector current; the transistor is *switched off*.

The operation of a common-emitter circuit is as follows. Assuming the input voltage at the base is converted to a base current, then if the input voltage increases, so does the base current. This causes an increase in collector current. Because one end of R3 is attached to +V, this increased current means the voltage across R3 must increase and so the voltage at the collector decreases. If the input voltage decreases, then so does the base current and the collector current. This causes less current through R3 and the collector voltage rises. It should be noted that the collector voltage does the opposite

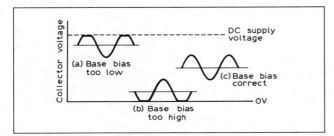

Fig 3.39. The effects of base bias on the collector voltage

to the input voltage, ie it is out of phase or inverted (ie 180°). Typical values for R1, R2, R3 and R4 might be 27kΩ, 8.2kΩ, 4.7kΩ and 1.5kΩ respectively.

One aspect not yet considered is how one circuit is affected by another one connected to it. For example, if one common-emitter amplifier cannot give enough gain then it can be followed by a second one in series. All electronic devices are made up by the connection of a series of basic building blocks. The second circuit obviously must take a signal from the first one and this leads to the question of how one circuit 'loads' another. This is commonly expressed by the concept of input and output impedances.

Ideally the input resistance should be high so that it does not load a previous circuit too much and the output resistance should be reasonably low so that most of the output voltage can be passed to the next circuit. For a typical common-emitter amplifier the input resistance is between 500Ω and 2kΩ and the output resistance between 5 and 20kΩ but the circuit resistors do have some effect on these figures. The common-emitter amplifier does not always represent an ideal arrangement and there are two other transistor configurations to consider – the common-collector (or emitter-follower) and common-base circuits.

Common-collector (emitter-follower circuit)

The name in brackets for this is the most popular, but the first one follows a logical sequence. It may also be referred to as a *buffer*. Fig 3.40 shows a typical circuit with values.

If the input voltage increases in this circuit, the base current rises and so does the collector current. As the emitter current is almost the same as the collector current, the current through the emitter rises and therefore the voltage at the emitter rises (one end of R3 is fixed to 0V and cannot change). If the input voltage decreases then the emitter voltage must also decrease. Because the base is always 0.6V greater than the emitter, the emitter voltage is always less than the base voltage; ie there is a voltage gain of less than unity. The input resistance of this circuit is about 100kΩ while the output resistance is maybe only 1kΩ (again, both are dependent on the effects of circuit resistors). This makes an ideal circuit in preventing loading of one circuit and feeding the next one with little voltage loss. It acts as a buffer between two circuits.

Common-base circuit

This is the third configuration and Fig 3.41 shows a typical arrangement. The signal is applied between base and emitter. If the input voltage increases, the emitter voltage will rise and cause less of a differential between emitter and base. This means that the transistor takes less base current and so the

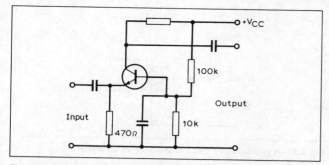

Fig 3.41. A typical common-base amplifier circuit

collector current drops. This in turn causes a rise in collector voltage. If the input voltage drops the reverse happens and the collector voltage drops. The collector voltage is in phase with the input voltage and so there is no phase inversion. The input impedance is very low, about 50–100Ω; therefore it is easy to match to a transmission line and/or antenna system. The output resistance is very high (at least 50kΩ).

Each of these circuits just discussed has its own specific properties as mentioned – these are summarised in Table 3.5. It must be stressed that these values are only typical as so much depends on other factors such as external resistors, transistor parameters and operating conditions. The negative sign in front of a gain figure shows that the output signal is out of phase with the input signal.

As the frequencies in use rise, so the internal capacitance effects of the transistor must be taken into account and the word 'resistance' in the above paragraphs must be replaced by 'impedance'. Generally the input impedance gets lower and so does the output impedance. The value of the internal capacitance has to be taken into account when designing adjacent circuitry but this is a matter above the present level of discussion.

Power amplifiers

This is the case of the large-signal amplifier. Power amplifiers are needed for both AF and RF applications. They are required to provide power to a load such as a loudspeaker or antenna. The basic circuits will be similar and the operation is the same as the small-signal amplifier but there will be differences in detail. There are also variations in order to keep the power dissipation as low as possible.

Class A operation

The common-emitter amplifier considered earlier provides an exact, but amplified, copy of the input signal – both positive and negative half-cycles of the input are amplified equally. This is defined as *Class A* operation and can be shown theoretically to have a maximum efficiency of 50%. At low power levels this is not important but if 50W is wanted in the load,

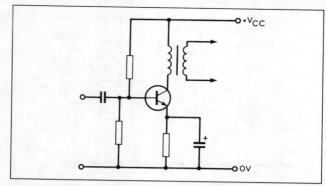

Fig 3.42. A Class A audio power amplifier circuit

then the transistor must dissipate 50W and the power supply has to provide 100W. This would be the ideal case; in practice the amplifier is more likely to be 40–45% efficient. This represents a high power wastage and of course means the provision of adequate heat sinks. The advantage of Class A operation is low distortion (ie low harmonic content). A Class A power amplifier will look very similar to Fig 3.38. The circuit in Fig 3.42 shows the case when the collector resistor is replaced by a transformer feeding a loudspeaker. This arrangement allows optimum power matching.

Efficiency and power wastage are a serious disadvantage of Class A and ways have been found to overcome this. The application will determine the approach. There are two other classes of operation – Class B and Class C.

Class B operation

This amplifier only amplifies half a cycle but theoretically is 78% efficient. In practice it should give at least 66% efficiency. Fig 3.43 shows a typical circuit which, as can be seen, looks identical to a Class A amplifier. The difference is that the bias resistors are chosen so that the base is only just at about 0.6V; as stated earlier, if it is taken lower than this the transistor stops passing current. On the positive half-cycle the base current will increase, as does the collector current. An inverted (but amplified) half-sine wave is produced. On the negative half of the input signal, the base is taken to less than 0.6V and so the transistor will not pass current (switches off) and does not amplify. Therefore only half of the input signal is amplified. For audio applications a Class B push-pull amplifier is used, as shown in Fig 3.44, while at radio frequencies the collector load is replaced by a tuned circuit.

In Fig 3.44 the top transistor amplifies the positive

Table 3.5. Characteristics of transistor configurations			
	Common emitter	Common collector	Common base
R in	1kΩ	100kΩ	50–100Ω
R out	20kΩ	1kΩ	50kΩ
Current gain	50	50	0.98
Voltage gain	–100	0.98	100

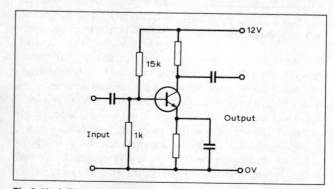

Fig 3.43. A Class B amplifier circuit

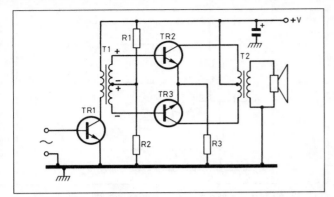

Fig 3.44. A Class B push-pull circuit

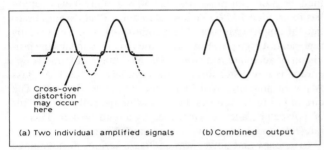

Fig 3.45. Typical combination of signals for the circuit of Fig 3.44

half-cycle and the other, the negative half-cycle. They are added together at the output. This is shown in Fig 3.45. One problem that can occur is that the two halves of the sine wave do not match exactly due to differences in the transistors, and crossover distortion occurs. To minimise this, some forward bias is applied so that the transistor is passing a small current with no input – this is Class AB operation.

Class C amplifiers

This amplifier amplifies less than half a cycle. A typical circuit is given in Fig 3.46. It will be noticed that there is no bias resistor from base to positive line, only one from base to ground.

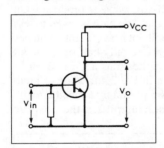

Fig 3.46. A Class C amplifier

The transistor is kept non-conducting by this resistor. For the transistor to conduct and to amplify, the base must be taken from 0 to 0.6V initially (ie part of the half-cycle has already started); the collector current then increases rapidly as the base becomes more positive. As the input decreases the transistor will switch off before the half cycle reaches 0V (ie at 0.6V). On the negative half-cycle of input, the transistor remains in a non-conducting state. The efficiency of this amplifier cannot be quoted exactly as it depends on how much of the half-cycle for which it conducts. However, it will be more efficient than a Class A or possibly Class B amplifier – assume about 66%. In a typical Class C transmitter the collector load is replaced by a tuned circuit. As with the Class B stage, the energy stored in the tuned circuit supplies the other half-cycle.

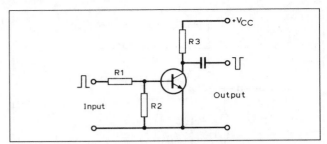

Fig 3.47. A typical circuit of a transistor as a switch

The transistor as a switch

A Class C amplifier is also used when the transistor is to act as a switch. In this case the criterion becomes "Is the transistor conducting or not?". This is the basis of digital circuits, ie ON or OFF; no intermediate state is wanted. A typical circuit is shown in Fig 3.47.

The operation of the circuit is similar to that of the Class C amplifier but the input is usually a rectangular pulse and not a sine wave. The resistor R2 keeps the transistor in a non-conducting state and R1 limits the base current during the pulse.

If the input signal exceeds 0.6V (assuming a silicon transistor) the transistor suddenly conducts and the output voltage, because of R3, drops to a low value, ie the signal is inverted. When the input falls to less than 0.6V then the transistor will no longer conduct. The collector resistor R3 could be replaced by a lamp or relay so that when an input signal is present current flows and the relay operates or the lamp lights. With no input signal the transistor will not conduct.

The transistor as a tuned amplifier

If the collector resistor of an amplifier is replaced by a parallel-tuned circuit, an amplifier can be created that will only amplify a selected range of frequencies. A typical circuit is shown in Fig 3.48.

From theory earlier in this chapter, we know that the dynamic resistance of the parallel-tuned circuit is maximum at resonance. Maximum output of the circuit will occur at this point. Going either side will give reduced output, ie maximum amplification occurs at the resonant frequency of the tuned circuit.

If the parallel resistance across a tuned circuit decreases, the dynamic resistance is reduced and so degrades the performance of the circuit, widening the band of frequencies

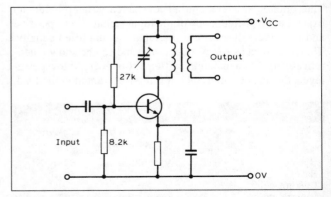

Fig 3.48. A typical tuned amplifier circuit

amplified. The input impedance of a following circuit appears across the tuned circuit. To minimise this degrading of the amplifier response, the output is usually taken from a secondary winding close to the tuned inductor in the collector circuit, ie it becomes a transformer with an untuned secondary winding (see p48).

If in Fig 3.48 the bias on the transistor is changed to Class C, the collector current is distorted and contains second and third harmonics. If the tuned circuit is resonant at one of these, the circuit would operate as a frequency doubler or tripler.

The transistor as an oscillator

At some point in a receiver or transmitter it is necessary to produce a continuous sine wave. This is accomplished by a circuit known as an *oscillator* and Fig 3.49 shows a basic circuit. The tuned circuit L-C determines the frequency of oscillation; the two coils L and L1 form the primary and secondary windings of a transformer; resistors R1, R2 and R3 set the bias conditions. The circuit is similar to a common-emitter amplifier that produces a 180° phase shift between input and output voltages.

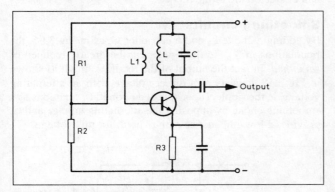

Fig 3.49. A basic oscillator circuit

When the circuit is switched ON there is a momentary surge which causes the circuit L-C to try to oscillate. This signal is fed back by the transformer action of L and L1. The phasing is such that this will cause a signal at the collector which adds to the original and so increases it. This is fed back again in the correct phase and so oscillations are maintained. The principle of the oscillator has been established.

Oscillators are amplifiers in which there is intentional positive feedback from the output to the input. This feedback can be achieved in several ways, and there are various oscillators, usually named after their originator, eg Colpitts, Hartley, Vackar, etc. The first two are the most common in amateur radio. In general there is little to choose between them.

When one end of the tuned circuit which determines the oscillator frequency is earthed, it can be replaced by a quartz crystal and the circuit becomes a *crystal oscillator*. The oscillator frequency is now determined by the crystal and the frequency stability is therefore very much higher, but the oscillator cannot be tuned.

The transistor as a mixer

Mixer circuits are used to change from one frequency to another and these rely on the non-linear property of a circuit. Mixers produce a range of output frequencies and the required output is chosen by means of a tuned circuit or filter. The

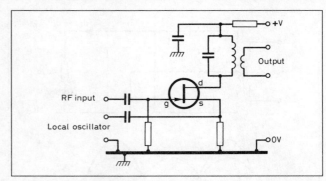

Fig 3.50. A typical junction FET mixer circuit

circuit in Fig 3.50 is the typical application of a junction FET as a mixer.

The local oscillator is fed in on the source, while the RF signal is fed (often by a tuned circuit) to the gate. These signals mix and the wanted mixing product is picked out by the tuned circuit in the drain circuit. The advantage of using a transistor or FET as a mixer is that it can provide gain at the same time.

The dual-gate MOSFET is also now very common as a mixer and a typical circuit is given in Chapter 4 (Fig 4.4).

INTEGRATED CIRCUITS

These are a development of transistor manufacturing techniques where complex electronic circuits are produced on a single silicon chip. Most low-power stages used in receivers and transmitters, such as amplifiers (RF, IF and AF), demodulators, oscillators, stabilisers etc are available as an integrated circuit. Few additional external components are required. The equipment has become smaller and more complex with extra facilities and at the same time, more reliable.

POWER SUPPLIES

Direct-current supplies of up to 12V which are required by solid-state circuits may be obtained from batteries of primary or secondary cells (for example, in mobile equipment). Fixed equipment is most conveniently served by a power unit which transforms, rectifies and smoothes the domestic 240V 50Hz supply.

Rectifying circuits

Silicon diodes are used as the rectifying elements. Fig 3.51 shows the half-wave rectifying circuit in which current flows

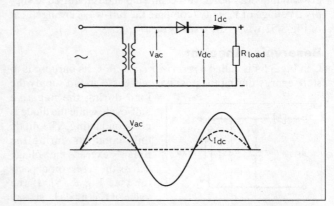

Fig 3.51. A half-wave rectifier circuit and waveforms

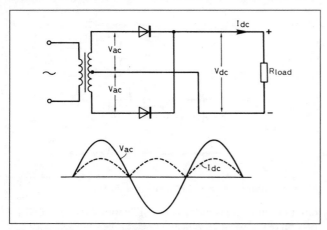

Fig 3.52. A full-wave rectifier circuit and waveforms

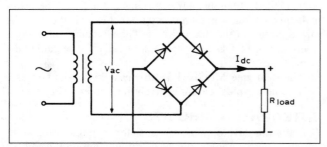

Fig 3.53. A bridge rectifier circuit

in the transformer secondary circuit (ie load, rectifier and secondary winding) only during the positive half-cycle. If the diode is reversed, then it is the negative half-cycle which is rectified.

Fig 3.52 shows the full-wave rectifier circuit. The diodes conduct on alternate half-cycles – the circuit is a combination of two half-wave circuits. The load current waveform varies considerably in amplitude but, as it does not change polarity, it is a direct current.

This variation in the amplitude of the output voltage (or current) of a rectifier circuit is known as the *ripple*.

The frequency of the ripple in the full-wave arrangement is 100Hz, while in the half-wave circuit it is 50Hz.

Fig 3.53 shows the bridge rectifier circuit. The output is full-wave, ie 100Hz ripple. At any one instant two of the diodes are in series carrying current. The transformer secondary winding does not have a centre tap and is required to supply a voltage of V_{ac} only (compare the full-wave arrangement of Fig 3.52 where the transformer supplies $2 \times V_{ac}$).

Reservoir capacitor

C in Fig 3.54 is called a *reservoir capacitor*. Its purpose is to store energy during the positive half-cycle and to supply the load during the negative half-cycle while the diode is non-conducting. The diode only conducts during the time V_{ac} exceeds the voltage across the reservoir capacitor (see Fig 3.55). If the value of C is made large, say 10,000µF, then a large pulse

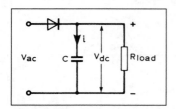

Fig 3.54. The reservoir capacitor

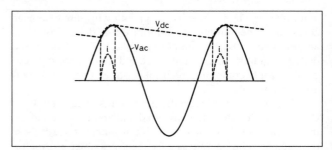

Fig 3.55. The output waveforms of a rectifier circuit using a reservoir capacitor

of current will be needed to charge it because the time during which the diode conducts is short.

The reservoir capacitor charges up to a voltage which equals the peak value of V_{ac}, ie 2 times V_{ac}. On the negative half cycle, polarities are reversed but the magnitude is the same. The maximum voltage across the diode is now $2 \times 2V_{ac}$. This value is known as the *peak inverse voltage* (PIV). The maximum PIV allowable across a rectifier diode is a very important characteristic of the diode.

Smoothing circuits

By adding a choke L_s and a capacitor C_s as in Fig 3.56, the fluctuations in V_{dc}, ie the ripple, can be greatly reduced or *smoothed*. In fact the output of the rectifier circuit as shown in Fig 3.58 consists of a direct voltage with an alternating voltage, ie the ripple, superimposed upon it. L_s functions as a smoothing choke by opposing the alternating voltage and C_s provides a low-impedance path to earth for this voltage.

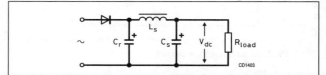

Fig 3.56. A smoothing circuit

A low-value resistor can be used in place of the choke but is not so effective. In the high-current supplies often required by transistor circuits, a smoothing choke is unacceptably large and expensive. In this situation a single high-value capacitor (eg 100,000µF) would be used for smoothing.

A power supply may contain other components as in Fig 3.57. The primary circuit contains the mains switch and a fuse. A metallic screen, placed between the primary and secondary windings, is connected to the earth terminal. This screen helps to reduce mains-borne interference, and to protect the secondary winding from the voltage on the primary, should a short-circuit occur between them. This screen is generally made of

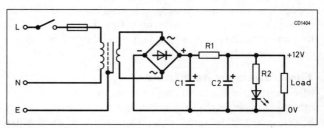

Fig 3.57. A practical power supply circuit

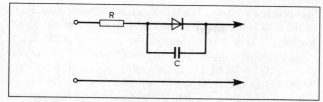

Fig 3.58. The surge protection diode

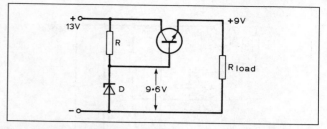

Fig 3.59. A simple voltage stabiliser

thin copper (0.1mm thick) and of course is not continuous, otherwise it would act as a short-circuited winding. C1 may have a value of 1000μF and C2 4700μF. R1 will help with smoothing but must have a comparatively low value to avoid excessive voltage drop across it. The light-emitting diode indicates the ON condition. The resistor R2 will be 470Ω ¼W. Note the symbol used in Fig 3.57 for a bridge rectifier.

Properties of silicon diodes

Silicon diodes have a low internal voltage drop and can rectify large currents. A rapid increase in voltage, eg a switching transient, may give rise to a large current pulse, especially if the reservoir capacitor has a large value, and such a 'surge' is likely to destroy a silicon diode.

The capacitor C (about 0.01μF) in Fig 3.58 reduces the amplitude of the *switching transient* (a short, but often high surge of current) when the diode turns off rapidly under bias conditions. The resistor R reduces the amplitude of the surge of current through the diode as the power supply is switched on and each time the reservoir (smoothing) capacitor charges up. The value of R must be chosen carefully to avoid an excessive voltage drop across it.

The PIV on each diode in a rectifier circuit depends on the circuit configuration and to a certain extent on the smoothing arrangement. In the half- and full-wave circuit, the PIV may be taken as approximately three times the direct output voltage of the power supply and in the bridge circuit it is one and a half times the output voltage. The mean current in each diode in the full-wave and bridge circuits is equal to one half of the DC output current.

Silicon diodes are commonly available with PIV from 50V up to about 1000V. Mean current capability varies from several amperes at the low PIV to an ampere or more at the higher voltage. Several diodes may be connected in series to provide a higher PIV capability. If this is done, a resistor (330kΩ) would be connected in parallel with each diode to equalise the voltage drop across each diode under reverse bias conditions.

Diodes and diode chains used in rectifying circuits should be very conservatively rated, eg five 50V diodes in series should be taken as a 200V diode.

Power supply characteristics

Most electronic circuits require a power supply which is very smooth, ie there is very little ripple voltage superimposed on the direct output voltage. Many circuits (particularly oscillators) require a supply which has an almost constant voltage irrespective of the amount of current being taken from the supply. Such a supply is said to have good *regulation*. Variation of the mains voltage will also cause the output voltage to change.

Variation of the output voltage of a power supply is caused by the fact that the load current also flows through the power supply circuits which inevitably have a certain resistance or impedance. The ideal power supply has a low *source impedance* (ie the internal resistance of a cell). Source impedance can be minimised by careful design, but a more effective solution is the use of a *stabilised* supply which also compensates for input voltage changes.

Stabilised power supplies

The simplest voltage stabiliser (or *regulator*) uses a zener diode as described earlier in this chapter (Fig 3.36). Reasonably constant supplies of up to 150V can be obtained in this way, and this circuit is often used for the supply of a VFO. A more effective method is to use a transistor as a regulator (the series or pass transistor) in series with the supply to the load as shown in Fig 3.59.

The base of the transistor is kept at a fairly constant forward voltage by the zener diode D. If the load increases, the voltage at the emitter will tend to fall. This in turn allows the transistor to conduct more easily and so maintain the output voltage. In order to maintain better control a balancing (bridge) circuit is used, with an extra transistor working as a DC amplifier. Let the voltage in Fig 3.60 divide equally between R2 and R3. The voltage between point B and chassis will be 6V. If the diode D is rated at 6V then there will be no difference of potential between points A and B. If the line voltage falls then the voltage across R3 will fall, but the voltage across D will remain at 6V. The voltage at A will now be higher than the voltage at B. This change of voltage can be applied to the base of a transistor and so provide a degree of control. Fig 3.61 shows a circuit using such a device.

If the voltage at C increases the voltage at point B will increase. The emitter voltage of TR2 stays constant due to the action of D. Due to the increased base-emitter voltage in TR2, the collector current (and therefore the voltage drop in R) will increase. The base-emitter voltage of TR1 is reduced, increasing the effective series resistance of TR1. This brings down the emitter voltage of TR1 and so point C returns to its normal voltage.

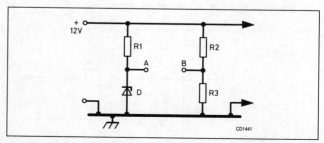

Fig 3.60. Voltage stabiliser – the basic balancing circuit

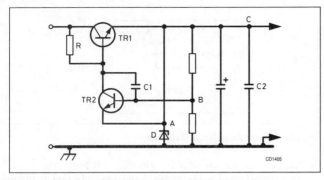

Fig 3.61. A voltage stabiliser using the balancing circuit

The small capacitors C1 and C2, about 0.1µF, prevent instability (self-oscillation) of the output voltage if the load is constantly varying. There are many refinements in stabilised supplies and manufacturers' literature gives much additional information.

The integrated-circuit stabiliser

The modern tendency in stabilised power supply design is to use an integrated circuit (IC) regulator. This contains in one small package the series element, reference voltage supply, a high-gain error amplifier and various sensing resistors and transistors. The more complex versions also contain protection circuits against too much voltage being applied to them and excess temperature rise. They are relatively cheap and are available up to a maximum regulated current of 10A. They may be connected in parallel for higher currents.

The simplicity of this type of power supply may be seen from Fig 3.62. The layout of this type of power supply can be critical and, in particular, the connections between the integrated circuit and the 2µF capacitors should be short to avoid any instability arising from parasitic oscillation.

Safety note

Safety precautions are important in the use and servicing of any power supply. It must be remembered that low-voltage power supplies operate from a 240V supply and that smoothing capacitors in such supplies do store a large amount of electrical energy.

Power supplies of the voltage discussed below should be regarded as lethal devices and treated accordingly.

See Chapter 2 for recommendations on the safety precautions to be observed when dealing with power supplies.

Power supplies for RF linear amplifiers using valves

The waveform of the SSB signal has a low average value and a high peak value as it represents the syllabic variations of

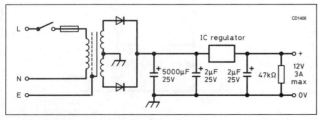

Fig 3.62. A practical power supply unit using an IC stabiliser

the speech waveform. The standing (no signal) current drawn by the SSB linear amplifier may be of the order of 30–40mA, but this is likely to rise to a peak value of around 250mA.

The voltage required will be about 600–700V in the case of an amplifier using TV line output valves and 1500–2300V if valves like the 572B or 813 are used. This supply voltage should not fall by more than 5% under the peak load referred to above.

The circuit generally used is the bridge rectifier arrangement shown in Fig 3.55. According to the PIV of the diodes used, several in series may be needed in each arm of the bridge. Across each diode should be a 0.01µF capacitor for surge protection and a resistor (order of 330kΩ) to equalise the voltage across each diode.

Smoothing is by means of a very-large-value reservoir capacitor; in fact it is this capacitor which supplies the peak load. This capacitor would be made up of a bank of series or series-parallel electrolytic capacitors according to availability with a total capacitance of not less than about 40µF. A resistor (330kΩ) across each capacitor equalises the voltage across each one and also serves as an HT bleed to discharge the capacitors on switch-off.

In order to provide maximum reliability of the power unit, the rating of each resistor, capacitor and diode should be such that it is under-run by a factor not less than 25%.

Power supplies of the voltage discussed above should be regarded as lethal devices and treated accordingly.

PRACTICE QUESTIONS FOR CHAPTER 3

1. The effective resistance of three 24Ω resistors connected in parallel is
   (a) 8Ω
   (b) 12Ω
   (c) 36Ω
   (d) 72Ω.

2. A sine wave has an RMS value of 12V. What is the peak-to-peak value?
   (a) 16.97V.
   (b) 24V.
   (c) 33.9V.
   (d) 36.4V.

3. A power gain of 4 is equivalent to
   (a) 3dB
   (b) 6dB
   (c) 10dB
   (d) 16dB.

4. A period of 50µs corresponds to a frequency of
   (a) 2kHz
   (b) 20kHz
   (c) 200kHz
   (d) 2MHz.

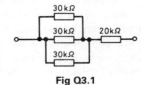

Fig Q3.1

5. The total resistance of the circuit shown in Fig Q3.1 is

(a) 5kΩ

(b) 15kΩ

(c) 20kΩ

(d) 30kΩ.

6. In a forward-biased PN junction, the electrons

(a) flow from P to N

(b) flow from N to P

(c) remain in the N region

(d) disintegrate.

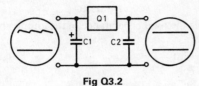

Fig Q3.2

7. Fig Q3.2 shows the circuit of part of a power supply. The waveforms present at two points in the circuit are shown in the insets. Device Q1 is a

(a) bridge rectifier

(b) voltage stabiliser

(c) single diode

(d) varicap diode.

8. Mutual inductance causes a voltage to be generated in a coil when

(a) a magnet is moved into the coil

(b) a magnet is moved out of the coil

(c) a current flows through another coil close to the first

(d) the coil is turned in a magnetic field.

9. An indirectly heated cathode in a thermionic valve is heated by

(a) an external heat source

(b) a heater element inside the cathode

(c) induction currents

(d) current flowing through the surface of the cathode.

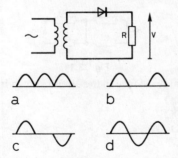

Fig Q3.3

10. Refer to the circuit shown in Fig Q3.3. Which one represents the output waveform?

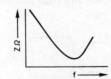

Fig Q3.4

11. The impedance-frequency curve shown in Fig Q3.4 shows the characteristic of

(a) a capacitance

(b) a parallel-tuned circuit

(c) an inductance

(d) a series-tuned circuit.

12. The peak value of the 240V domestic mains is

(a) 168V

(b) 339V

(c) 480V

(d) 678V.

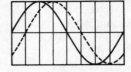

Fig Q3.5

13. The phase difference between the two sine waves shown in Fig Q3.5 is

(a) 0 degrees

(b) 45 degrees

(c) 90 degrees

(d) 180 degrees.

Fig Q3.6

14. The symbol shown in Fig Q3.6 represents a

(a) dual bipolar transistor

(b) dual diode

(c) dual varactor diode

(d) dual-gate MOS FET.

15. A forward-biased PN junction allows

(a) current to flow from P to N region

(b) current to flow from N to P region

(c) no current to flow

(d) electrons to flow from P to N region.

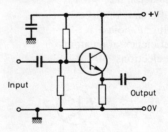

Fig Q3.7

16. The circuit shown in Fig Q3.7 is

(a) a common-emitter amplifier

(b) an emitter follower

(c) an oscillator

(d) a common-base stage.

17. In the circuit shown in Fig Q3.7 the phase difference between input and output voltages is

(a) 0 degrees

(b) 45 degrees

(c) 90 degrees

(d) 180 degrees.

18. The output impedance of the circuit shown in Fig Q3.7 is
    (a) very high
    (b) infinite
    (c) very low
    (d) inductive.

19. One use of the circuit shown in Fig Q3.7 would be as a
    (a) buffer between an oscillator and load
    (b) high-gain voltage amplifier
    (c) voltage inverter
    (d) frequency multiplier.

20. An integrated circuit is
    (a) a passive device only
    (b) a complete set of capacitors
    (c) an encapsulated complex circuit
    (d) a discrete component circuit.

21. The tolerance of a resistor is given as 10%. If the nominal resistor value is 4.7kΩ, its actual value must lie between
    (a) 4230 and 5170Ω
    (b) 4653 and 4747Ω
    (c) 4230 and 4747Ω
    (d) 4653 and 5170Ω.

Fig Q3.8

22. The circuit shown in Fig Q3.8 is that of a
    (a) series-tuned circuit
    (b) low-pass filter
    (c) high-pass filter
    (d) parallel-resonant circuit.

23. N-type material has
    (a) a deficiency of electrons
    (b) additional holes
    (c) a deficiency of an atom
    (d) free electrons.

Fig Q3.9

24. The symbol shown in Fig Q3.9 represents
    (a) a PNP transistor
    (b) an NPN transistor
    (c) a P-type FET
    (d) an N-type FET.

25. The main purpose of a varicap diode is
    (a) tuning
    (b) rectification
    (c) voltage regulation
    (d) display.

26. In a Class B amplifier, using an NPN transistor, the base bias potential is
    (a) much greater than the emitter potential
    (b) the same as the collector potential
    (c) about 0.6V above the emitter voltage
    (d) less than the emitter voltage.

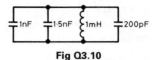

Fig Q3.10

27. What is the total capacitance in the circuit shown in Fig Q3.10?
    (a) 0.15nF.
    (b) 2.7nF.
    (c) 4.5nF.
    (d) 202.5nF.

28. Two resistors are connected in series across a DC supply. The voltage across one resistor is 12V and the other 24V. The supply voltage is
    (a) 6V
    (b) 12V
    (c) 24V
    (d) 36V.

29. As frequency rises the reactance of a capacitor
    (a) stays constant
    (b) decreases
    (c) increases
    (d) becomes infinite.

30. A tuned circuit can be made to oscillate if
    (a) additional damping is included
    (b) more capacitance is added
    (c) more inductance is added
    (d) an amplifier is added in order to make up for circuit losses.

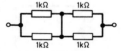

Fig Q3.11

31. The total resistance in the circuit shown in Fig Q3.11 is
    (a) 250Ω
    (b) 500Ω
    (c) 1kΩ
    (d) 4kΩ.

32. The quiescent current of a Class C amplifier is
    (a) zero
    (b) infinite
    (c) the same as the full load value
    (d) just above zero.

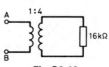

Fig Q3.12

33. Refer to Fig Q3.12. What is the impedance between terminals AB?

(a) 0Ω.
(b) 250Ω.
(c) 1000Ω.
(d) 4000Ω.

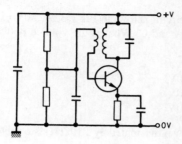

Fig Q3.13

34. The circuit shown in Fig Q3.13 is typical of
    (a) an L-C oscillator
    (b) a common-base stage
    (c) a Class C tuned amplifier
    (d) a crystal oscillator.

35. Integrated circuits that perform logic functions come under the general classification of
    (a) linear circuits
    (b) amplifiers
    (c) mixers
    (d) digital circuits.

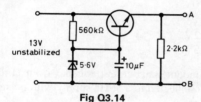

Fig Q3.14

36. Refer to Fig Q3.14. The output voltage between A and B will be about
    (a) 2.2V
    (b) 5V
    (c) 10V
    (d) 13V.

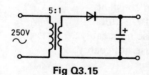

Fig Q3.15

37. The PIV rating of the diode in the circuit shown in Fig Q3.15 should not be less than
    (a) 50V
    (b) 75V
    (c) 150V
    (d) 250V.

38. The phase relationship between input and output voltage of a common-emitter stage is
    (a) zero
    (b) 90 degrees
    (c) 180 degrees
    (d) 270 degrees.

39. The power dissipated in a pure inductor is
    (a) zero
    (b) small
    (c) large
    (d) very large.

40. A light bulb (lamp) is rated at 12V, 3W. What is the current drawn when it is connected to 12V?
    (a) 250mA.
    (b) 750mA.
    (c) 4A.
    (d) 36A.

41. 100mW is equivalent to
    (a) 0.001W
    (b) 0.01W
    (c) 0.1W
    (d) 1.0W.

42. Two 10kΩ resistors are connected in parallel across a 5V DC supply. Total current taken is
    (a) 50μA
    (b) 0.5mA
    (c) 1mA
    (d) 1A.

43. Two 10μF capacitors are placed in parallel across a 10V, 1kHz supply. The phase difference between applied voltage and current drawn is
    (a) 0 degrees
    (b) 45 degrees
    (c) 60 degrees
    (d) 90 degrees.

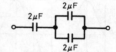

Fig Q3.16

44. The total capacitance in the circuit shown in Fig Q3.16 is
    (a) 1.33μF
    (b) 3μF
    (c) 3.5μF
    (d) 6μF.

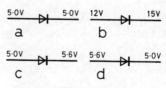

Fig Q3.17

45. Fig Q3.17 shows diodes with various bias conditions. Which diode is conducting?

46. P-type material has
    (a) free electrons
    (b) an atom deficiency
    (c) too many electrons
    (d) holes where electrons could be.

47. Colpitts, Hartley, are types of
    (a) power supply
    (b) amplifier
    (c) oscillator
    (d) modulator.

48. A varicap diode acts like a variable
    (a) resistor
    (b) voltage stabiliser
    (c) capacitor
    (d) inductor.

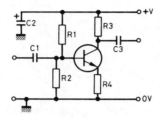

Fig Q3.18

49. The circuit shown in Fig Q3.18 is
    (a) an emitter-follower
    (b) a common-emitter amplifier
    (c) a common-collector amplifier
    (d) a voltage stabiliser.

50. In the circuit shown in Fig Q3.18, the purpose of R1 and R2 is
    (a) biasing
    (b) amplification control
    (c) feedback
    (d) filtering.

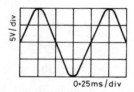

Fig Q3.19

51. Fig Q3.19 shows a trace on an oscilloscope. What is the frequency of the displayed waveform?
    (a) 100Hz.
    (b) 1kHz.
    (c) 10kHz.
    (d) 100kHz.

52. What is the peak-to-peak value of the waveform shown in Fig Q3.19?
    (a) 1V.
    (b) 2V.
    (c) 10V.
    (d) 20V.

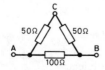

Fig Q3.20

53. In Fig Q3.20 10V is applied between points A and B. What is the total current flow?

    (a) 0.002A.
    (b) 20mA.
    (c) 200mA.
    (d) 2A.

54. In the circuit shown in Fig Q3.20, 50V exists between points A and C. What is the voltage between points A and B?
    (a) 50V.
    (b) 100V.
    (c) 150V.
    (d) 200V.

55. The power dissipated by a 10Ω resistor with 2A flowing through it is
    (a) 5W
    (b) 20W
    (c) 40W
    (d) 200W.

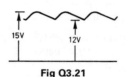

Fig Q3.21

56. The waveform at the output of a power supply is shown in Fig Q3.21. What is the value of the ripple?
    (a) 1V.
    (b) 3V.
    (c) 12V.
    (d) 15V.

57. The fundamental output frequency from a full-wave rectifier connected to a 50Hz supply with no smoothing is
    (a) 25Hz
    (b) 50Hz
    (c) 100Hz
    (d) 200Hz.

58. If the base voltage on an NPN transistor operating in Class B is increased, the collector current will
    (a) remain constant
    (b) decrease a little
    (c) increase noticeably
    (d) decrease noticeably.

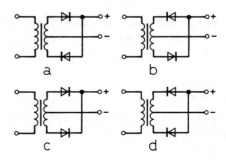

Fig Q3.22

59. Which one of the circuits shown in Fig Q3.22 gives full-wave rectification with the polarity shown?

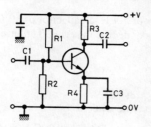

Fig Q3.23

60. The purpose of C3 in the circuit shown in Fig Q3.23 is
    (a) biasing
    (b) decreasing the amplifier gain
    (c) stopping DC drift
    (d) bypassing the emitter resistor.

61. The purpose of C1 and C2 in the circuit shown in Fig Q3.23 is
    (a) DC coupling
    (b) AC coupling
    (c) biasing
    (d) RF biasing.

62. If the capacitor C3 is removed from the circuit shown in Fig Q3.23, the voltage gain will
    (a) increase
    (b) stay the same
    (c) decrease
    (d) fall to zero.

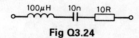

Fig Q3.24

63. The resonant frequency of the circuit shown in Fig Q3.24 is
    (a) 1.59155kHz
    (b) 15.9155kHz
    (c) 159.155kHz
    (d) 1591.55kHz.

64. The peak-to-peak value of the 240V mains is
    (a) 170V
    (b) 240V
    (c) 339V
    (d) 679V.

65. The reactance of a choke can be calculated by
    (a) $1/2\pi fL$
    (b) $2\pi fL$
    (c) πfL
    (d) $2fL$.

66. A high-voltage power supply has a number of rectifier diodes connected in series. Each diode should have
    (a) a resistor in series
    (b) a resistor in parallel
    (c) a second diode in parallel
    (d) an inductor in parallel.

67. The main use of a Zener diode is
    (a) rectification
    (b) tuning
    (c) voltage stabilisation
    (d) display.

68. When a bipolar transistor is conductive, the emitter-base junction is
    (a) reverse biased
    (b) open-circuit
    (c) short-circuit
    (d) forward biased.

69. The terminals of a bipolar transistor are labelled
    (a) emitter, base, collector
    (b) emitter, drain, source
    (c) drain, source, collector
    (d) drain, gate, base.

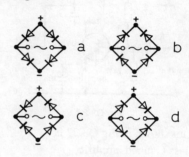

Fig Q3.25

70. Which one of the diagrams in Fig Q3.25 is the correct arrangement for a bridge rectifier?

71. In a varicap diode the capacitance
    (a) is constant irrespective of applied reverse voltage
    (b) increases as reverse bias is increased
    (c) decreases as reverse bias increases
    (d) decreases as reverse bias decreases.

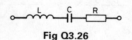

Fig Q3.26

72. At resonance the impedance of the circuit shown in Fig Q3.26 is
    (a) R
    (b) infinity
    (c) C
    (d) L

73. The primary of a transformer has five times as many turns as the secondary. If the primary is connected to 250V mains, what is the expected secondary voltage?
    (a) 10V.
    (b) 25V.
    (c) 50V.
    (d) 1250V.

74. The phase difference between voltage and current in a purely resistive circuit is
    (a) 0 degrees
    (b) 45 degrees
    (c) 90 degrees
    (d) 180 degrees.

75. The effective capacitance of three 33pF capacitors in series is
    (a) 11pF
    (b) 22pF

(c) 33pF

(d) 99pF.

76. The input resistance of a common-emitter amplifier stage is about

(a) 5Ω

(b) 50Ω

(c) 2kΩ

(d) 200kΩ.

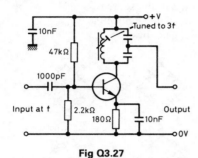

Fig Q3.27

77. The circuit shown in Fig Q3.27 is

(a) a Class C tuned amplifier

(b) an oscillator

(c) a multiplier

(d) a buffer circuit.

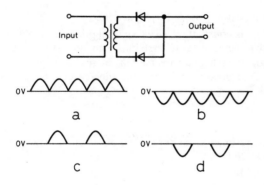

Fig Q3.28

78. Which of the waveforms will be present at the output of the circuit shown in Fig Q3.28?

79. To switch an NPN transistor OFF, the base must be

(a) at the collector potential

(b) at the emitter potential

(c) midway between collector and emitter

(d) positive to the emitter.

80. In a semiconductor diode the depletion layer widens with

(a) decrease in reverse bias voltage

(b) increase in forward bias voltage

(c) increase in forward current flow

(d) increase in reverse bias voltage.

81. The power dissipated in a pure 1µF capacitor at 10kHz with 12V (RMS) across it is

(a) zero

(b) 0.9W

(c) 9W

(d) 90W.

82. An inductor of 50µH, a capacitor of 50pF and a resistor of 50Ω are connected in series. The impedance at resonance is

(a) 16.66Ω

(b) 50Ω

(c) 150Ω

(d) frequency dependent.

83. A resistor having a value of 100Ω has 10V across it. Its minimum power rating must be

(a) 0.125W

(b) 0.25W

(c) 1W

(d) 10W.

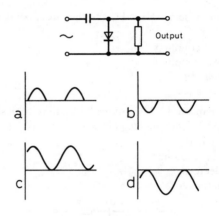

Fig Q3.29

84. An alternating voltage is applied to the circuit shown in Fig Q3.29. Which one will be the output waveform?

85. A bipolar transistor is

(a) current controlled

(b) voltage controlled

(c) a thermionic device

(d) a magnetically operated device.

86. A Class C amplifier operates over

(a) the complete cycle

(b) three-quarters of a cycle

(c) exactly half a cycle

(d) less than half a cycle.

87. The input resistance of an emitter follower is about

(a) 10Ω

(b) 1kΩ

(c) 10kΩ

(d) 100kΩ.

88. A reverse-biased diode exhibits

(a) no resistance

(b) low resistance

(c) high resistance

(d) high inductance.

89. If the base potential of an NPN transistor is held at the emitter potential, the collector current will be

(a) zero

(b) always 1A

(c) between 10mA and 2A

(d) very high.

90. Two 20kΩ resistors are connected in parallel across a 10V DC supply. The total current drawn from the supply is

(a) 50mA

(b) 0.5mA

(c) 1mA

(d) 1A.

91. As the frequency rises, the reactance of an inductor

(a) stays constant

(b) decreases

(c) increases

(d) increases to a maximum and then falls.

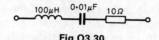

Fig Q3.30

92. The resonant frequency of the circuit shown in Fig Q3.30 is about

(a) 1.6kHz

(b) 16kHz

(c) 160kHz

(d) 1600kHz.

93. A power gain of 100 is equivalent to

(a) 3dB

(b) 6dB

(c) 10dB

(d) 20dB.

94. The output impedance of an emitter-follower buffer amplifier is

(a) infinite

(b) very high

(c) zero

(d) fairly low.

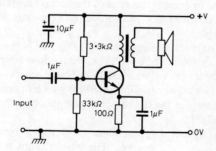

Fig Q3.31

95. The circuit shown in Fig Q3.31 shows

(a) an audio amplifier

(b) a microphone amplifier

(c) a mixer

(d) an audio oscillator.

96. A light bulb is rated at 12V, 48W. The current drawn when used on a 12V supply is

(a) 250mA

(b) 750mA

(c) 4A

(d) 36A.

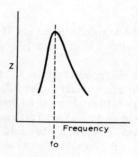

Fig Q3.32

97. The impedance-frequency curve shown in Fig Q3.32 is the characteristic of

(a) a capacitor

(b) a parallel-tuned circuit

(c) an inductor

(d) a series-tuned circuit.

98. A varicap diode is

(a) heat dependent

(b) current dependent

(c) voltage dependent

(d) light dependent.

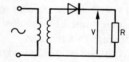

Fig Q3.33

99. The circuit shown in Fig Q3.33 is for

(a) half-wave rectification

(b) full-wave voltage stabilisation

(c) reverse bias protection

(d) voltage multiplication.

100. A Class A amplifier conducts over

(a) the complete cycle

(b) three-quarters of a cycle

(c) exactly half a cycle

(d) less than half a cycle.

Check your answers using the key in Appendix 4.

4 Receivers, transmitters and transceivers

BEFORE discussing radio receivers, it is necessary to explain certain terms which are used to define their characteristics.

Sensitivity is the ability of a receiver to receive weak signals. The sensitivity of a receiver is normally quoted as being that level of signal which produces a standard ratio of signal-to-background noise, eg 1μV input to give not less than 10dB signal-to-noise ratio. This means that a 1μV signal will be such that the level of the signal is about three times the level of the noise with the antenna removed and replaced by a 50Ω dummy load. The sensitivity of a communication receiver can usually be varied by means of an RF gain control.

Selectivity is the ability of a receiver to receive one signal and reject others on adjacent frequencies. On crowded amateur bands it is necessary for stations to operate on frequencies very close to each other. In order to be able to receive the desired signal with the minimum amount of adjacent-channel interference, a receiver with a high selectivity must be used. Selectivity may be quoted, for example, as follows: 2.5kHz at 6dB down; 4.1kHz at 60dB down.

Bandwidth. A receiver with high selectivity is said to have a narrow bandwidth. In the above example, the receiver has a bandwidth of 2.5kHz at 6dB down.

Frequency stability is the ability of a receiver to remain tuned to the desired signal. If a receiver is not stable it is said to drift. Stability is determined by the design and construction of the oscillator stage in a receiver.

Dynamic range is the range of input signal over which a receiver will function satisfactorily, ie it is the difference in level between the maximum signal the receiver will accept and the minimum signal which will give a usable output. The dynamic range is quoted in decibels (dB); in a good receiver it would be of the order of 90–105dB.

Automatic gain control (AGC) is the automatic control of the sensitivity of a superheterodyne receiver by the strength of the signal to which the receiver is tuned. For weak signals, the sensitivity needs to be high, but for strong signals a low sensitivity suffices. AGC is useful when there is fading on a signal; the sensitivity is varied in accordance with the signal to produce an almost constant audio output level.

THE SUPERHETERODYNE RECEIVER

The poor selectivity and lack of gain of the early receivers led to the development of the *supersonic heterodyne* principle in around 1920. In the supersonic heterodyne (or *superhet* as it is commonly known) receiver, the frequencies of all incoming signals are changed to a fixed, fairly low frequency at which most of the gain and the selectivity of the receiver is obtained.

Because this fixed frequency is lower than the signal frequency but higher than the audio frequency, it became known in the early days of the superhet as the *intermediate frequency* (IF). As the circuits operating at the intermediate frequency, once adjusted, need no further tuning, high amplification and good stability are possible.

In order to convert the signal frequency to the intermediate frequency, a frequency-mixing process is necessary. In the mixer the signal frequency is mixed with the output of an oscillator, the frequency of which is varied by the receiver tuning control. This oscillator is called the *local oscillator*.

The resulting *intermediate frequency* is amplified and fed to demodulator and audio amplifier stages. The output of the IF amplifier is used to provide a voltage, the amplitude of which is proportional to the amplitude of the input signal. This is used to control the gain of the receiver, giving automatic gain control (AGC) to compensate for variation of the received signal.

In order to receive telegraphy (CW) signals, it is necessary to provide a signal to beat with the intermediate frequency to produce a beat note which is audible. This signal is generated by the *beat frequency oscillator* (BFO) which operates at the same frequency as the IF but is variable about this frequency by about ±3kHz.

Fig 4.1 is a block diagram of the simplest possible superhet receiver. The basic design features of each stage of a superhet receiver will now be discussed in greater detail.

Mixers

The mixing process of the superhet receiver is shown in Fig 4.2. As is expected in the mixing process, two frequencies appear at the mixer output, these being the sum and difference of the signal and local oscillator frequencies. Only one of these is wanted as the intermediate frequency, and in fact only

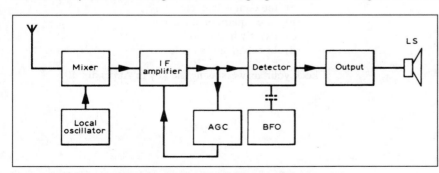

Fig 4.1. The block diagram of a simple superheterodyne receiver

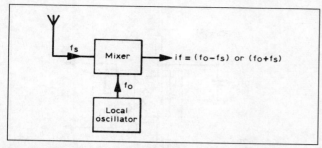

Fig 4.2. The superheterodyne mixing process

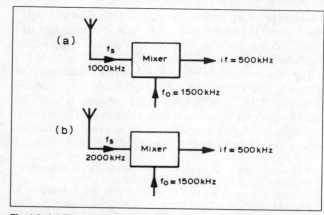

Fig 4.3. (a) The wanted signal. (b) The image frequency

one frequency is accepted by the following IF amplifier. The reason for this will be seen later.

To take a simple numerical example, assume an IF of 500kHz; if the signal frequency is 1000kHz, the frequency of the local oscillator must be 1500kHz; see Fig 4.3(a).

$$IF = f_0 - f_s$$
$$500kHz = 1500kHz - 1000kHz$$

However, a strong signal on a frequency of 2000kHz, that is, a frequency which is twice the IF (ie 2×500kHz) away from the first frequency (1000kHz), can also produce an intermediate frequency of 500kHz; see Fig 4.3(b).

$$IF = f_s - f_0$$
$$500kHz = 2000kHz - 1500kHz$$

Two signals, the wanted one on 1000kHz and an unwanted one on 2000kHz, can both result in an intermediate frequency of 500kHz. The unwanted signal (on 2000kHz) is called the *image* or *second channel*.

This phenomenon appears as the reception of two signals apparently on the same frequency and at the same time. The reception of the unwanted signal is known as *image (second-channel) interference* and it is a spurious response of the receiver in question.

Image interference can only occur when there is a signal on the second channel which is strong enough to reach the mixer. The most common example is the reception in the 20m amateur band of some of the powerful 19m broadcast stations on a simple general-coverage receiver having an IF of 455 to 465kHz (the frequency separation between parts of the 20m amateur and 19m broadcast bands is about 920kHz).

As the existence of image interference depends on the response of the signal input circuit of the mixer to a frequency which is

separated from the resonant frequency of the input circuit by twice the IF, it is clear that increasing the IF will reduce the possibility of image interference.

As a result of the selectivity of the tuned circuits included, one or two RF stages between the antenna and the mixer was accepted as the preferred method of providing considerable attenuation of the second channel. This is now rarely the case and the signals from the antenna are applied directly to the mixer. A high value for the IF and the selectivity given by a *preselector* are sufficient to reduce the image interference to acceptable levels.

The preselector is normally a pair of tuned circuits which have a bandwidth of just a little greater than the band being used so that all required stations are passed to the mixer but the image signals are greatly attenuated. Fig 4.4 shows a typical mixer/oscillator arrangement using transistors. Bipolar transistors, FETs and MOSFETs are all suitable for this application, and the typical arrangement shown here is a Colpitts oscillator, the collector supply being stabilised by a 6.8V zener diode. The oscillator output is fed to a buffer stage to provide isolation between the oscillator and the mixer. The mixer uses a dual-gate MOSFET which is particularly suitable

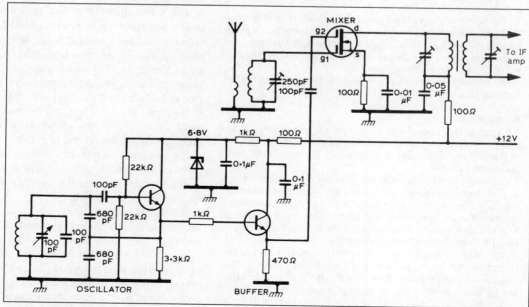

Fig 4.4. A mixer/oscillator circuit

for this type of application, having two gates. The input (RF) tuned circuit is between gate 1 and earth, and the output (IF) tuned circuit is between the drain and the 12V supply. The oscillator voltage is applied to gate 2.

The receiver local oscillator has the same requirements of frequency stability etc as the VFO in a transmitter. The discussion of VFO stability later in this chapter is therefore equally applicable to receiver local oscillators. The situation is complicated by the necessity for the receiver local oscillator to be switched to cover a number of frequency bands.

▶Generally the local oscillator frequency is on the high side of the signal frequency. The reason for this is as follows.

Assume a receiver tunes to signals in the range 1500kHz to 4500kHz and has an IF of 1000kHz. The signal frequency range has a ratio of 3 to 1 (4500 to 1500) and because $f \propto 1/\sqrt{C}$, the change in capacitance must therefore have a ratio of 9 to 1, say, 20pF to 180pF.

If on the low side, the oscillator would have to tune from 500kHz to 3500kHz, a frequency range of 7 to 1, requiring a capacitance range of 49 to 1, say 20pF to 980pF.

Alternatively, if the oscillator is on the high side it would need to tune from 2500kHz to 5500kHz, a frequency range of 2.2 to 1, requiring a capacitance range of only 4.8 to 1, say 20pF to 96pF. A capacitor having a range of 20pF to 96pF is obviously very much more practical than one which has a range of 20pF to 980pF.

Tracking

The tuned circuit of the local oscillator must maintain throughout its tuning range a constant frequency separation equal to the IF from the mixer tuned circuit (if any are present). This requisite is known as *tracking*.

The need for tracking arises because the oscillator and mixer tuned circuits cannot be identical in inductance and capacitance. For example, for a signal frequency range of 5–10MHz with an IF of 500kHz, the mixer tuned circuit must cover 10MHz to 5MHz (ratio 2:1), while if the oscillator is on the high side, its tuned circuit must cover 10.5MHz to 5.5MHz (ratio 1.9:1). The oscillator tuning capacitor often has a smaller capacitance than the mixer capacitor to allow for this.

The wider the frequency range, the more difficult tracking becomes; in practice the optimum solution generally considered is that tracking should be correct at both ends of the tuning range and also at a point near the middle.

Tracking was generally achieved in the better class of receiver by the careful adjustment of a small trimming capacitor in parallel with the oscillator tuning capacitor at the high-frequency end of each range, and the inductance of the tuning coil (by means of a dust core) at the low-frequency end.

An untuned front-end (as is normal modern practice) renders tracking unnecessary.

RF amplifiers

RF amplifiers, ie tuned amplifiers operating at the signal frequency, were employed in some high-quality receivers and also in transceivers. The tuning is ganged with the mixer/local oscillator tuning control.

Basically, an RF stage improves the sensitivity of the receiver, ie it increases the signal/noise ratio. The additional selectivity resulting from the extra tuned circuits may be advantageous in a number of ways, ie the chance of image interference is reduced, as is radiation from the local oscillator via the antenna. This additional RF selectivity is always useful.

The older receivers with an IF of around 465kHz always employed two RF stages and the image interference then only became unacceptable above about 30MHz. If the IF was 1.6MHz, one RF stage could be considered to be adequate.

The big disadvantage of an RF amplifier is the probability of it becoming overloaded by strong signals with resulting

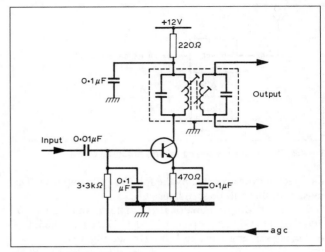

Fig 4.5. An IF amplifier circuit

cross-modulation (strong signals modulating one another cannot be separated by any subsequent selectivity).◀

The intermediate-frequency amplifier

The function of the intermediate-frequency (IF) amplifier is to amplify the output of the mixer before demodulation; it is a tuned amplifier, ie it operates at a single fairly low frequency (the IF). High gain and stability are easily achieved, in fact it is the IF amplifier which provides virtually all the selectivity and most of the gain of the superhet receiver. Its importance is therefore obvious.

The selectivity of the IF amplifier can be achieved by means of tuned circuits or band-pass filters. It is desirable to be able to change the bandwidth of the IF amplifier to suit the signal being received, ie from about 2.7kHz ('wide') for SSB to about 300Hz ('narrow') for CW.

The tuned circuits are designed as *coupled pairs* (see Chapter 3). An IF transformer is such a pair in a screening can (see Fig 4.5). A typical IF amplifier may consist of two or three such stages in cascade.

The value of the IF will depend upon the selectivity required and the need to minimise image interference. These requirements are incompatible, ie low image interference requires a high IF whereas high selectivity requires a low IF (see Chapter 3). One solution to this problem is the *double superhet*, having two different intermediate frequencies. The first is fairly high, typically 1.6 to 3MHz for good image rejection; this is then converted by means of a second mixer and local oscillator to a second IF which is low to provide high selectivity. The second IF may be as low as 50 to 100kHz.

Fig 4.6 shows the typical selectivity of an IF amplifier based on tuned circuits. The achievement of wide and narrow bandwidths in such an amplifier presents difficult electrical and mechanical design problems.

A better IF selectivity characteristic can be obtained by the use of a *band-pass filter*. One version is based on the use of quartz crystals; two, three or four pairs of crystals carefully matched in frequency may be used. The older general-purpose receiver used a crystal filter which employed a single crystal in conjunction with a phasing capacitor. This simple arrangement gave a nose bandwidth of less than 0.5kHz and so was very useful for receiving telegraphy. However, the

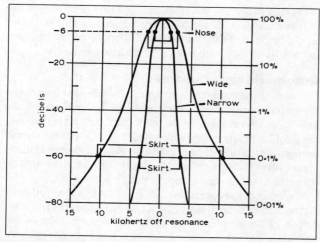

Fig 4.6. Curves showing the typical overall selectivity of an IF amplifier based on tuned circuits

skirt bandwidth, being determined mainly by the tuned circuits, was often very wide.

▶Another form of band-pass filter is the mechanical type. This is a mechanically resonant device which receives electrical energy, converts it into a mechanical vibration which is then converted back into electrical energy at the output. The mechanical vibration is set up in a series of six to nine metal discs by the magnetostrictive effect.

Filters of the band-pass type have a much flatter top to the selectivity curve and shape factors of 1.5–2.5. They are made in various bandwidths from 0.3–10kHz at frequencies of commonly 455kHz and 3–9MHz. Such filters of the desired bandwidth can be switched into an IF amplifier, and the design of the IF transformers used then becomes relatively unimportant as the overall selectivity is determined by the filters. They are compact but tend to be expensive. This type of filter has a sufficiently steep characteristic (ie low shape factor) to filter out the unwanted sideband of a double-sideband signal and is therefore the basis of the filter method of single-sideband generation. It is also used in the receive function of the SSB transceiver.◀

The detector

The purpose of the detector is to rectify or demodulate the output of the IF amplifier, so that the modulation originally superimposed upon the carrier wave at the transmitter can be recovered as a varying voltage superimposed on DC. This can then be amplified and converted into sound by the loudspeaker.

For optimum performance, each mode of modulation requires that a particular demodulating circuit is used in the receiver.

If the carrier is unmodulated, as in telegraphy, it is necessary to mix with the IF amplifier output another signal of a slightly different frequency which is generated by a *beat frequency oscillator* (BFO) in order to produce a difference frequency in the audible range, ie an audible beat note which is then recovered by the detector.

Diode or envelope detector

The simplest detector is a single diode operating as a half-wave rectifier as shown in Fig 4.7. The output is developed across the resistor (the diode load) and then fed to the following audio amplifier. This arrangement

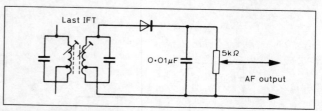

Fig 4.7. The basic circuit of a diode detector

is also known as an *envelope detector* as its object is to recover the modulation envelope. It is the circuit normally used for the detection of an amplitude-modulated signal and, in conjunction with a BFO, for CW telegraphy.

Detection of an FM signal

The ratio detector is a circuit which has been widely used in both entertainment and amateur receivers. The basic circuit is shown in Fig 4.8.

Because the primary voltage is injected into the centre tap of L2 by L3, the voltages at the ends of L2 depend on the phase difference between L1 and L3. At resonance, at the centre frequency, the voltages applied to the diodes are equal. As the frequency increases, the voltage at one end increases and decreases at the other end. The reverse occurs when the frequency decreases from the centre value. The voltages at the ends of L2 are rectified by the diodes and so the rectified voltages appearing across C1 and C2 vary, giving rise to an output at point A.

The output is therefore proportional to the ratio of the voltages which appear across C1 and C2. The total voltage across C1 and C2 is held constant (ie its amplitude does not vary) by the capacitor C3, which is at least 8µF.

Detection of an SSB signal

In this mode of transmission the carrier and one sideband are suppressed and only the remaining sideband is received by the receiving antenna.

The detection of a single-sideband (SSB) signal necessitates the insertion of a signal into the detector to simulate the carrier wave which was suppressed in the transmitter. This signal is generated in the receiver by the *carrier insertion oscillator* (CIO).

This function can be carried out by the BFO of an AM/CW receiver and, by the use of the usual diode envelope detector, reasonably satisfactory results may be obtained. However, the diode detector system has directly opposite requirements for optimum CW detection and optimum SSB detection. A

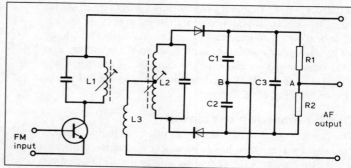

Fig 4.8. The basic circuit of a ratio detector

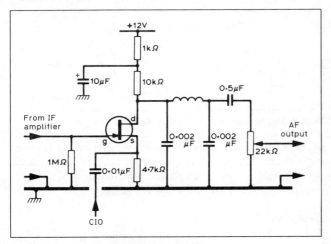

Fig 4.9. The circuit of a product detector

very small input signal from the BFO is preferable for CW whereas SSB detection requires a much larger BFO signal. As the BFO injection voltage is never adjustable, it should be set to suit whichever mode is of most interest. A large BFO voltage is likely to affect the operation of the AGC system as discussed later in this chapter.

The *product detector* is the preferred circuit arrangement for the resolution of an SSB signal. This is a mixer circuit, and one of several varieties is shown in Fig 4.9. The frequencies involved in this mixing process are the receiver IF and the frequency to which the BFO (or CIO) is set. The BFO frequency will have been adjusted to produce an acceptable audible beat frequency. The mixer output frequencies are the audio frequency required (difference) and the sum of the intermediate and BFO frequencies – the following stages will not operate at the sum frequency because of the selectivity provided by a narrow-band filter. The circuit shown uses an FET. The IF amplifier output is connected to the gate and the BFO/CIO injection voltage is taken to the source.

The product detector is also a very effective demodulator of CW telegraphy signals. A further advantage is that the BFO injection voltage necessary is small and is the same for SSB and CW.

Thus the modern all-mode receiver will include two detectors, ie a diode envelope detector for AM and a product detector for SSB/CW. The VHF receiver is most likely to also include a ratio detector for FM.

Beat frequency oscillator

The BFO is a conventional oscillator which operates at the IF of the receiver. Its frequency is generally variable by ±3–4kHz by means of a front-panel control in order to provide the audible beat note discussed earlier, and to enable this note to be set at a frequency which is acceptable to the operator. The BFO is switched on and off by a front-panel control. Coupling between the BFO and detector is very loose; 5pF or so, or even by stray capacitance.

Carrier insertion oscillator

The carrier insertion oscillator generates a signal to replace the carrier wave which has been suppressed in the transmitter. It also performs the same function as the BFO when receiving telegraphy.

In order to achieve the frequency stability necessary in an SSB system, the CIO would be crystal controlled, a separate crystal being used for each sideband. The crystal frequencies are usually ±1.5kHz from the intermediate frequency.

Automatic gain control

The gain of the receiver is automatically adjusted by a voltage which is dependent on the strength of the received signal. The object is to ensure that the output of the receiver remains constant or nearly so, irrespective of the incoming signal strength which may change considerably due to propagation conditions (fading) or simply due to the relative signal strengths of the several stations operating in a net.

The basis of the operation of an AGC system is as follows. As the received signal strength increases, so does the receiver output, and a sample of this is taken from some point in the later IF or early AF stages and fed back in such a way as to reduce the overall gain of the receiver. As the signal fades or a weaker signal is being received, the output falls and a lower control voltage results, increasing the receiver gain.

The gain of the IF amplifier is controlled by feeding the AGC voltage to the base of each transistor in order to vary the emitter current and therefore the gain.

In a simple receiver the AGC voltage would be taken from the detector diode circuit. A separate diode to develop the AGC voltage, fed via a small capacitor (say, 33pF) from the same point as the detector diode, provides a more flexible arrangement.

The simplest circuit is shown in Fig 4.10. R1/R4 form a divider which provides the diode with a small forward bias to make it more sensitive to weak signals. Any increase or decrease in voltage at point A due to changing signal strength will be applied to the base of the first IF amplifier transistor. Any audio component is filtered out by R2 and C1.

Effective AGC for CW reception presents a number of difficulties. The rectified BFO voltage may well reduce the gain even in the absence of a signal. For this reason AGC is often switched out of operation (by S1 in Fig 4.10, ganged to the BFO on/off switch) when receiving CW signals.

A receiver intended for CW/SSB reception will invariably employ a product detector. This provides much better isolation between the locally generated BFO/CIO voltage and the AGC circuit, and the AGC on CW reception is much more effective.

The AGC voltage in an SSB receiver is sometimes obtained by sampling and rectifying the audio at some point in the

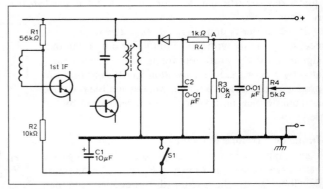

Fig 4.10. The basic configuration of an AGC system

audio amplifier. There is not much to choose between the two methods.

A well-designed AGC system can provide a characteristic which exhibits little change in output level (less than 4dB) for a very large change in input signal (90–100dB). However, a more significant characteristic, particularly for SSB with the intermittent nature of the signal and its syllabic variations, is the speed of operation of the AGC system. The AGC must take effect quickly: the attack time must be of the order of 2ms but the release should be much slower, about 200–300ms. These times are governed by the time constants (ie products of resistance and capacitance) in the AGC circuit.

Audio stages

The audio side of the communication receiver is conventional in every way, bearing in mind the restricted audio bandwidth necessary for communication purposes. The audio power output is normally 1–2W peak to a small loudspeaker located within the receiver cabinet. Generally provision is made to plug in a pair of headphones at the input side of the output stage.

The inclusion of some form of additional selectivity or filter in the audio chain is quite common in the more complex receiver, particularly in the older general-purpose receiver.

This may take two forms, one being a sharp notch filter, in which the notch can be tuned across the audio band. The gain in the notch is very much reduced and so it can attenuate a particular interfering frequency. Alternatively a sharp peak of amplification at a particular frequency, say 1000Hz, may be provided and, by careful adjustment of the BFO to give a 1000Hz beat note, the overall selectivity for CW may be improved.

Calibration oscillator

This is a crystal oscillator arranged to produce a high level of harmonics and operating usually at 100kHz. It provides a calibration 'pip' every 100kHz throughout the receiver tuning range. Generally provision is made to adjust the tuning scale or the pointer slightly to enable the calibration to be corrected at the 100kHz points. In the better class of equipment there are facilities for checking the accuracy of the crystal frequency against a standard frequency transmission.

▶ Noise limiters and noise blankers

Much electrical interference to reception arises from the short pulse of energy radiated whenever a spark occurs from a faulty switch or a car ignition system. The noise limiter is an arrangement of diodes which clip off those interfering pulses which exceed the amplitude of the modulation. The level at which clipping occurs is normally adjustable. The noise limiter is a simple and quite effective circuit.

Fig 4.11 shows the wanted signal and the unwanted interfering waveform.

The noise blanker is a much more complex circuit in which the interfering noise pulses are selected, amplified and inverted. The resulting waveform is then fed back into the receiver via a gate circuit. If the amplitude of the pulse fed back equals that on the signal, the interfering pulse waveform is 'blanked' out before it reaches the output stage of the receiver.

Squelch circuits

Squelch is the name given to a facility which is normally part of an FM communication receiver (or transceiver). The object is to switch off the audio output of the receiver in the absence of a signal or when the incoming signal strength is inadequate for

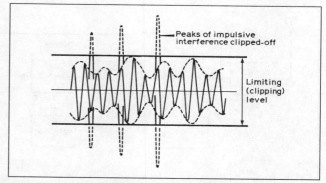

Fig 4.11. Illustrating the action of a noise limiter

satisfactory communication, ie when the receiver is just at the maximum range of a particular transmitter. In this way the annoying hiss produced by the receiver in the absence of a signal is eliminated. The level at which the squelch circuit comes into operation is normally adjustable. ◀

Signal-strength meters

Most commercial receivers now incorporate a signal-strength meter (S-meter). Normally this consists of a sensitive milliammeter, often in a bridge circuit, which is used to monitor the AGC control voltage. This of course varies in sympathy with the incoming signal.

The meter is calibrated in S-units up to S9 and decibels up to 40 or 60 above S9. There is no generally agreed definition of an S-unit (it may be 4 or 6dB) or of the zero point of the meter. Unless an S-meter has been specially calibrated against a signal generator on each band, no great reliance should be placed on its readings. In spite of this failing the S-meter does provide a useful comparison of the signal strengths of different stations.

A COMPLETE RECEIVER

A block diagram of a double-superhet receiver incorporating the points discussed so far in this chapter is shown in Fig 4.12. It is known as a *communication receiver* because it is intended for communication purposes and not entertainment.

Examination of Fig 4.12 raises the query as to which local oscillator is tuned. In fact, either can be tuned as follows:

(a) LO1 tuned and LO2 fixed frequency;
(b) LO1 fixed frequency and LO2 tuned.

For stability reasons, the fixed-frequency oscillator should be crystal controlled.

The arrangement (a) allows, by appropriate design of the RF/mixer/local oscillator tuned circuits, each amateur band to be spread over the whole of the tuning scale which is obviously a very convenient arrangement.

In arrangement (b) the RF/mixer/local oscillator tuned circuits are designed to cover a small range, usually 500kHz. Each amateur band apart from 28MHz can be covered in one such range; for full coverage of the 28MHz band four 500kHz segments are required.

The second local oscillator frequency (crystal controlled) is chosen to convert the above RF ranges to the IF range required, which may be for example 5000–5500kHz. The rest of the receiver is therefore a single-superhet having a single tuning range of 5000–5500kHz.

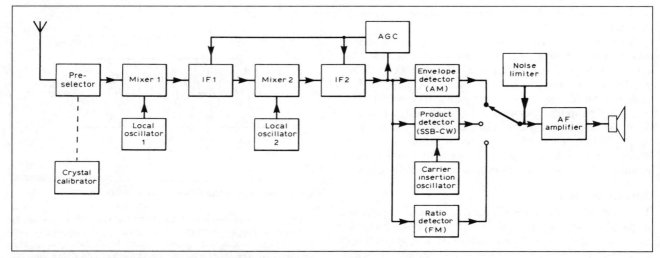

Fig 4.12. The block diagram of a double superheterodyne receiver

The intermediate frequency would be typically 455kHz and the IF amplifier would ideally contain crystal filters having bandwidths of about 0.4kHz, 3kHz and 6kHz which would be switched in to suit the mode in use.

This is a very common arrangement – it provides a constant tuning rate on each band which is slow enough for satisfactory tuning of an SSB signal, ie a tuning rate of no more than 25kHz per revolution of the tuning knob.

▶Transverters
The transverter enables an HF bands transceiver to operate on bands other than those for which it was designed. It combines the function of transmit frequency conversion (generally upwards) and receive frequency conversion (generally downwards) using a common oscillator.

The most common application is to provide operation on the VHF and UHF bands, but they have also been designed to transvert to 1.8MHz. Fig 4.13 is a block diagram of an HF bands transceiver (tuned over the 28MHz band) transverted to 144MHz. The transverter oscillator frequency is 116MHz.◀

VHF RECEIVERS
The principles discussed in this chapter apply to receivers for the VHF and higher frequency ranges, although somewhat higher values of intermediate frequencies may be used.

Alternatively an HF receiver may be used on the higher frequency bands by means of a converter. This is a separate unit consisting of an RF stage, a mixer and crystal-controlled local oscillator. Typically this may convert 144–146MHz to 28–30MHz, the output from the mixer at this frequency being taken to the antenna input of a receiver which tunes over 28–30MHz.

Such converters are commercially available to convert the popular VHF and UHF bands to a number of different output frequencies.

▶Direct-conversion receivers
The basis of the superhet is the conversion of all signals to a fixed intermediate frequency, followed by demodulation and AF amplification to drive a loudspeaker. The incoming signals can, however, be converted directly to AF, and a much simplified type of superhet results. This is known as the *synchrodyne*. It is not a new principle but has become popular in amateur radio as the direct-conversion receiver.

The local oscillator operates very close to the signal frequency so that the output of the mixer (which is equivalent to a product detector) is in the AF range. This is normally followed by a low-pass filter to restrict the audio bandwidth to about 3kHz and a high-gain audio amplifier to drive a loudspeaker.

The mixer is usually preceded by a simple untuned RF stage. Due to the difficulties of making a sufficiently stable oscillator, the direct-conversion receiver is often restricted to the lower-frequency amateur bands where it is capable of surprisingly good performance, although obviously not in the same class as a good-quality communication receiver.

The oscillator followed by a buffer amplifier can also be used to drive a power amplifier, so creating a low-power transceiver, and a number of these are now available commercially.◀

TRANSMITTERS
Radio transmitters, irrespective of their application, must:

(a) produce the output power required;
(b) not drift in frequency, ie the frequency shall not change for any reason once it has been set to the desired value;
(c) generally be capable of operating on several frequencies and probably in more than one mode;
(d) have a pure output waveform, ie it should not contain harmonics or any other unwanted frequencies, as may be caused by parasitic oscillations.

A transmitter therefore consists of a *power amplifier* (PA) to provide the necessary output power which is preceded by low-power drive circuits to generate the RF input to the PA at

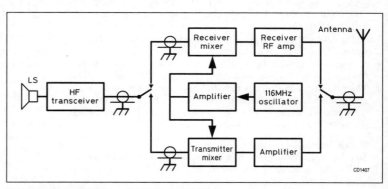

Fig 4.13. Block diagram of 28MHz/144MHz transverter

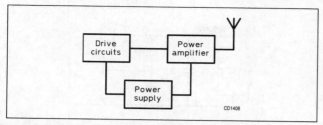

Fig 4.14. A simple block diagram of a transmitter

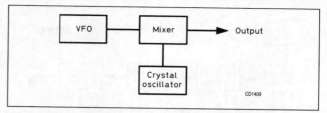

Fig 4.15. The block diagram of a basic mixer-VFO

the required frequencies. The drive circuits may well include the means by which modulation of the transmitter is achieved (see Fig 4.14).

An amateur transmitter is required to operate on any frequency in a number of different bands. As *netting* (that is, stations in communication operating on the same frequency) is almost universal in amateur radio, it is necessary to be able to set the transmitter frequency to any particular value.

A variable frequency oscillator (VFO) is therefore the basic RF source for the drive circuits.

TRANSMITTER DRIVE CIRCUITS

The transmitter drive circuits may consist of:

(a) a frequency multiplier chain;
(b) a mixer VFO; or
(c) a frequency synthesiser.

The frequency multiplier chain

Table 4.1 lists the limits of the original HF amateur bands, ie up to 30MHz, and the harmonic relationship between them.

▶It will be seen from Table 4.1 that the output of a VFO which is tuneable over a frequency range of 1.75MHz to 2MHz can be multiplied to produce frequencies in all bands up to 28MHz.

It should be noted that any undesired change in the frequency of the VFO is also multiplied in the frequency multiplier circuit; in the worst case by a factor of 16, ie 1.8MHz to 28MHz.

It is particularly important to prevent the radiation of the harmonics other than the required one which are generated in this arrangement.

Harmonics of frequencies in the HF amateur bands will occur around 42MHz, 56MHz and 63MHz. These are liable to cause breakthrough to radio services operating near these frequencies. The frequency multiplier chain cannot be extended to include the WARC bands, ie 10MHz, 18MHz and 24MHz, because these bands are not in harmonic relationship to each other or to the original bands. This circuit is now rarely used commercially, but it provides a simple solution for the home constructor who is interested only in CW operation on the original HF bands.◀

The mixer-VFO circuit

Coverage of all the HF bands can be achieved by mixing the outputs of a VFO and a fixed-frequency (crystal) oscillator.

By the use of a crystal of the appropriate frequency this circuit, generally known as a *mixer VFO*, can produce an output at almost any frequency. Harmonic relationship is not necessary as the desired frequency is the result of the addition of two frequencies and not the multiplication of one (see Fig 4.16).

Typically the frequency coverage of the VFO would be 500kHz in the range of 3MHz to 8MHz. Any unwanted change in the frequency of the VFO remains the same at all output frequencies because it is not multiplied as in the arrangement of Fig 4.15. In this way the overall frequency stability is significantly improved.

For reasons which will be explained later in this chapter, the mixer VFO must be used in an SSB transmitter.

The frequency synthesiser

The term *frequency synthesiser* has been applied to the mixer VFO just described, but today it normally implies a complex circuit which can produce a large number of equally spaced frequencies, the basic stability of which is determined by a single quartz crystal.

Such a circuit could replace the VFO or the local oscillator as the controlling frequency source in a transmitter and/or receiver in a communication system utilising a large number of equally spaced frequency channels.

The basis of the frequency synthesiser is a *phase-locked loop* (PLL). This is an electronic feedback loop and is shown in outline in Fig 4.16.

A *voltage-controlled oscillator* (VCO) is an oscillator whose frequency can be controlled by the variation of a voltage, eg variation of the frequency of an L-C oscillator by a varicap diode. The VCO frequency f_0 is fed back to a phase detector circuit in which it is compared with a reference frequency f_r. The output of the phase detector is an 'error' voltage. This is a varying direct voltage which is proportional to the difference in frequency and phase between f_r and f_0. The error voltage is filtered to remove any high-frequency components from the output of the phase detector and is then fed back to the VCO where it causes the VCO frequency to change in order to reduce the difference between f_r and f_0. This process continues until the two frequencies are equal. The loop is then said to be *phase locked*.

Table 4.1. Harmonically related HF bands	
Limits of HF bands (kHz)	**Equivalent to**
1810–2000	1810–2000 × 1
3500–3800	1750–1900 × 2
7000–7100	1750–1775 × 4
14,000–14,350	1750–1794 × 8
21,000–21,450	1750–1787 × 12
28,000–29,700	1750–1856 × 16

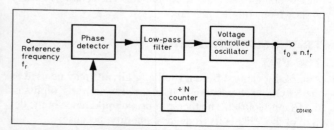

Fig 4.16. A block diagram of a basic phase-locked loop

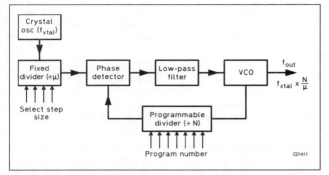

Fig 4.17. The block diagram of a basic frequency synthesiser

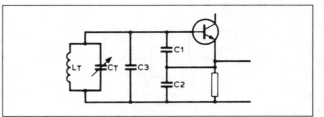

Fig 4.18. The connection between the tuned circuit (L$_T$, C$_T$) and the transistor in a Colpitts-type oscillator

The phase-locked loop may be used in conjunction with a conventional oscillator to provide a frequency stability which is greater than that of the oscillator itself. However, when it is used with a divide-by-*n* counter, it becomes the basis of the *frequency synthesiser*.

A divide-by-*n* counter is a digital logic integrated circuit which produces a single output pulse for every *n* input pulses; *n* of course is a whole number.

Many counters are available, capable of dividing by fixed ratios according to the way in which they are connected. These can be connected in cascade to give greater ratios. For example, if three counters which divide by 10, divide by 6 and divide by 5 are connected in cascade, they will divide by 300 (10 × 6 × 5). A more useful version is the *programmable counter* which typically can divide by any number between 1 and 10 according to whether the appropriate pin on the IC is grounded or not.

A basic block diagram of a frequency synthesiser is shown in Fig 4.17. The reference frequency is obtained from a low-frequency crystal oscillator (typically 1MHz to 5MHz) followed by a divider. By selection of the divide ratio of the reference frequency divider and the programmable divider in the feedback loop, a stable and programmable output frequency is obtained. This output frequency cannot be adjusted in a continuous manner as in a VFO but is tuned in a number of discrete steps. In FM equipment it is convenient to make these steps equal to the channel spacing, ie 25 or 12.5kHz. In the case of an SSB transceiver the step needs to be much smaller in order to ensure that the signal can be resolved correctly. 100Hz should be regarded as the maximum step size on SSB unless some other form of fine tune is available.

The actual programming of a frequency synthesiser is achieved in a number of ways, from simple switches to microcomputers. Tuning knobs coupled to electro-mechanical or mechanical-optical switches are also used to simulate conventional tuning. The method used depends upon the complexity and the price of the equipment. The actual frequency is shown on a digital display.

TRANSMITTER DESIGN
The VFO

Any of the many different oscillator circuits may be used as the VFO, but the generally used circuits are the Colpitts or the Clapp-Gouriet. The factor of prime importance in the design of the VFO is its frequency stability, because:

(a) the frequency must not drift outside the permitted band;

(b) the frequency must not drift outside the pass band of the receiver which is tuned to the transmission.

Frequency stability is particularly important in a transmitter intended for single sideband operation.

The frequency of an oscillator is determined by the resonant frequency of its tuned circuit:

$$f = \frac{1}{2\pi\sqrt{LC}}$$

Therefore the magnitude of *L*, the inductance of the coil, and of *C*, the capacitance necessary to tune *L* to the required frequency, should not vary under any circumstances.

The factors which may cause *L* and *C* to vary are:

(a) mechanical shock:

   (i) The coil must be tightly wound (preferably under tension) on a grooved former, preferably ceramic or made from a low-loss material.

   (ii) The variable capacitor should be of good quality, ie mechanically sound.

   (iii) The wiring between the coil and capacitor should be as short and rigid as possible, so that it cannot move.

(b) change in ambient temperature:

The coil and capacitor inevitably have a temperature coefficient, the effects of which are show up as a mechanical movement, therefore (a) (i) and (a) (ii) above are doubly important.

Preferably the coil should be air-cored as any form of dust-iron core will cause an additional variation of the inductance of the coil with temperature. The effect of temperature on the tuned circuit may be minimised by locating it as far as possible from any source of heat.

In the Colpitts and similar oscillators, the effect of change in transistor capacitances is minimised by the particular circuit configuration (see Fig 4.18). C1 and C2 are large and swamp the transistor capacitances, but they are part of the frequency-determining capacitance, and so their change in value with temperature is important. These capacitors should be of good quality, preferably having mica or polystyrene as the dielectric. These will have a small positive temperature coefficient which may be compensated for by the experimental addition of a low-value ceramic dielectric capacitor which has a large negative temperature coefficient (C3 in Fig 4.18).

To summarise, the tuned circuit of a VFO must be soundly made and use best-quality components.

External influences on the VFO

The VFO should be considered as a source of a small output voltage at a constant frequency. It should not be close to any

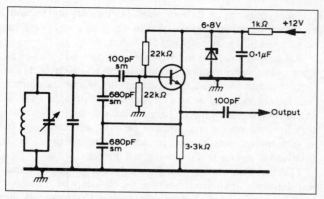

Fig 4.19. A typical Colpitts oscillator circuit

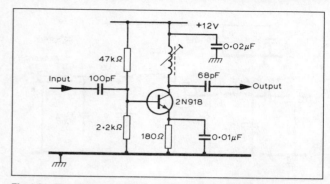

Fig 4.20. The basic circuit of a frequency multiplier

source of heat. The VFO should be lightly loaded by the following stage; excess loading may ultimately stop the oscillation, and any change in loading, if heavy (eg during keying), may well cause a change in frequency ('chirp'). The VFO should ideally be followed by an isolating stage such as a Class A buffer amplifier.

Variation of supply voltage can cause a change in transistor parameters and hence in frequency. For this reason stabilisation of the supply voltage is advisable. This is normally achieved by the use of a zener diode (see Chapter 3).

For frequency-stability reasons, it is considered inadvisable to key a VFO and it should also operate at the lowest possible frequency. This is because the effects of the likely sources of frequency drift increase as the frequency increases. It should be noted that some frequency drift is inevitable during the first few minutes of operation after switch on from cold; it is the drift after this period which must be reduced to the minimum.

Fig 4.19 is the circuit diagram of a Colpitts VFO.

Frequency multiplication

Frequency multipliers are normally low-power transistors operating in Class C in order to produce a collector current which is rich in harmonics. The circuit of such a stage is shown in Fig 4.20.

The tuned circuit is resonant at $n \times f$, where f is the frequency of the input voltage and n is usually 2 or 3. Higher multiplications may be used but the output is rather low. The tuned circuit may consist of a small coil and variable capacitor or a slug-tuned coil and fixed capacitor.

Exciters for VHF and UHF transmitters

A stable frequency source followed by a multiplier chain is a convenient arrangement for the VHF (70 and 144MHz) and UHF (430MHz) bands as the transmitters used at these frequencies are generally single-band transmitters. Due to the increased circuit losses at the higher frequencies, a buffer amplifier may be necessary before the output stage.

For stability reasons, crystal oscillators (frequencies in the region of 6MHz, 8MHz or sometimes 12MHz) can be used, but phase-locked loops are usual. A block diagram of an exciter for 144MHz is shown in Fig 4.21.

It will be seen that the addition of a further tripler stage will give an output at

432MHz and that with a slightly different crystal frequency, the first two multiplying stages will provide an output at 70MHz.

Transistor power amplifiers

Transistor RF power amplifiers differ significantly in circuit design from valve amplifiers. This arises mainly because of the much lower input and output impedances of the transistor compared with the thermionic valve. These impedances decrease as the power level increases.

It must be remembered that transistors have very little thermal overload capacity and so the standard precautions for their use are particularly important in high-power amplifiers, ie close attention must be paid to the de-rating factor and heat sinking. Considerable de-rating may be advisable if amplitude modulation is to be used, and therefore SSB or NBFM is to be preferred.

Layout and bypassing of the collector supply must be carefully considered to avoid instability and probably interference (see Chapter 5). The antenna must be accurately matched to the transmitter output as transistor output stages are very sensitive in this respect.

Adjustment and operation are generally more critical.

Overloading of the output stages can easily be caused by mis-matching (a high SWR), and solid-state output devices are liable to failure if this occurs. To minimise the risk *automatic level control* (ALC) is used. This monitors the SWR and reduces the drive to the output device as the SWR increases. Normally it is only possible to realise the full output of a solid-state device if the SWR is 1.5 or lower. The same system may be used with a thermionic valve output stage but the requirement is less critical.

Power amplifiers at VHF

For low powers, ie less than 25W (output) or so, the transistor is a relatively cheap and very convenient solution, particularly for mobile or portable operation when the power level desired can be obtained from a 12V supply.

The preferred output arrangement for a transistor PA at

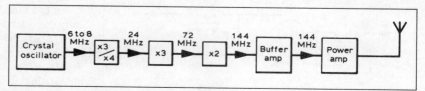

Fig 4.21. The block diagram of a 144MHz transmitter

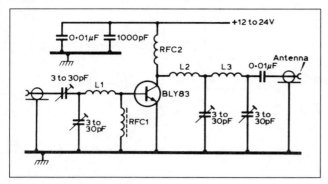

Fig 4.22. A low-power PA for 144MHz

144MHz is the L-pi circuit. This is a combination of the series-tuned L and the conventional pi circuit.

A typical circuit is shown in Fig 4.22. This uses a Mullard BLY83 and gives an output of 7W for a collector supply voltage of 12V, and 12W at 24V. These powers are capable of very good performance at VHF due to the much more effective antennas which are possible at these frequencies. The collector supply is decoupled by 0.01μF and 1000pF capacitors in parallel. The 0.01μF capacitor next to the output socket is for DC blocking. The relative simplicity of the circuit, which was built on a printed circuit board measuring 127 by 38mm, should be noted.

Power amplifiers at HF

A similar arrangement to that of Fig 4.22 can be used for single-band low-power work on the HF bands, but in general the requirements here tend to be a great deal more severe, ie higher powers are generally called for with operation over all bands.

The lower input and output impedances of transistors, which were referred to earlier, mean that in a PA having an output of 100W, these impedances will be of the order of 1–10Ω. Conventional pi-network designs at such low impedances lead to impractical values of inductance and capacitance.

The solution adopted at high power is to transform the impedance of the RF input to a transistor PA down from 50Ω and then transform the output impedance of the transistor back up to the normal 50Ω. The basic arrangement is shown in Fig 4.23. The transformers used have ratios of about 4:1 and two such transformers may be used in cascade to provide a higher ratio.

These transformers are known as *transmission line* or *broad-band transformers* and typically consist of relatively

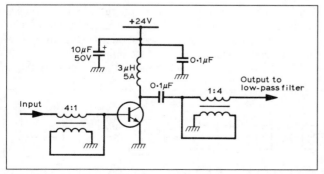

Fig 4.23. A basic circuit diagram of a PA for use on the HF bands

few turns of wire on a toroidal core. The primary and secondary windings are wound together as a pair of wires (a *bifilar* winding) which may be twisted together.

Because this type of transformer is broad-band, it can operate over a wide frequency range, ie from 3–30MHz. If the drive circuits are similarly designed, the whole transmitter becomes broad-band, ie apart from the VFO no band switching or retuning is required. This is obviously highly satisfactory from the operational point of view; however, the design of such transformers is complex and the constructional work involved is not for the inexperienced amateur.

The fact that the RF circuits are broad-band means that any harmonic or spurious frequency which may be generated is also amplified and appears at the output. Consequently the output must be filtered to avoid the radiation of any unwanted frequencies. A separate (switched) filter for each band is often used.

MODULATION

The output of a transmitter is known as the *carrier wave*. This is an alternating waveform of the desired amplitude and frequency. Ideally it is a pure sine wave, ie it should not contain harmonics, nor any other unwanted frequencies which might cause breakthrough to other services (TV, broadcast etc). The amplitude of the carrier wave depends upon the power and the output impedance of the transmitter which is most likely to be 50 to 75Ω.

In order that a transmitter may be used to convey a message or other information to a listener, the carrier could be switched on and off (ie keyed) in order to produce the dots and dashes of the Morse code (CW telegraphy). Alternatively, some characteristic of the carrier wave may be varied in sympathy with the message. This process is called *modulation*.

Modulation may be achieved by the periodic variation of:

(a) amplitude, giving *amplitude modulation* (AM); or
(b) frequency, producing *frequency modulation* (FM).

The rate of variation of amplitude or frequency of the carrier wave, ie the *modulating frequency* (f_m) is assumed to be low compared with the carrier frequency (f_c).

For optimum performance, each mode of modulation requires a particular form of demodulation circuit in the receiver. These are described earlier in this chapter.

Sidebands

In all modulation processes frequencies above and below the carrier wave are produced, these being termed *side frequencies*. The bands of side frequencies are called *sidebands*.

In AM, the highest side frequency is the sum of the carrier frequency (f_c) and the highest modulating frequency (f_m), eg if f_c is 1950kHz and f_m is 5kHz, the highest and lowest side frequencies are 1955kHz and 1945kHz, ie the sidebands extend from 1955kHz to 1945kHz as shown in Fig 4.24. The bandwidth occupied by this transmission is 10kHz.

For FM this situation is much more complex and theoretically the sidebands in an FM system are infinitely wide. The change, which is both positive and negative, in the frequency of the carrier (known as the *centre frequency*) is called the *deviation*. The deviation is proportional to the amplitude of the modulating signal, so that the limits of the 'swing', ie twice the deviation, are determined by the peaks of the modulating

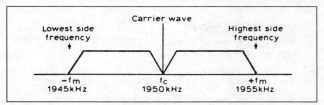

Fig 4.24. The relationship between the carrier and sidebands in an AM system

voltage. The rate at which the carrier frequency is deviated is equal to the frequency of the modulating signal, eg if a carrier wave of 7075kHz is modulated by a 3kHz tone of specified amplitude to produce a deviation of 2.5kHz, the carrier frequency will swing between 7072.5 and 7077.5kHz (ie the swing is 5kHz) 3000 times per second. If the amplitude of the 3kHz tone were doubled, the carrier frequency would swing between 7070 and 7080kHz but the rate of variation would still be 3kHz.

The ratio of the deviation to the frequency of the modulating signal is the *modulating index*. This ratio is obviously not constant, as the deviation depends on the amplitude of the modulating signal. Its limiting value, or the ratio of the maximum deviation to the highest modulating frequency, is called the *deviation ratio*. In the example quoted earlier, the deviation ratio is 2.5kHz divided by 3kHz or 0.833 for the first given amplitude, and 5.0kHz divided by 3kHz or 1.67 when the amplitude of the modulating signal is doubled.

Bandwidth necessary for communication

For the faithful reproduction of speech and music, it is necessary to transmit frequencies over the whole audible range (ie approximately 20Hz to 16kHz). In a communication system, intelligibility rather than fidelity is of prime importance and in the overcrowded conditions of the present-day amateur bands it is obviously most important to ensure that no transmission occupies a greater bandwidth than is absolutely necessary for intelligible communication.

Experience shows that the intelligible transmission of speech requires that only frequencies of up to 2.5–3kHz need be transmitted. Therefore the bandwidth of an AM transmission should not be greater than about 5–6kHz. This restriction of the audio bandwidth is achieved by the use of a low-pass filter having a cut-off frequency of about 2.5kHz in the low-level stages of the modulating circuits.

In FM, as applied to communication, the deviation should be restricted so that the bandwidth occupied is approximately the same as in an AM transmission. This is known as *narrow-band frequency modulation* (NBFM) and the deviation used is ±2.5kHz or so (as compared with the ±75kHz of the high-fidelity broadcast station).

Depth of modulation

The amplitude-modulated wave is shown graphically in Fig 4.25. Here (a) represents the unmodulated carrier wave of constant amplitude and frequency which, when modulated by the audio-frequency wave (b), acquires a varying amplitude, as shown at (c). This is the modulated carrier wave, and the two curved lines touching the crests of the modulated carrier wave constitute the modulation envelope. The modulation amplitude is represented by either x or y (which in most

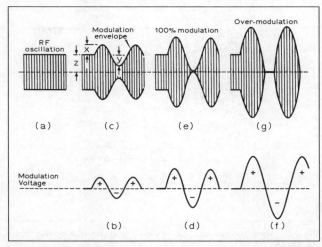

Fig 4.25. Graphical representation of an amplitude-modulated wave

cases can be assumed to be equal), and the ratio of this to the amplitude of the unmodulated carrier wave is known as the *modulation factor* or *modulation depth*. This ratio may also be expressed as a percentage. When the amplitude of the modulating signal is increased, as at (d), the condition (e) is reached, where the negative peak of the modulating signal has reduced the amplitude of the modulated wave to zero, while the positive peak increased the carrier amplitude to twice the unmodulated value. This represents 100% modulation, or a modulation factor of 1.

Further increase of the modulating signal amplitude, as indicated by (f), produces the condition (g), where the carrier wave is reduced to zero for an appreciable period by the negative peaks of the modulating signal. This condition is known as *over-modulation*. The breaking up of the carrier in this way causes distortion and the introduction of harmonics of the modulating frequencies, which are radiated as spurious sidebands; this causes the transmission to occupy a much greater bandwidth than necessary, and considerable breakthrough is likely to be experienced in nearby receivers (see Chapter 5). The radiation of such spurious sidebands (sometimes known as *splatter*) must be avoided at all costs.

There is no direct equivalent of over-modulation in an FM system; an increase in the amplitude of the modulating signal will cause an increase in the deviation produced by the transmitter. The recommended deviation would therefore be exceeded and the transmission would occupy a wider bandwidth, ie it would be FM rather than NBFM.

Ultimately the maximum deviation possible is restricted by the design of the RF circuits in the transmitter and the receiver, and attempts to exceed this will result in a distorted signal. However, this would require gross maladjustment and really excessive audio input to the frequency modulator.

Single-sideband operation

Consideration of Fig 4.24 indicates two significant aspects of an amplitude modulation system.

(a) The carrier wave itself does not contain any intelligence, its frequency being f_c.

(b) Both sidebands are identical as they both result from the modulating frequency f_m and the width of each is equal to

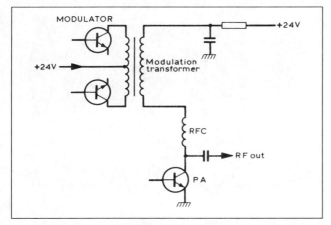

Fig 4.26. Amplitude modulation using transformer coupling to the PA stage

the highest modulating frequency. Both sidebands therefore carry the same intelligence.

It follows that the carrier need not be transmitted and, as both sidebands contain the same intelligence, only one of them need be transmitted. This has led to the adoption of the system known as *single sideband suppressed carrier*, generally abbreviated to 'SSB'.

Keying

Keying is the switching on and off (by a Morse key) of a transmitter in order to break up the carrier wave into the dots and dashes of the Morse code. Keying implies the switching of an electric circuit and therefore, in order to minimise sparking at the contacts of the key, it should take place at a point in the circuit where the power or current is at a minimum.

In order to avoid the possibility of causing 'chirp' and small changes in transmitter frequency, it is recommended that the VFO itself should not be keyed. The logical point to key is therefore the stage after the VFO, which ideally should be an isolating buffer amplifier, although it may be the first frequency multiplier stage.

The process of keying may cause serious interference. This and steps to overcome it are discussed in Chapters 5 and 6.

MODULATION METHODS

►Amplitude modulation

It can be shown that the effective power in a carrier wave modulated to a depth of 100% by a sinusoidal modulating signal (ie a single pure tone) is 1.5 times the unmodulated carrier power. In order to fully modulate the carrier, the power in it must be increased by 50%.

This extra power, which is in fact 'added' to the HT supply to the transmitter PA stage, must be supplied by the *modulator*, which is a fairly high-power audio-frequency amplifier. To fully modulate a transmitter operating at an input of 150W to the PA stage would require an AF power of 75W.

The output of the modulator is coupled into the HT supply to the PA by the modulation transformer as shown in outline in Fig 4.26. The ratio of this transformer is determined by the output impedance of the modulator and the modulating impedance of the PA stage.

This is the most effective method of amplitude modulation as the PA stage operates in Class C, giving the highest efficiency.

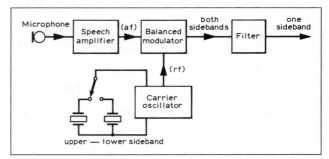

Fig 4.27. A block diagram of an SSB generator

The disadvantage is that large and expensive modulating equipment is necessary for full-power operation, ie as indicated above the basic power required would be 75W, to which must be added an allowance to cover losses in the modulation transformer, so that the design aim should be 100W or so. ◄

Frequency modulation

Frequency modulation is modulation of a carrier wave created by the variation of the carrier frequency by the modulating voltage. The variation (deviation) is positive and negative from the actual carrier frequency (ie the centre frequency).

FM may be achieved by the direct action on the tuned circuit of the fundamental oscillator by a varactor diode. This is shown in outline in Fig 3.37. The diode would be biased so that the variation in capacitance upwards and downwards by the modulating voltage is both equal and linear.

It must be remembered that when the final frequency of an FM transmitter is obtained by multiplication, the deviation of the fundamental is also multiplied.

At VHF, crystal control is common, eg at 144MHz multiplication of ×18 is typical. For a final deviation of 2.5kHz, the fundamental oscillator has to be deviated by less than 200Hz. The frequency of an 8MHz crystal oscillator can be pulled by this small amount by means of a varicap diode.

Single sideband

The single-sideband (SSB) transmitter performs two distinct functions. These are:

(a) suppression of the carrier wave;
(b) elimination of one sideband.

The carrier is suppressed by feeding the output of the carrier frequency oscillator and the modulating voltage into a circuit known as a *balanced modulator*. This is a form of bridge circuit which, when correctly balanced, will cause the RF input to be suppressed, so only the two sidebands appear at the output. The unwanted sideband is removed by a band-pass filter about 2.7kHz wide. If for any reason suppression is not 100%, the possibility of some unwanted radiation occurring outside the band must be borne in mind if one is operating right on the band edge.

This combination, shown in block form in Fig 4.27, is called the *sideband generator*. The single sideband produced is in fact a band of frequencies corresponding to one sideband of an AM system. It can be produced at a fairly low frequency, typically 455kHz, in which case the frequency band is 455–458kHz. Alternatively the sideband can be generated in the megahertz region, eg at 9MHz, in which case the frequency band would be 9–9.003MHz.

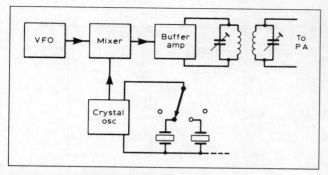

Fig 4.28. A block diagram of a mixer-type VFO

Output		Input (W)	
(dbW)	(W)	Class C	Class B
26	400	600	720
20	100	150	180
16	40	60	72
9	8	12	14

Fig 4.28 is a block diagram of a mixer-type exciter in which the outputs of a VFO and a crystal oscillator are mixed to produce an output in the required amateur band.

The VFO will typically cover a range of 500kHz; its actual frequency (order of 3–8MHz) and the crystal frequencies must be chosen so that the wanted and unwanted products in the output of the mixer are as far apart in frequency as possible. The mixer is followed by a tuned amplifier having coupled tuned circuits in the output to improve the rejection of the unwanted product.

This exciter followed by a conventional PA is a preferred, although complex, alternative to the frequency multiplier circuit for the following reasons:

(a) the absence of internally generated frequencies which may be radiated and so cause interference to other services; and

(b) the overall frequency stability is improved because it is constant and not dependent on the band in use.

For the reasons discussed earlier it must be used in the SSB transmitter.

Depending upon the frequency at which the sideband is generated, one or more mixing processes may be required to reach the final frequency and to introduce the output of a VFO.

Fig 4.29 is a block diagram of an SSB transmitter in which the SSB is generated at a high frequency, say 9MHz, and therefore only one mixing process is needed to translate the SSB generation frequency to the output frequency. This diagram is a combination of Figs 4.27 and 4.28.

The PA of the SSB transmitter has to amplify a modulated RF signal without distortion. It therefore operates in Class B rather than Class C and is known as a *linear amplifier* as the relationship between the output and input is linear.

By convention the lower sideband is transmitted at radio frequencies below 10MHz and the upper sideband above 10MHz. The sideband required is selected by switching the crystal in the sideband generator (see Fig 4.27).

For a number of reasons, the sideband transmitter is combined with the appropriate receiver giving rise to the *transceiver*.

The modulation systems described above are utilised for the transmission of telephony. The UK licence also permits the use of other more specialised modes of transmission such as radio teletype (RTTY), high-definition television, slow-scan television (SSTV) etc.

These modes are achieved by basically similar forms of modulation. Their use is quite small compared with telegraphy and telephony; they are not included in the RAE syllabus and are not covered in this manual.

TRANSMITTER POWER LEVEL

The UK amateur licence now defines maximum power on all bands and modes in terms of output rather than input. The actual levels are quoted in 'dBW', ie so many decibels above one watt (see Chapter 3).

Powers in watts and dBW are:

$$26\text{dBW} = 400\text{W} \qquad 16\text{dBW} = 40\text{W}$$
$$22\text{dBW} = 160\text{W} \qquad 15\text{dBW} = 32\text{W}$$
$$20\text{dBW} = 100\text{W} \qquad 9\text{dBW} = 8\text{W}$$

In a CW, AM or FM transmitter it is considerably easier to measure input power than output power. This is because input power is the product of the direct voltage applied to the output stage and the direct current drawn by the output stage. This current does not vary.

The inputs corresponding to the maximum carrier powers now permitted for modes other than SSB (note that there is no change as regards SSB) are shown in Table 4.2. They assume an output stage efficiency of 66 and 55% for output stages operating in Class C and Class B respectively.

Derivation of the SSB power level

In an AM transmitter, the maximum output power permitted (in the absence of modulation) is 100W (20dBW).

When the transmitter is 100% modulated, the amplitude of the peaks of the modulation envelope is

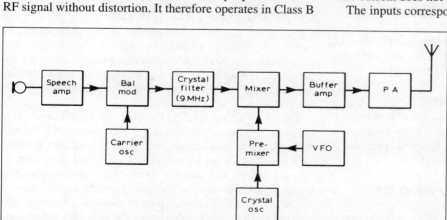

Fig 4.29. A block diagram of an SSB transmitter

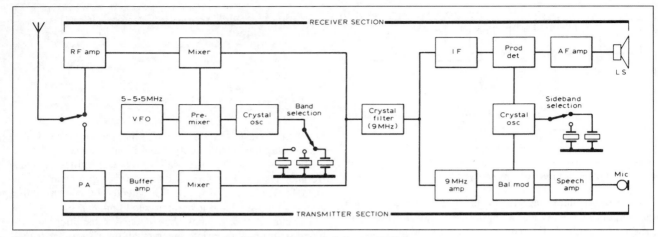

Fig 4.30. A block diagram of an SSB transceiver (from *A Guide to Amateur Radio*)

twice that of the unmodulated carrier wave (see Fig 4.12). As we are considering a voltage waveform, and since power equals V^2/R (R is the value of the load resistor and V is the unmodulated carrier amplitude), the output power of each cycle of RF energy at the peaks of modulation is $(2V)^2/R$ (because V is the unmodulated carrier amplitude and the modulated carrier amplitude is $2V$). This is equal to $4V^2/R$ or four times the unmodulated carrier power. The power at the peak of the modulation envelope or the peak envelope power is 4×100 or 400W. This is the maximum power permitted by the UK amateur licence.

▶**Speech processors**
The speech waveform has a high peak but quite low average value. When this is amplified to increase the modulation level, excess deviation, distortion and spreading signal will occur at the peaks. The action of a speech clipper is to limit the peaks. The resulting waveform is filtered as it is now somewhat distorted by the clipping action.
Most modern transmitters incorporate a moderate amount of speech processing which can be switched in and out.◀

COMPARISON OF MODULATION METHODS
AM is now not commonly used; operation is in Class C but efficiency is low due to the audio power required.

FM is widely used for hand-held and mobile operation at VHF and UHF. It gives good coverage over a relatively small area (greater when used via a repeater) but has little use at HF.

SSB is the most effective system from the point of view of bandwidth and power efficiency, and is less adversely affected by disturbances inherent in ionospheric propagation.

TRANSMITTER INTERFERENCE
A high-power transmitter is a potential source of interference to TV, other radio services and domestic AF equipment. All relevant aspects of the installation and antenna system of a transmitter are discussed in Chapters 5 and 7.

THE ADJUSTMENT AND TUNING OF TRANSMITTERS
Testing and adjustment of transmitters should be done on a dummy load.

The most important adjustment is in the audio level. Excess

audio will cause over-modulation in all its forms and consequent interference to other users of the bands.

An oscilloscope is invaluable for adjustment of an SSB transmitter (see Chapter 8).

THE TRANSCEIVER
The frequency stability of the transmitter and receiver are especially important in an SSB communication system. The carrier re-insertion process also must be done accurately. Unless the local signal is within 25Hz of the original (suppressed) carrier frequency there will be distortion, and if the frequencies differ by much more than that figure, the SSB transmission will be unreadable.

A narrow band filter (2.5–3kHz) is required to remove one sideband in the transmitter and a similar filter is advantageous in the receiver. Both require a very stable VFO.

For these reasons, the transmitter and receiver circuits can be combined to produce the *transceiver* in which the same VFO and filter are used in both the transmit and receive functions. This is now the preferred arrangement for SSB operation; it can also be used for telegraphy.

The modern transceiver is compact and inevitably complex in design. It is often followed by a separate linear amplifier to boost the transmitter power to the legal maximum. Fig 4.30 is a block diagram of a typical SSB transceiver.

INTRODUCTION TO VALVES
Valves function by the *thermionic emission* of electrons (negative) from a heated cathode in a vacuum. The electrons are attracted to an anode which is maintained at a positive potential. The electrons flow from the cathode to the anode, but the 'conventional' current is considered to flow in the opposite direction.

The cathode may be *directly heated*, in which case it is a tungsten wire which is heated by the passing of a current through it. An *indirectly heated* cathode consists of a thin tube which is coated with various compounds of barium or thorium and is maintained at the required temperature by a heater which is inside and insulated from the cathode tube.

The basic two-electrode valve or *diode* is a one-way device, ie it can rectify an alternating current. This application has now been taken over by the solid-state diode.

The addition between the cathode and the anode of a metal

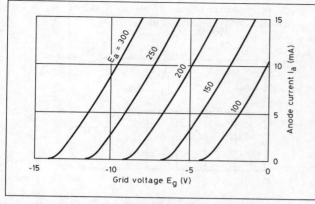

Fig 4.31. Anode current/grid-voltage characteristics

grid (control grid g₁), maintained at a negative potential, enables the electron current to be changed by varying the voltage applied to the latter. In this way the anode current is controlled. The relationship between anode current (I_a) and grid voltage (E_g) (negative) is shown in Fig 4.31, while Fig 4.32 shows how a valve functions as an amplifier. The anode load is a tuned circuit in an RF amplifier. The similarity to the transistor situation should be noted; it must be emphasised that a valve is a high-impedance device, whereas the transistor is of low impedance.

The terms *Class A*, *Class B* etc are used to indicate the proportion of the input waveform over which the anode current flows. In Class A anode current flows over the whole of the input wave, and so on. Again the similarity to the transistor operation should be noted.

A second grid, the *screen grid* (g₂) can be located between the control grid and the anode, and then the valve is termed a *tetrode*. The anode current is now much less dependent on the anode voltage: see Fig 4.33. The amplification and the impedance are increased, but the capacitance between the control grid and the anode is reduced from the order of 5–10pF to the order of 0.02pF. This is particularly significant because in a triode the higher grid/anode capacitance is in effect connected between the output and the input of the amplifier circuit. There is sufficient positive feedback through this capacitance to cause oscillation. The capacitance must be neutralised by a small external capacitor. The low capacitance of the tetrode is unlikely to cause oscillation unless the mechanical layout of the circuit is poor.

Alternatively the input to an RF amplifier may be applied to the cathode of the valve, with the control grid connected to

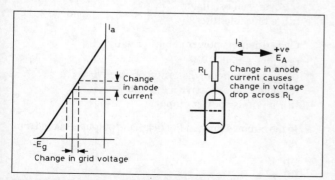

Fig 4.32. How the triode valve functions as an amplifier

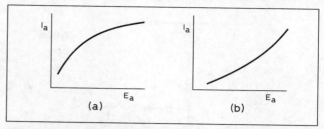

Fig 4.33. The anode current/anode voltage curves of (a) a tetrode and (b) a triode

earth. This is known as *grounded-grid operation*. In this way the control grid acts as a screen between input (the cathode) and the output (the anode).

The amplification of an SSB waveform must be achieved with the minimum of distortion; a linear amplifier will meet this need.

This requirement is met by a grounded-grid triode amplifier operating in Class AB. Such an amplifier is also suitable for telegraphy.

Important characteristics of valves are:

1. Heater/filament voltage and current.
2. Maximum anode voltage and current.
3. Control grid voltage.
4. Maximum anode dissipation, ie the heat which can be dissipated safely at the anode.

VALVES AS RF POWER AMPLIFIERS

The main use of valves as RF power amplifiers is now as a separate amplifier unit driven by the standard transceiver. The amplifier is generally a *linear amplifier* operating in the grounded-grid mode as it is required to amplify an SSB waveform. These amplifiers are readily available commercially at ratings well above the UK licence limit. They are quite often home-made as the circuit is quite simple, using relatively few, but some large, components.

▶Two categories of valve are in use. The first category is the medium-power transmitting valve. Such types with their approximate outputs are: two 572B valves (800–1000W), three 811A valves (600W), two 813 valves (1000W), one 3-5000Z valve (1000W). At VHF and UHF the 4CX250B is used. These valves require a power supply of about 2000V (see Chapter 3).

The other category is colour-TV line output valves with up to four connected in parallel. These are indirectly heated tetrodes used as triodes by connecting both grids together. They have a maximum anode voltage of about 700V (peak E_a is 7kV), with maximum anode current of the order of 350mA. These are not continuous ratings, so the anode dissipation is 25–30W. Such valves are satisfactory at the peaky nature of the SSB waveform. They have been used in commercial equipment and are used in home-built amplifiers. Typical types are 6JS6, 6KD6, 6LQ6 and 6HF6 (American) and PL509 (European, 40V 0.3A heater); they provide an output of about 400W at an anode voltage around 700V.◀

In the grounded-grid mode it is necessary to isolate the filament of a directly heated valve from ground at RF. This is achieved by supplying the filament via a bifilar choke wound on a ferrite rod as shown in Fig 4.34. There is generally sufficient isolation between cathode and ground at RF if the cathode is indirectly heated. The remainder of the circuit is as that of the standard Class C RF stage. The anode tuned circuit

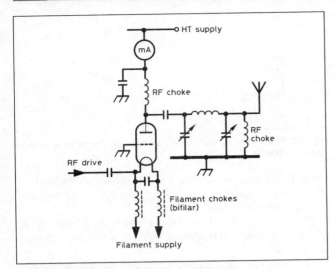

Fig 4.34. A grounded-grid RF power amplifier

is the standard 'pi' arrangement to attenuate unwanted frequencies.

The input drive power required by the grounded-grid circuit is somewhat greater than in the grid-driven amplifier. This is offset by the fact that a portion of the drive power appears in the output. The drive power required is within the output capability of most transceivers.

It must always be remembered that an overdriven linear amplifier can create serious interference due to the resulting non-linearity, distortion and excess bandwidth. In other words, a linear amplifier should not be used at more than about 75% of its rating.

High-power solid-state amplifiers are commercially available; designs for home-built units have been published. No doubt others are available in the application reports of the transistor manufacturers. Problems such as protection against high SWR and power supply failure are likely to be worse at higher powers.

PRACTICE QUESTIONS FOR CHAPTER 4

1. AGC stands for

    (a) amplified gain control
    (b) auxiliary gain cut-off
    (c) automatic ganging control
    (d) automatic gain control.

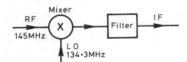

Fig Q4.1

2. In the circuit shown in Fig Q4.1, image interference could be experienced at

    (a) 123.6MHz
    (b) 134.3MHz
    (c) 145MHz
    (d) 155.7MHz.

3. A high first IF allows easier filtering to prevent

    (a) power supply ripple
    (b) local oscillator breakthrough

    (c) image interference
    (d) second IF breakthrough.

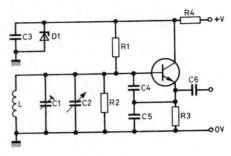

Fig Q4.2

4. The circuit shown in Fig Q4.2 is

    (a) an RF preamplifier
    (b) a crystal oscillator
    (c) a mixer
    (d) a VFO.

5. In the circuit shown in Fig Q4.2 what is the reason for the use of D1?

    (a) Visual indicator.
    (b) Frequency stability.
    (c) Frequency modulation.
    (d) Amplitude modulation.

6. The use of a thermionic valve as a PA will

    (a) give a high SWR
    (b) give minimum distortion on receive
    (c) make the problem of a poor SWR less acute
    (d) minimise power consumption.

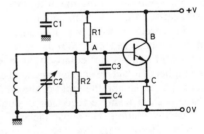

Fig Q4.3

7. The circuit shown in Fig Q4.3 is

    (a) a Colpitts oscillator
    (b) an RF preamplifier
    (c) a crystal oscillator
    (d) a tuneable filter.

8. Over-driving a power amplifier will

    (a) give a high SWR
    (b) give minimum distortion on receive
    (c) generate excessive harmonics
    (d) minimise power output.

9. In the circuit shown in Fig Q4.3, the output is taken from

    (a) A
    (b) B
    (c) C
    (d) D.

10. The coil forming part of the frequency-determining elements in a VFO should be
   (a) wound on a steel former
   (b) made of resistance wire
   (c) self-supporting
   (d) of sound mechanical construction.

11. The output stage of an SSB transmitter must be a
   (a) switch
   (b) linear amplifier
   (c) non-linear amplifier
   (d) multiplier.

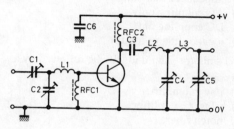

Fig Q4.4

12. In the circuit shown in Fig Q4.4, C1, C2 and L1 are for
   (a) frequency stability
   (b) bias adjustment
   (c) gain adjustment
   (d) impedance matching.

13. The power supply to a VFO should be
   (a) stabilised
   (b) straight from the smoothing circuit
   (c) unstabilised
   (d) AC only.

14. The typical deviation of an amateur NBFM signal is
   (a) 5kHz
   (b) 7.5kHz
   (c) 10kHz
   (d) 25kHz.

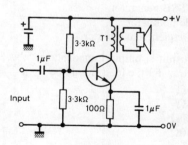

Fig Q4.5

15. The circuit in Fig Q4.5 is
   (a) an audio amplifier
   (b) an RF amplifier
   (c) a mixer
   (d) a BFO.

16. In the circuit shown in Fig Q4.5 T1 is for
   (a) voltage amplification
   (b) impedance matching

   (c) power amplification
   (d) gain control.

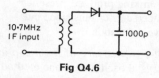

Fig Q4.6

17. The circuit shown in Fig Q4.6 is
   (a) a power rectifying circuit
   (b) an FM discriminator
   (c) a varactor tuner
   (d) an AM detector.

18. For reception of CW signals, the beat note produced by the BFO should be about
   (a) 200Hz
   (b) 800Hz
   (c) 2kHz
   (d) 456kHz.

19. If the value of the capacitor in the VFO of a receiver increases with temperature, then for increased temperature the frequency of the VFO will
   (a) stay the same
   (b) fall to zero
   (c) increase
   (d) decrease.

20. The sensitivity of a receiver specifies
   (a) the bandwidth of the RF preamplifier
   (b) the stability of the VFO
   (c) its ability to receive weak signals
   (d) its ability to reject strong signals.

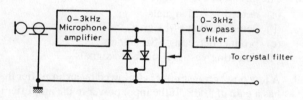

Fig Q4.7

21. The circuit shown in Fig Q4.7 allows
   (a) RF clipping
   (b) control of deviation
   (c) amplitude modulation
   (d) SSB generation.

22. If the power supply to an output stage is modulated, this produces
   (a) AM
   (b) FM
   (c) NBFM
   (d) PM.

23. A crystal oscillator has
   (a) poor frequency stability
   (b) FM components
   (c) good frequency stability
   (d) vibration problems.

24. The output of a balanced mixer has

    (a) the full carrier present
    (b) many mixing products present
    (c) a reduced carrier plus sidebands
    (d) the two sidebands.

25. Varying the capacitance of a varicap diode connected across a crystal oscillator is one method of producing

    (a) amplitude modulation
    (b) double sideband modulation
    (c) CW signals
    (d) frequency modulation.

26. The L-C circuits immediately following an RF power amplifier allow

    (a) harmonic analysis
    (b) harmonic amplification
    (c) impedance mismatching
    (d) impedance matching.

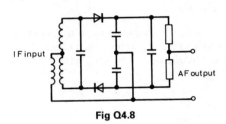

Fig Q4.8

27. The circuit shown in Fig Q4.8 is

    (a) an envelope detector
    (b) a crystal detector
    (c) a ratio detector
    (d) a varactor multiplier.

28. The circuit in Fig Q4.8 is used for

    (a) detecting AM signals
    (b) demodulating FM signals
    (c) product detecting SSB signals
    (d) detecting vestigial sideband signals.

29. A low power transmitter is followed by an amplifier that has a gain of 10dB. If the input power to the amplifier is 1W, the output is

    (a) 1dBW
    (b) 3dBW
    (c) 10dBW
    (d) 20dBW.

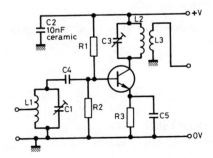

Fig Q4.9

30. The circuit shown in Fig Q4.9 is

    (a) a mixer
    (b) an RF amplifier
    (c) an AF amplifier
    (d) an oscillator.

31. The purpose of C2 in the circuit shown in Fig Q4.9 is

    (a) DC smoothing
    (b) tuning
    (c) AC coupling
    (d) RF decoupling.

32. The tapping on L1 in the circuit shown in Fig Q4.9 is for

    (a) impedance matching
    (b) AC coupling only
    (c) DC coupling only
    (d) local oscillator input.

33. An oscillator should ideally be followed by a

    (a) buffer
    (b) power amplifier
    (c) Class C amplifier
    (d) notch filter.

34. Theoretically frequency modulation has

    (a) an infinite number of sidebands
    (b) only two sidebands
    (c) no sidebands
    (d) only one sideband.

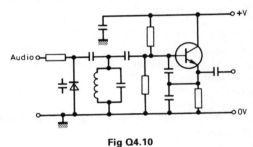

Fig Q4.10

35. The circuit shown in Fig Q4.10 is

    (a) an amplitude modulator
    (b) an SSB generator
    (c) a demodulator
    (d) a frequency modulator.

36. If a transmitter output impedance is 50Ω, for optimum power transfer the load should be

    (a) 50Ω
    (b) 75Ω
    (c) 100Ω
    (d) 150Ω.

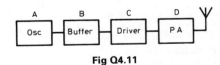

Fig Q4.11

37. A CW transmitter is shown in Fig Q4.11. The key should be connected to

    (a) A
    (b) B
    (c) C
    (d) D.

38. In a receiver, narrow bandwidth usually gives
    (a) poor selectivity
    (b) no selectivity
    (c) high selectivity
    (d) negative selectivity.

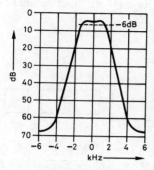

Fig Q4.12

39. The diagram in Fig Q4.12 represents the response of a filter. It would be most suitable in a receiver for
    (a) wide-band FM signals
    (b) AM signals
    (c) fast-scan TV signals
    (d) SSB signals.

40. Referring to the diagram in Fig Q4.12 the skirt bandwidth at −60dB is
    (a) 3kHz
    (b) 5kHz
    (c) 8kHz
    (d) 9kHz.

41. A calibration oscillator in a receiver is based on
    (a) a crystal
    (b) an L-C circuit
    (c) an R-C circuit
    (d) a transformer.

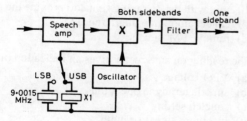

Fig Q4.13

42. The block diagram in Fig Q4.13 shows an SSB generator. The filter is specified as 9MHz. What is the expected frequency of X1?
    (a) 8.9970MHz.
    (b) 8.9985MHz.
    (c) 9.0000MHz.
    (d) 9.0030MHz.

43. In Fig Q4.13 what is the function of box X?
    (a) Balanced mixer.
    (b) Balanced filter.
    (c) Balanced demodulator.
    (d) Non-balanced mixer.

44. A typical bandwidth for the speech amplifier shown in Fig Q4.13 is
    (a) 6kHz
    (b) 5kHz
    (c) 4kHz
    (d) 2.5kHz.

45. The process of modulation allows
    (a) information to be impressed on to a carrier
    (b) information to be removed from a carrier
    (c) voice and CW to be combined
    (d) AF to be extracted from the signal.

46. The RF power output from an FM transmitter
    (a) is constant irrespective of modulation
    (b) varies with the modulation
    (c) is zero with no modulation
    (d) reduces to 50% with modulation.

47. For optimum stability a VFO should be
    (a) kept away from varying heat sources
    (b) kept in a varying draught
    (c) next to the power amplifier compartment
    (d) air cooled.

48. For CW reception, the difference in frequency of the BFO and final IF should be about
    (a) 1kHz
    (b) 10kHz
    (c) 455kHz
    (d) 10.7MHz.

49. In some AF output stages in a receiver the loudspeaker is driven via a step-down transformer. This provides
    (a) higher AF gain
    (b) matching of amplifier to loudspeaker
    (c) better audio quality
    (d) economy of the power supply.

50. If a station is being received on 14.24MHz and the first IF of the receiver is 10.7MHz, image interference could arise from a signal at
    (a) 10.7MHz
    (b) 14.54MHz
    (c) 24.31MHz
    (d) 35.64MHz.

51. In the detection of SSB signals there is normally a carrier insertion oscillator. In a high-quality receiver this is
    (a) a VFO
    (b) varicap controlled
    (c) inductor controlled
    (d) crystal controlled.

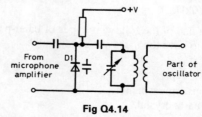

Fig Q4.14

52. Fig Q4.14 shows part of an FM transmitter. The purpose of D1 is to

(a) prevent overloading of the AF amplifier

(b) rectify any RF to provide a DC supply

(c) vary the oscillator frequency

(d) provide a DC voltage to drive the relative power output meter of the transmitter.

53. When generating an SSB signal, a balanced modulator is used. The filter following this used to remove one of the sidebands should have a bandwidth of

(a) 300Hz

(b) 2.4kHz

(c) 2.4MHz

(d) 10.7MHz.

54. If the output level of a transmitter is quoted as 20dBW, this is equivalent to an

(a) input power of 20W

(b) output power of 20W

(c) output power of 100W

(d) input power of 100W.

55. The efficiency of a power amplifier is the ratio of

(a) RF power out to RF power in

(b) RF power input to DC power input

(c) RF power output to DC power input

(d) RF power input to RF power output.

56. In order to demodulate CW transmissions in an AM only receiver, which one of the following is required?

(a) a BFO.

(b) an FM detector.

(c) a crystal multiplier.

(d) a Morse key.

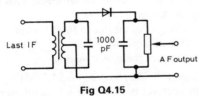

Fig Q4.15

57. The diagram shown in Fig Q4.15 is

(a) an envelope detector

(b) a mains single-phase rectifier

(c) a discriminator

(d) a phase detector.

58. If a receiver uses a final IF of 455kHz, a suitable BFO frequency to obtain a 1kHz signal when receiving CW is

(a) 456kHz

(b) 457kHz

(c) 460kHz

(d) 470kHz.

59. Which one of the following types of band-pass filter is likely to have the narrower bandwidth?

(a) R-C type.

(b) L-C type.

(c) Ceramic resonator.

(d) Quartz crystal.

60. Stability of the local oscillator in a transceiver is partially determined by

(a) good rigid mechanical construction

(b) the use of electrolytics for tuning

(c) the use of resistance wire for the coil

(d) unregulated dc supply to VFO.

61. An amplifier is quoted as having a gain of 16dB. The RF output for a 1W RF input should be

(a) 4W

(b) 16W

(c) 40W

(d) 160W.

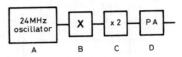

Fig Q4.16

62. Fig Q4.16 shows a block diagram of a typical 144MHz transmitter using multipliers. The box marked 'X' is a

(a) doubler

(b) tripler

(c) quadrupler

(d) buffer.

63. An ideal place to key a CW transmitter is the

(a) VFO

(b) whole power supply

(c) power amplifier

(d) buffer after the VFO.

64. A 145MHz transmitter uses a ×12 multiplier and a deviation of 5kHz. The oscillator deviation would be

(a) 0kHz

(b) 0.417kHz

(c) 5kHz

(d) 60kHz.

65. A BFO is used in a receiver to

(a) make a CW signal using A1A audible

(b) mix with the incoming signal to provide the first IF

(c) cancel amplitude interference

(d) remove FM signals.

66. The reading on an S meter gives an indication of

(a) VFO voltage

(b) superheterodyne operation

(c) squelch setting

(d) incoming signal strength.

67. The advantage of a superheterodyne receiver over a direct conversion type is

(a) cheaper components can be used

(b) greater selectivity can be achieved

(c) the VFO need not be as stable

(d) it is much simpler in construction.

68. The frequency difference between the wanted RF signal and the so-called image is

(a) twice the third IF

(b) twice the wanted RF

(c) twice the first IF

(d) the wanted RF plus the first IF

69. In order to minimise variation of audio output with variation of RF input, a receiver is fitted with

    (a) automatic gain control
    (b) audio gain limiting
    (c) audio filters
    (d) audio bias control.

70. Apart from a discriminator, FM signals can be demodulated by

    (a) a ratio detector
    (b) balanced modulators
    (c) resistive dividers
    (d) zener diodes.

71. To produce a double sideband, suppressed carrier signal, which one of the following should be used?

    (a) Balanced mixer.
    (b) Crystal filter.
    (c) Single transistor mixer.
    (d) Single diode mixer.

72. In a transmitter VFO it is found that the inductance of the coil rises with temperature and that the capacitor is very stable. The effect of this as temperature rises is

    (a) VFO frequency drifts high
    (b) VFO frequency drifts low
    (c) VFO output remains constant
    (d) chirp occurs.

73. When compared with valves, transistors are

    (a) more susceptible to overload
    (b) less susceptible to overload
    (c) less efficient
    (d) magnetically controlled.

74. The frequency difference between the wanted RF signal and the so-called image is equal to

    (a) the RF input
    (b) the frequency of the LO
    (c) twice the first IF
    (d) the frequency of the preselector.

75. The effect of the AGC on receipt of a very strong incoming signal is to reduce

    (a) the VFO output
    (b) the gain of the RF and IF amplifiers
    (c) the power supply voltage
    (d) a filter response.

76. A high first IF allows easier filtering to prevent

    (a) power supply ripple
    (b) local oscillator breakthrough
    (c) image interference
    (d) second IF breakthrough.

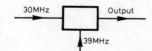

Fig Q4.17

77. The principal outputs from the circuit in Fig Q4.17 are

    (a) 9 and 39MHz
    (b) 9 and 69MHz
    (c) 30 and 39MHz
    (d) 39 and 69MHz.

78. To produce double sideband, suppressed carrier signal, which of the following should be used?

    (a) Balanced mixer.
    (b) Sideband filter.
    (c) Transistor oscillator.
    (d) VDU.

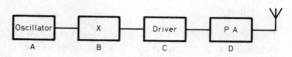

Fig Q4.18

79. The diagram in Fig Q4.18 represents a CW transmitter. The box marked 'X' is a

    (a) VFO
    (b) buffer
    (c) BFO
    (d) IF amplifier.

80. The output amplifier of an SSB transmitter must

    (a) be a Class C amplifier
    (b) be a linear amplifier
    (c) be in a non-linear mode
    (d) act as a multiplier.

81. The output power from an FM transmitter

    (a) is unaffected by modulation
    (b) varies with modulation
    (c) is zero with no modulation
    (d) reduces to 70% with modulation.

82. If a transmitter output impedance is 50Ω for optimum power transfer, the load should be

    (a) 25Ω
    (b) 50Ω
    (c) 100Ω
    (d) 150Ω.

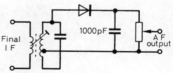

Fig Q4.19

83. The circuit in Fig Q4.19 shows

    (a) an AM detector
    (b) a single-phase mains rectifier
    (c) an FM detector
    (d) a phase detector.

84. In the detection of SSB signals there is normally a carrier insertion oscillator. In a high-quality receiver this is

    (a) a VFO
    (b) varactor controlled
    (c) free running
    (d) crystal controlled.

85. One advantage of FM over AM is
    (a) increased distance range
    (b) narrower bandwidth required
    (c) freedom from most sources of 'man-made' inter-
        ference
    (d) no antenna is needed.

86. For CW reception, the difference in frequency of the
    BFO and final IF should be about
    (a) 800Hz
    (b) 4kHz
    (c) 10kHz
    (d) 15kHz.

87. The frequency of a VFO depends on an L-C circuit. The
    frequency is determined by the square root of the
    (a) difference between L and C
    (b) sum of L and C
    (c) ratio L/C
    (d) product of L and C.

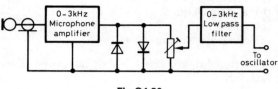

Fig Q4.20

88. Fig Q4.20 shows part of a transmitter. It is typical of
    (a) an RF filter
    (b) a deviation control
    (c) an amplitude modulator
    (d) an SSB generator.

Check your answers using the key in Appendix 4.

5 Transmitter interference

BEFORE studying this chapter, it is necessary to study Chapter 4 (Receivers, transmitters and transceivers). It is also useful to study Chapter 8 (Measurements).

This chapter covers frequency stability, spurious emissions and frequency checking in relation to an amateur transmitter. An understanding of how to avoid causing interference to fellow radio amateurs and to other services using radio frequencies is one of the most important subjects which radio amateurs need to know about. It is also one of the most technical sections of the Radio Amateurs' Examination syllabus. Questions on transmitter interference make up 17.5% of the total question paper, so it is important to devote sufficient attention to this subject.

If interference appears to be caused by an amateur transmitter, there may be three possible causes:

(a) The amateur transmitter is producing unwanted signals due to a fault, poor design or incorrect operation.

(b) There is nothing wrong with the transmitter but:

   (i)   the affected equipment has insufficient immunity to the wanted signal from the amateur transmitter.

   (ii) the problem is caused by poor station design.

This chapter deals with avoiding case (a). Case (b), (i) and (ii), are dealt with in Chapter 6 (Electromagnetic compatibility), which deals with good station design and methods of minimising interference in the home and to immediate neighbours.

If interference is caused by a deficiency in an amateur transmitter, it may be classified broadly into two groups:

- Interference to users of immediately adjacent frequencies.
- Interference to users of frequencies much further away, possibly outside the amateur band.

In either case, interference may be caused at great distances from the transmitter so a radio amateur has a heavy responsibility to ensure that his or her transmissions do not attract criticism or, worse still, break the conditions of the amateur licence. It is important to realise that the fact that a transmitter is of commercial manufacture does not necessarily mean that is free of interference problems. The following examples of possible transmitter defects and shortcomings apply both to home-constructed and commercial equipment.

POOR FREQUENCY STABILITY

If a transmitter has poor frequency stability, this is likely to result in drift, chirp or both.

Drift

Drift is a gradual change of frequency over a period of minutes or hours and has the following effects.

- On CW (A1A), the pitch of the received CW note changes gradually.
- On SSB (J3E), the pitch of the received voice changes gradually. With SSB, even a small change of the transmitting frequency requires the receiver to be retuned. After having established contact on one frequency, two stations may slowly drift away from each other, ending up several kilohertz apart. This not only occupies an unnecessary space in the RF spectrum but a drifting signal may drift onto a frequency which is in use by another station. In severe cases, drift may result in transmissions ending up outside the edges of the amateur bands.

The frequency stability of an oscillator is often expressed in parts per million (PPM). For example, a frequency change of 10 PPM corresponds to a change of 10Hz in an oscillator operating at 1MHz or 50Hz in an oscillator operating at 5MHz. The frequency change in parts per million is given by the following formula:

$$\frac{\Delta f \times 1{,}000{,}000}{f}$$

where f is the operating frequency and Δf is the change in frequency.

Causes of drift

In a VFO-controlled transmitter, care is required to achieve good frequency stability, as explained in Chapter 4. The main points affecting VFO stability are:

- Changes in temperature
- Changes in supply voltage
- Mechanical shock
- Changes in output loading.

A change in temperature generally causes a small change in the resonant frequency of an L-C tuned circuit. This is due to a small change in the inductance of the inductor and/or the capacitance of the variable capacitor or fixed capacitors. Drift due to temperature changes can be minimised as follows:

- The VFO should be located away from sources of heat.
- The coil should be wound tightly on a ceramic grooved coil former. The coil should be air-cored rather than having a ferrite core.
- The variable capacitor should be a good-quality type and the fixed capacitors should have a low temperature coefficient.
- The Q factor of the L-C tuned circuit should be as high as possible.

Mechanical shock can cause a slight frequency change if the mechanical stability of the circuit and its components is poor.

A knock may cause the components or wiring to move slightly, leading to a small change in the stray capacitance between different parts of the circuit. This effect can be minimised by housing the VFO in a rigid box with sound mechanical construction and rigid wiring.

To minimise frequency changes due to change in supply voltage, a VFO should be powered from a well-stabilised DC supply whose voltage does not change significantly with temperature.

If the impedance of the load connected to the VFO output changes, this may affect the frequency. To minimise this effect, there should be a buffer amplifier at the output of a VFO to ensure low loading.

Chirp

Chirp is a characteristic of A1A mode Morse (CW) signals. It is a rapid change of frequency which occurs for a fraction of a second after the Morse key is depressed. Undesirable effects of chirp include the following:

- The CW signal is more difficult to copy.
- The CW transmission occupies more bandwidth than necessary.
- There is a risk of out-of-band emissions if transmitting near the band edge.

Causes of chirp include:

- *Poorly regulated VFO DC voltage supply.* The transmitter draws more current from the power unit during key-down conditions which causes the voltage of some DC supply rails to fall. The supply to the VFO must be well stabilised so that it does not change during 'key down'.
- *Changes in loading of the VFO output.* A buffer amplifier should be used at the VFO output to minimise loading. The VFO should not be keyed but should run continuously otherwise chirp may occur as the VFO starts up.
- *RF feedback.* Unwanted feedback of the transmitted signal into the VFO circuit can cause chirp. This is most likely to occur if the VFO runs at the final transmitted frequency so it is common practice to mix or to multiply the VFO signal to obtain the required transmitter output frequency. RF feedback can be avoided by adequate screening of the VFO which should be housed in a metal box with good filtering of its DC power leads. It is also possible for RF signals from the transmitter to be fed back into the VFO output. This effect can be minimised by using a buffer amplifier following the VFO stage.

SPURIOUS EMISSIONS – CAUSES AND METHODS OF PREVENTION
Transmitter harmonics

Harmonics are unwanted outputs from a transmitter which occur at exact multiples of the transmitted frequency, for example, the second, third, fourth and fifth harmonic. These harmonics fall in other amateur bands or in bands used by other services.

VHF bands are no longer used for television broadcasting in the UK although they are still used in some other countries. Harmonics from an amateur HF transmitter are therefore most unlikely to cause interference to UHF TV broadcasting in the UK. If such interference occurs, it is likely that the cause is insufficient immunity of the affected equipment

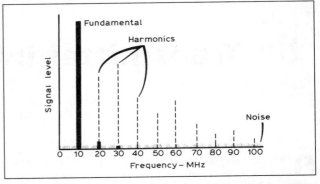

Fig 5.1. Example of possible harmonics transmitted by a 10MHz station. With poor station design, harmonic levels may be excessive (shown dotted). With good design it will be difficult to detect even the second or third harmonics above the received general noise level

(see Chapter 6), in which case fitting a filter to the amateur transmitter would not cure the problem. Nevertheless, harmonics from some HF amateur bands fall in bands used by other services including mobile radio and Band II FM broadcasting, so high standards for unwanted transmitter outputs must be maintained. There is a good chance that an amateur will live close to users of other radio services (even next door), and very low levels of unwanted outputs could cause severe interference. Harmonics which fall below about 30MHz may not be as troublesome because users of HF are relatively few and hence likely to be more remote. With the relatively high levels of HF background noise and interference, low levels of unwanted signals may go unnoticed.

Without attention to filtering there is a progressive (if somewhat erratic) drop in the level of the higher harmonics. Fig 5.1 shows the comparison of harmonic levels of a 10MHz transmitting station, illustrating the improvement obtained by good station design. Harmonics from the lower frequency amateur bands may fall within a higher band (eg 2×3.53MHz = 7.06MHz, thus interfering with other amateurs) or outside the HF end (eg 2×3.7MHz = 7.4MHz, thus interfering with other services).

In the case of the 50–52MHz amateur band, the second harmonic falls at 100–104MHz which is within the 88–108MHz FM broadcast band. Some harmonics of 144MHz fall in the UHF TV band, for example the fourth harmonic of the 144–146MHz band falls between 576 and 584MHz which is within UHF TV channel 34 and the 5th harmonic is at 720 and 730MHz which is within TV channel 52 or 53. Further examples are given in Chapter 6.

Harmonics occur because amplifiers are to some extent non-linear, ie they distort the signal waveform. They are produced mainly in the high-power stages in a transmitter, especially those which use Class C amplification. This may be the most efficient, but it is highly non-linear. Even the relatively linear Class A and Class B amplifiers used in SSB transmitters are by no means harmonic-free. Clearly, there will be less need for filtering to reduce harmonics if the transmitter is designed to generate lower levels of harmonics in the first place. Some measures which help to reduce harmonics include the following:

- The use of a push-pull output stage as this reduces even harmonics (second, fourth etc).

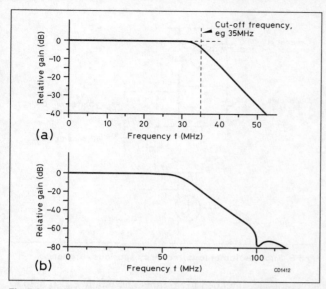

Fig 5.2. (a) Example of a low-pass filter for use between an HF transceiver and an antenna. (b) Example of a low-pass filter for the 50MHz band with a trap to increase rejection of the second harmonic frequency

- The use of inductive link coupling for interstage coupling in a driver stage.
- Avoiding unnecessarily high drive levels in power amplifiers.

Most transmitters with a tuned PA stage use *pi-network* output tuning (or some variation, such as *L-pi*). Fig 4.9 is a typical example. This acts as a built-in low-pass filter and greatly reduces harmonic levels. In HF transmitters with a solid-state, wide-band (untuned) power amplifier, different band-pass or low-pass filters are often used (being selected as required by the transmitter bandswitch).

Provided a transmitter is designed to avoid direct radiation of harmonics as explained below, the only way out for RF signals is via the antenna socket. Any harmonics can therefore be reduced by a suitable filter fitted in the feed to the antenna system. A suitable type of filter is a low-pass or band-pass filter. Fig 5.2(a) shows an example of the frequency response of a low-pass filter for use with an HF transmitter. This filter has a low loss (ideally zero) in the pass band which extends up to at least 29.7MHz. Somewhere above this frequency there is a cut-off frequency at typically 35MHz. Above the cut-off frequency, the loss increases as frequency increases. The response shown in Fig 5.2(a) has a loss of 40dB at 56MHz so if it is used with a 28MHz transmitter, the level of the second harmonic at the output of the filter would be 40dB lower than the second harmonic level at the input of the filter.

As explained above, in the case of 50MHz amateur transmissions, it is particularly important to minimise the level of the second harmonic. For this band, a low-pass filter may be used with a trap to give increased rejection of the second harmonic as shown in Fig 5.2(b).

For single-band transceivers, particularly at VHF, a band-pass filter may be used. This allows the fundamental to pass through with low loss but

attenuates frequencies above and below the fundamental. For HF bands, the use of an antenna matching unit also reduces harmonics because it acts as a band-pass filter for the band in use.

Direct radiation

Stages carrying RF signals should be individually screened and their power feeds well decoupled in order to prevent RF signals and harmonics from being carried around inside the transmitter via the internal wiring. A transmitter should be screened using a good-quality metal case with no large holes, gaps or slots which would allow RF leakage.

An example of stages in a transmitter which could directly radiate unwanted signals is shown in Fig 5.3(a). This shows a crystal-controlled 144MHz band transmitter using a multiplier chain. There is a possibility of unwanted signals being radiated at 8, 24 or 72MHz if the screening and/or filtering of the intermediate stages is inadequate.

Fig 5.3(b) shows some measures which minimise unwanted radiation from an oscillator. A metal box prevents direct radiation of the oscillator frequency. Effective filtering and decoupling of the DC supply rail prevents unwanted signals from getting out (or in) via the supply rail.

Unwanted mixer products

Many transmitters use mixing processes to obtain the required output frequency – especially for SSB transmitters and VFO-controlled VHF transmitters. An ideal mixer (frequency changer or converter) produces only the wanted sum and difference frequencies (see Chapter 2). In practice, mixers also produce various other undesirable signals. The most significant are generally the harmonics of the local oscillator injection and harmonic mixing products. These are outputs created when the self-generated oscillator harmonics mix with the input signal to produce a large number of sum and difference signals.

Fig 5.4 shows a block diagram of part of an SSB transmitter for the 3.5 and 14MHz bands. The SSB signal is generated at a fixed frequency which is typically around 9MHz. It must be converted to the required frequency for transmission which can be done by mixing the 9MHz SSB signal (f_1) with a VFO on 5MHz (f_2). This generates the sum and difference

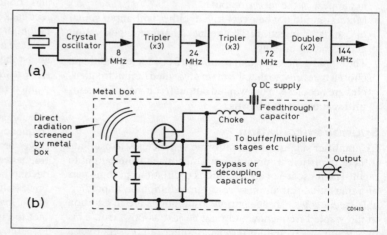

Fig 5.3. (a) Multiplier chain showing frequencies which could give rise to unwanted outputs. (b) An oscillator, showing the need for screening and filtering

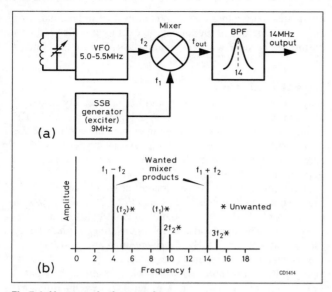

Fig 5.4. Unwanted mixer products

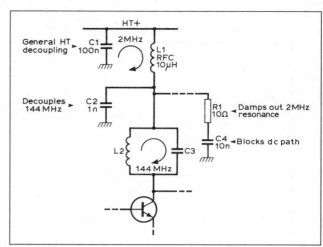

Fig 5.5. Suppression of low-frequency spurious resonance

frequencies of $f_1 + f_2$ (14MHz) and $f_1 - f_2$ (3.5MHz). Either of these frequencies can be selected by means of a suitable band-pass filter (BPF). In Fig 5.4, the 14MHz output is selected. There are, however, other unwanted outputs from the mixer. These include the input frequencies, f_1 and f_2, and their harmonics such as $2f_2$ at 10MHz and $3f_2$ at 15MHz. The mixer may also generate the fifth harmonic of f_2 which will mix with the 9MHz and appear at 16MHz (5×5MHz $-$ 9MHz = 16MHz).

The unwanted products at 15 and 16MHz must be well filtered to ensure that they are at a sufficiently low level by the time that they reach the transmitter output. This may not be easy to achieve in practice because the band-pass filter must pass 14.0–14.35MHz but must have sufficient rejection of 15MHz. To simplify subsequent filtering, the generation of unwanted mixer products should be minimised as follows:

- Although there are many types of mixer, such as a single diode, bipolar transistor or FET, for transmitter use, a *balanced or double-balanced mixer* should be used. If the balance is perfect, the oscillator signal and its harmonics do not appear at the mixer output.
- Mixers should not be over-driven, either with input signal or oscillator injection. This reduces harmonic generation and harmonic mixing.
- The signal generation and oscillator frequencies should be chosen carefully so that the main unwanted output frequencies are not close to the wanted output frequency. This simplifies subsequent filtering.

Spurious oscillation

RF amplifier stages have an unfortunate tendency to oscillate if there is sufficient (unintentional) feedback from output to input. The presence of such spurious oscillations in some part of a transmitter circuit may result in radiation on unpredictable frequencies. These spurious oscillations are in addition to the wanted frequency and may be just as powerful. This may result in severe interference to other radio users over a wide area.

In many respects the techniques of filtering, decoupling,

screening etc, intended to minimise harmonics, also help to prevent spurious oscillations. However, some additional precautions may be necessary. Note that if particularly violent oscillations occur, some transistors (especially the more expensive devices used at VHF and UHF) may be instantly destroyed. Take great care when investigating oscillations. It is wise to operate the suspected stage at a reduced voltage and with some current-limiting resistance in series with the DC supply. Spurious oscillation of a transmitter may be divided into two distinct categories, self-oscillation and parasitic oscillation.

Self-oscillation may occur at or near the working frequency of a stage, especially if both input and output are tuned to the same frequency. It may only occur when no RF input drive is present, eg between words on SSB or with key-up on CW. Its frequency will be fairly unstable and the transmitter may continue to give a noticeable RF output when the power level should read zero. Conversely, the oscillation may occur only when the stage is being driven. The result may be burbly, splashy speech and a rough CW note, with chirps and key-clicks. The cure for this problem is to minimise the feedback by ensuring that input and output circuits are screened from each other. DC feeds may also provide another feedback path and should be adequately decoupled. There may be enough feedback through the amplifying device itself to cause oscillation, in which case the stage will have to be *neutralised*. In the case of valve power amplifiers, it is often necessary to re-adjust the neutralisation after replacing the valves.

Parasitic oscillations are generally far above or below the wanted frequency. If they occur at a much lower frequency, they can sometimes modulate the RF signal, appearing as sidebands (often multiple) either side of the wanted output frequency. These may be the result of instability in audio stages or in regulated DC power supplies (often at supersonic frequencies) or by unwanted resonances of RF chokes and decoupling capacitors, often in the DC feeds to certain stages. For example, VHF transistors often have a very high gain at much lower frequencies, and care must be taken to ensure that the decoupling of the DC supplies is effective at these low frequencies. Fig 5.5 shows how a hidden parallel resonant circuit exists. To prevent the danger of oscillations the resonance must be damped. One way to do this is to use a very low-Q (ie *lossy*) choke for L1. This can be made by winding a choke on a carbon resistor. Alternatively, R1 and C4 can be added to the existing circuit.

VHF and UHF parasitic oscillations may occur in HF transmitters because of a poor choice of circuit layout, and the type and style of components used. This often results in capacitor leads, earth returns and other interconnections which are rather long, and are therefore somewhat inductive. Coils also may have long leads which are not part of the winding. In addition, any inductor has a self-resonant frequency where the stray capacitance of the winding resonates with the inductance of the coil. Capacitors have a stray series inductance which depends on the lead length and the type of capacitor. This stray inductance can be a very important factor which limits the performance of capacitors at radio frequencies, particularly at VHF. For a supply rail decoupling capacitor in an RF power amplifier, for example C2 in Fig 5.5, the type of capacitor with the best high-frequency performance is generally a *ceramic capacitor*. This should have the *shortest possible leads*. Better still, a ceramic leadless disc capacitor should be used.

Although small stray inductances and capacitances may not have any adverse effect at HF, they can form resonances at much higher frequencies with the stray capacitances in the circuit. Indeed, these *parasitic resonances* may affect even well-laid-out circuits where lead lengths cannot be shortened and the correct style of components are used. As with low-frequency resonances, the cure is to make these resonances well damped. Low-Q VHF chokes (eg coils wound on resistors or on lossy ferrite beads) may be added at suitable points in the circuit to break up the parasitic resonances.

In some cases, parasitic oscillation in a VHF transistor amplifier can be cured by threading a ferrite bead onto a transistor lead such as the collector. This introduces a small inductance in series with the transistor lead but, due to the characteristics of the ferrite, this inductance is lossy at VHF and its self-resonance is well damped.

TRANSMISSIONS WHICH OCCUPY EXCESSIVE BANDWIDTH

On the crowded amateur bands, the amateur must not make excessive use of the space available. Consequently, the bandwidth of amateur transmissions should be limited to the minimum necessary for effective communication.

A signal which consists only of a single carrier wave occupies a single spot frequency but conveys no information. The information is conveyed by modulating the carrier which produces sidebands (see Chapter 4) and it is really these which contain the information. The complete transmission therefore occupies a range of frequencies known as the *radio frequency bandwidth* of the transmission. The RF bandwidth of a transmission is affected by the characteristics of the signal which modulates the transmitter. This applies to all modes of transmission, eg CW, speech, data modes or amateur television (slow or fast scan).

Key-clicks

Morse (CW, A1A mode) is usually transmitted by on-off keying of an otherwise continuous wave, and is usually referred to by amateurs as *CW*. Methods of keying vary. In high-power transmitters, the supply current or a bias voltage

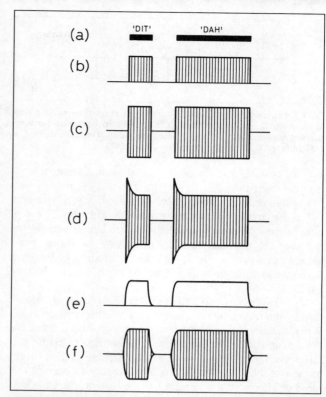

Fig 5.6. Comparison of keying waveforms with and without filtering. (a) The Morse letter 'A'. (b) The supply current to the keyed stage without filtering. (c) The resulting RF signal envelope. Note the sharp edges. (d) The RF envelope when power supply regulation is poor. (e) The slowing of the rise and fall of the keying current using a key-click filter (see Fig 5.7). (f) The resulting RF signal envelope with soft edges and hence minimal key-clicks

in a low-power stage is keyed. In low-power transmitters the PA stage itself may be keyed. Whichever method is used, care must be taken to prevent key-clicks being produced. Only a relatively narrow bandwidth is needed for Morse – a few hundred hertz at the most at normal keying speeds. However, if the keying turns the transmitter on and off instantaneously, a signal with a very wide bandwidth is produced.

Fig 5.6 shows the transmission of the Morse character 'A'. The instantaneous switching of the signal from zero to full power and back to zero is equivalent to 100% amplitude modulation by a rectangular-waveform audio signal. The sharp edges of the waveform produce sidebands which, on adjacent frequencies, are audible as clicks each time the key is pressed or released. The sharper the edge, the greater is the bandwidth occupied by the sidebands. Fig 5.6(c) shows the waveform without filtering, where the clicks may be audible over 100kHz away from the signal carrier frequency. However, although the keying may sound 'hard' (and probably rather tiring after some time), the disruption caused to users of nearby frequencies may not be realised by listening to the signal itself.

The situation is made worse if the transmitter PA power supply suffers from poor regulation and the DC voltage rises considerably during the key-up period. At the instant the key is pressed, the supply voltage is at its higher unloaded level and rapidly falls to a lower level under load. This produces a waveform as shown in Fig 5.6(d) which accentuates the

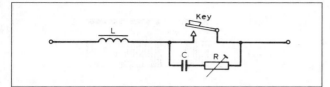

Fig 5.7. Typical key-click filter. L serves to prevent too rapid a rise of current. C, charging through R, serves to continue flow of current momentarily when key contacts open. Typical values: L = 0.01 to 0.1H, C = 0.01 to 0.1µF, R = 10 to 100Ω

key-clicks and gives the received signal an unpleasant, thumping characteristic.

Key-clicks are suppressed by slowing down the rise and fall of the keying waveform, as shown in Fig 5.6(e). This in turn softens the transitions of the power output waveform, reducing the sideband spread and making the signal more pleasant to listen to. Fig 5.6(f) shows the correct RF signal envelope where both the rising and falling edges are controlled.

Fig 5.7 shows a simple filter circuit suitable for use where the key interrupts the DC current flow in a transmitter stage. When the key closes, the rise of current is slowed down by the inductor in series with the key. When the key opens, the fall of current is slowed down by the charging of the capacitor across the key. The resistor is necessary to prevent the rapid discharge of the capacitor at the instant when the key closes. Without it, sparking would occur at the key contacts.

SSB, AM, FM

Most amateur speech transmissions use single sideband (SSB, mode J3E) or FM (mode F3E) while AM (A3E mode) is rarely used these days. All may occupy excessive bandwidth unless certain precautions are taken. Any attempt to transmit high-quality audio (which contains frequencies up to 15kHz) would result in the use of excessive RF bandwidth leading to *splatter* across adjacent channels. The audio frequency range required for voice communication is normally stated as 300Hz–3.4kHz which is the bandwidth used in the public telephone system. For amateur radio communication purposes, however, the upper frequency limit can be further reduced in order to

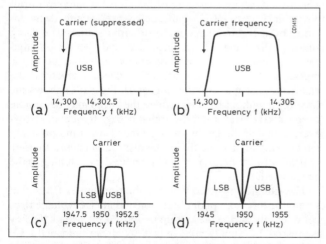

Fig 5.8. (a) SSB with 2.5kHz audio bandwidth. (b) SSB with 5kHz audio bandwidth. (c) AM with 2.5kHz audio bandwidth. (d) AM with 5kHz audio bandwidth

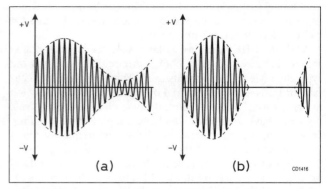

Fig 5.9. AM transmitter (a) with 80% modulation, (b) over-modulated

reduce the RF bandwidth of the transmitted signal while still maintaining acceptable intelligibility. In any amateur speech transmitter, the transmitter audio stages should be designed to have an overall low-pass filter characteristic with a sharp cut-off above about 2.5–3kHz. Some other sources of transmitted audio such as simple computer interfaces for slow-scan TV (SSTV) or packet radio may have an almost square-wave audio output and additional low-pass audio filtering may be required.

In SSB transmissions, the RF bandwidth is equal to audio bandwidth. Fig 5.8(a) shows an example of the RF spectrum of an SSB signal with a carrier frequency of 14.300kHz and 2.5kHz audio bandwidth. This results in 2.5kHz RF bandwidth which is acceptable for SSB. Fig 5.8(b) shows that if the audio bandwidth is increased to 5kHz the RF bandwidth also increases to 5kHz which is unnecessarily wide for SSB.

In double sideband AM transmissions, the RF bandwidth is twice the highest audio frequency. Fig 5.8(c) shows an example of the RF spectrum of an AM signal with a carrier frequency of 1950kHz and 2.5kHz audio bandwidth. This results in 5kHz RF bandwidth which is acceptable for AM. Fig 5.8(d) shows that if the audio bandwidth is increased to 5kHz the RF bandwidth increases to 10kHz which is unnecessarily wide for AM.

In FM transmissions, the audio bandwidth must also be restricted because it affects the overall RF bandwidth occupied by the FM signal. The RF bandwidth is also affected by the FM deviation (see below).

Over-modulation

In an AM signal, severe splatter will result if the carrier is *over-modulated*. This occurs when too much audio signal is applied to the carrier, resulting in breaks during the modulation. Fig 5.9(a) shows the waveform of an AM signal with 80% modulation which is acceptable and Fig 5.9(b) shows the effect of over-modulation which should be avoided.

Too little audio makes the signal appear weak, so to ensure maximum intelligibility the modulation should approach but not exceed 100%. It is advantageous to use some form of automatic audio compression or limiting circuit which, when adjusted correctly, ensures a consistently high level of modulation but prevents over-modulation.

In SSB transmissions, all the power of the signal is concentrated into one sideband only. Ideally, the unwanted sideband and the carrier would be totally suppressed and transmitted bandwidth would be that of the original audio modulating

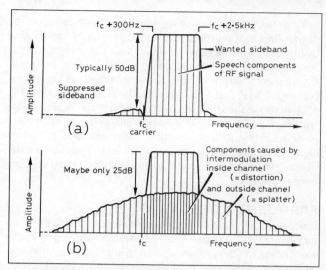

Fig 5.10. Spectrum of an SSB signal (a) when first generated, (b) after passing through an over-driven 'linear' amplifier

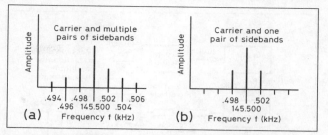

Fig 5.12. (a) NBFM transmitter on 145.500MHz driven by a 2kHz audio tone with excessive deviation. (b) NBFM transmitter on 145.500MHz driven by a 2kHz audio tone with low deviation

signal (ie somewhat less than half that required for AM). In practice the suppression is typically 50dB. The spectrum of an upper-sideband SSB signal is shown in Fig 5.10(a). It can be seen that the signal will occupy excessive space if the sideband suppression is insufficient. Poor carrier suppression may cause annoying heterodyne whistles to those trying to operate on adjacent frequencies.

The SSB signal in a transmitter is usually generated in an early stage and the required transmitter power obtained by using a linear amplifier which should cause negligible distortion. However, if the amplifier is over-driven in order to obtain a power output of which it is not really capable, serious distortion will result due to intermodulation.

Fig 5.11 shows the effect of intermodulation. Suppose for example that an SSB transmitter with a carrier frequency of 14,300kHz is set to upper sideband and is modulated by an audio signal consisting of two tones at 1kHz and 2kHz. An ideal SSB transmitter would only produce signals on 14,301kHz and 14,302kHz as shown in Fig 5.11(a). If the transmitter or a linear amplifier is overdriven, however, this generates intermodulation products as shown in Fig 5.11(b). These intermodulation products are new, unwanted signals which cause the RF signal to occupy a greater bandwidth than before amplification. With a complex audio signal such as speech, an overdriven SSB transmitter would produce a spectrum similar to Fig 5.10(b) with intermodulation products both inside the transmitted channel (resulting in audible distortion) and outside (resulting in splatter across adjacent frequencies).

Over-driving can occur if the microphone gain in an SSB transmitter is too high. It can be prevented by the use of compression or limiting circuits, which may operate either at audio or at radio frequencies.

Excessive FM deviation

When using FM, the audio signal causes the frequency of the transmission to deviate from the nominal carrier frequency. Increasing the amplitude of the audio signal increases the amount of frequency deviation. Amateur FM transmissions are referred to as *narrow-band FM* (NBFM), as opposed to wide-band FM which is used for high-quality sound broadcasting. Frequency modulation generates sidebands in a manner somewhat similar to AM but with FM there are multiple sets of sidebands. For example, an audio tone of 2.5kHz creates sidebands not only at ±2.5kHz, but also at multiples of 2.5kHz (ie 5, 7.5, 10kHz etc). Fig 5.12(a) shows an example of an amateur transmission on 145.500MHz modulated with a 2kHz audio tone. There are multiple sets of sidebands caused by over-deviation. As well as causing severe splatter over adjacent frequencies, a noticeable characteristic of over-deviated FM signals is that, even when correctly tuned in, the received audio sounds distorted on modulation peaks, and the receiver S-meter kicks noticeably downward.

It is possible to reduce the additional FM sidebands to an insignificant level if the deviation is kept sufficiently low. The RF bandwidth is then comparable to an AM transmission. An example of such an FM frequency spectrum is shown in Fig 5.12(b). For amateur NBFM, the exact deviation depends on whether the channel spacing is 12.5 or 25kHz on the band in question but in any case, the maximum deviation should not exceed ±2.5kHz. Even with this deviation, the higher sidebands are not entirely negligible so to prevent out-of-band radiation, FM transmissions must not be less than 10kHz from the edge of the amateur band.

To minimise the RF bandwidth of an FM signal, it is therefore essential that both the audio bandwidth and the audio amplitude are kept within well-defined limits. This is particularly important with data modes such as packet radio where over-deviation may be less obvious than with speech. To avoid over-deviation, audio compression or limiting is used in almost every FM transmitter.

Frequency synthesisers

Modern commercial transmitters rarely use the low-frequency VFO and frequency multiplier system. Instead, a phase-locked loop (PLL) frequency synthesiser replaces the VFO and may operate at very much higher frequencies where a VFO would be far too unstable. Synthesisers contain a crystal

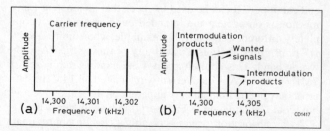

Fig 5.11. Effect of overdriving SSB. (a) USB transmitter on 14,300kHz driven by 1kHz and 2kHz audio tones. (b) USB transmitter on 14,300kHz overdriven by 1kHz and 2kHz audio tones

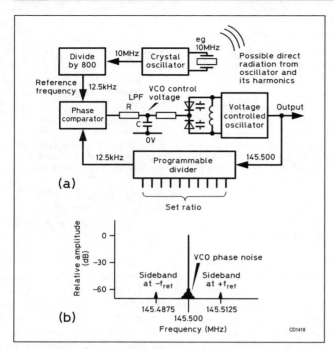

Fig 5.13. (a) Block diagram of frequency synthesiser for 144–146MHz. (b) Example of the spectrum of a PLL frequency synthesiser

oscillator (typically 1 to 15MHz), a voltage-controlled oscillator (VCO) and digital divider circuits. For some types of transceiver, particularly HF, the synthesiser is complex with multiple loops and additional frequency multipliers and mixers. For a single-band FM transceiver, however, a relatively simple single-loop PLL synthesiser can be used.

Fig 5.13(a) shows an example of a PLL frequency synthesiser for a 144MHz band FM transceiver with 12.5kHz channel spacing. A 10MHz crystal oscillator is divided by 800 to produce the reference frequency of 12.5kHz. The VCO is tuned by means of varicap diodes but is too unstable to be allowed to 'free run'. Instead, the VCO frequency is divided down using digital techniques and is compared to the reference frequency. The phase comparator controls the VCO and keeps it on the required frequency. For example, if an output frequency of 145.500MHz is required, the divider is set to 11640 which forces the VCO to run at 11640×12.5kHz = 145.500MHz.

On most synthesised transceivers with a digital frequency display, the frequency shown is not the *measured frequency* but the frequency which the PLL should produce. There is a possibility that the PLL may fail to lock, due to a fault or incorrect adjustment. If this occurs, the VCO does not run at the frequency shown on the display but is *uncontrolled, unstable and could transmit out of band*. This error condition must be detected by means of a lock detection circuit (not shown) which prevents a signal from being radiated if the PLL is out of lock. When constructing or converting a PLL synthesiser for amateur use, it is important to ensure that lock detection is included and that it is working correctly.

A synthesiser circuit must be adequately screened and filtered to ensure that it does not radiate into or pick up from other parts of the transmitter. This could result in the transmission of signals on some unexpected frequencies, for example harmonics of the crystal oscillator.

Even the wanted output signal can be troublesome if the design does not minimise unwanted frequency modulation by noise (inherently greater than with a VFO or crystal oscillator) or by the reference frequency. This is often the smallest frequency step available and in channelised equipment (as used at VHF and UHF) is typically 12.5kHz or 5kHz. Fig 5.13(b) shows the spectrum of an otherwise unmodulated signal which could give rise to complaints of 'hash' or 'whine' on adjacent frequencies. Note that when modulated, the whole signal (and not just the carrier) will carry modulation sidebands, giving the distinct impression that the signal is being over-modulated.

FREQUENCY CHECKING

It is essential that no transmissions be made outside the amateur bands, and signals should be located sufficiently inside band edges to allow for the spread of sidebands and for possible inaccuracy in the frequency measuring equipment (see Chapter 8). The requirements of the RA for frequency checking and measuring equipment are dealt with in Chapter 1.

Absorption wavemeters

An inductively coupled absorption wavemeter is a useful test instrument during the construction or alignment of a transmitter. For example, when tuning up a multiplier chain of the type shown in Fig 5.3(a), an absorption wavemeter can be used to check that the multiplier stages are tuned to the correct harmonic of the input. In the case of Fig 5.3(a), this means ensuring that the doubler stages are amplifying the second harmonic and the tripler stages are amplifying the third harmonic.

For day-to-day operation of an amateur station, it is more convenient to use a modified form of absorption wavemeter which has a short whip antenna to detect strong nearby signals. This is sometimes called a *tuneable field-strength meter* although this is not an appropriate name as it only indicates relative field strength, not absolute field strength in volts per metre. Fig 8.7 shows the circuit diagram of such an instrument. If the whip antenna receives a sufficiently strong signal at the resonant frequency of the tuned circuit, this is detected by the diode detector and drives the microammeter. The variable capacitor has a calibrated tuning scale which gives an approximate indication of the frequency to which the wavemeter is tuned. The whip antenna is positioned so that it picks up sufficient but not excessive RF energy from the transmitter. The tuning dial of the wavemeter is rotated until the meter pointer moves. This shows that RF energy is present at or near the frequency indicated by the tuning scale.

It is important to note what an absorption wavemeter can and cannot do. It can be used to check that an amateur transmission is on or near the intended band and not on a completely different frequency. For example, when tuning a valve HF transmitter, there is a possibility of tuning the PA to the wrong band. This could happen if the band switch is set for 7MHz but the PA is inadvertently resonated on 14MHz. This error may not be immediately apparent on the station receiver but would be apparent if an absorption wavemeter is used.

As an absorption wavemeter only gives an approximate indication of frequency, it cannot be used to check whether a transmitter is operating just inside or just outside a particular amateur band. It can be used to check for the presence of harmonics but it cannot measure the level of a harmonic relative to the carrier and is not particularly sensitive. It cannot detect spurious signals which are close to the wanted frequency and neither can it detect over-modulation or inter-modulation products.

Heterodyne wavemeter

A heterodyne wavemeter is used for measuring the frequency of a transmitter and is accurate enough to check that the transmitter is operating within an amateur band. A heterodyne wavemeter contains a variable frequency oscillator (VFO) with a calibrated frequency scale. The oscillator output and the unknown frequency from the transmitter are fed to a mixer which produces a difference frequency or *heterodyne* which is amplified to drive headphones or a loudspeaker. This allows the frequency of the VFO to be adjusted until it is very close to the unknown frequency (within 100Hz or less). The unknown frequency can then be measured using the calibrated frequency scale of the VFO. A heterodyne wavemeter normally contains a crystal calibrator (see below) for checking the accuracy of its own frequency scale.

Crystal calibrator

If a separate transmitter and receiver are used, it is useful to have available a crystal calibrator, preferably built into the receiver. This allows the receiver tuning accuracy to be checked at frequent intervals. A good-quality crystal and a few low-cost digital integrated circuits can provide frequency calibration markers typically at intervals of every 10MHz, 1MHz, 100kHz, and 10kHz. The frequency of the amateur transmission (and indeed any other signal) can then be checked against these markers. An output frequency of 100kHz is suitable for checking the transmitter frequency at band edges which are multiples of 100kHz. For example, if the output of a 100kHz crystal calibrator is received on the 28–29.7MHz band, harmonics will be received at 28.0, 28.1, 28.2MHz, and so on up to the band edge at 29.7MHz. In the case of the 14.0–14.35MHz band, however, it would be necessary to use a 50kHz marker to check the transmitter frequency at the upper edge of the band.

If a transceiver is used, it is not possible to transmit and receive at the same time. In these circumstances only the receiver can be calibrated, and further checks should be made to verify that the transmitting and receiving frequencies really are the same. Where the equipment incorporates a digital frequency display it is unwise to assume that this is absolutely accurate. The transmission frequency in particular should be checked, and due allowance made for possible inaccuracies when operating near band edges.

Digital frequency counters

Nowadays, digital frequency counters are widely used for transmitter frequency checking instead of the techniques described above. The principle of a digital frequency counter is explained in Chapter 8 (Measurements). It is important to note that the number of digits on a frequency counter determine its resolution, that is, the smallest change of frequency which can be detected. Resolution is not the same as accuracy, however. The accuracy of a digital frequency counter is limited by the accuracy of its timebase which is controlled by a crystal oscillator. This typically operates at 10MHz but its

frequency may drift slightly due to temperature variations and crystal ageing. The timebase crystal should therefore be regularly calibrated by comparison with a standard frequency source (see below). For example, the frequency of the crystal oscillator in a frequency counter might change by up to ±10ppm in a year due to ageing of the crystal which corresponds to an error of ±1.44kHz at 144MHz.

Standard frequency transmissions

Any equipment used to measure frequency (crystal calibrator, heterodyne wavemeter, digital frequency counter etc) should be checked regularly and, if necessary, adjusted against a source of known high accuracy. Standard frequency transmissions on HF may be received on 2.5, 5 or 10MHz from various transmitters in Europe or the USA, although they are no longer broadcast from the UK. The frequency of the 198kHz BBC Radio 4 long-wave transmissions is also maintained to a high degree of accuracy and can be used for calibration purposes.

PRACTICE QUESTIONS FOR CHAPTER 5

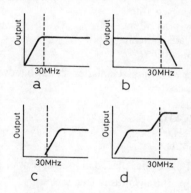

Fig Q5.1

1. Which one of the filters shown in Fig Q5.1 would minimise harmonic output from an HF transmitter?

2. The first odd harmonic of 144.690MHz is
   (a) 145.000MHz
   (b) 289.380MHz
   (c) 434.070MHz
   (d) 723.450MHz.

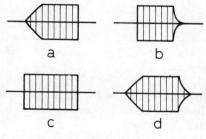

Fig Q5.2

3. Which one of the traces shown in Fig Q5.2 is likely to give minimum interference due to key clicks?

4. To maintain good screening of equipment with hinged metal lids it is advisable to connect across the hinge a

(a) plastic retainer

(b) good earth strap

(c) polystyrene capacitor

(d) ferrite bead.

5. Which one of the following operating conditions of the power amplifier stage of a transmitter is likely to produce the highest harmonic content in the output waveform?

(a) Class C.

(b) Class B.

(c) Class AB.

(d) Class A.

6. An absorption wavemeter can be used to check for

(a) over-modulation

(b) receiver overloading

(c) signals close to the band edge

(d) correct selection of harmonic from a multiplier circuit.

7. It is imperative that a broad-band transistor PA should be followed by a

(a) high-pass filter

(b) low-pass filter

(c) resistive attenuator

(d) mains filter.

8. In order to minimise splatter, audio bandwidth should be restricted to

(a) 3kHz

(b) 12.5kHz

(c) 25kHz

(d) 465kHz.

9. A band-pass filter placed after a VHF transmitter will

(a) stop all transmitting frequencies

(b) allow all harmonics to be passed

(c) allow all sub-harmonics to be radiated

(d) pass the desired frequency range.

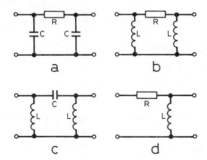

Fig Q5.3

10. Which of the circuits in Fig Q5.3 would provide low-pass filtering for a microphone circuit in order to minimise bandwidth?

11. Key-clicks from a CW transmitter heard on a receiver can be reduced by

(a) using an unscreened lead to the key

(b) using a key-click filter

(c) using a very small gap on the key

(d) sending more quickly.

12. To generate an accurate and stable frequency, a frequency synthesiser should

(a) have a crystal reference oscillator

(b) have no oscillator

(c) run from a modulated DC supply

(d) use the mains as a reference frequency.

13. Which one of the following arrangements will give the greatest accuracy when trying to check the carrier frequency of an FM transmitter?

(a) An oscilloscope and an unmodulated carrier.

(b) Digital frequency counter and a modulated carrier.

(c) Digital frequency counter and an unmodulated carrier.

(d) Absorption wavemeter and an unmodulated carrier.

14. Over-deviation in an FM transmitter causes

(a) no sidebands to be generated

(b) only a single sideband to be generated

(c) several sets of sidebands to be generated

(d) the carrier frequency to be suppressed.

15. Which one of the following antenna combinations is least likely to radiate harmonics?

(a) A dipole fed with coaxial cable.

(b) A dipole fed with balanced feeder.

(c) An inverted L-Marconi with vertical feeder.

(d) A long-wire antenna end fed.

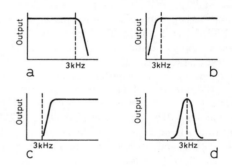

Fig Q5.4

16. Which one of the plots shown in Fig Q5.4 represents a filter suitable for following a microphone in order to limit the bandwidth?

17. In order to minimise unwanted radiation, a mixer stage should be

(a) AF decoupled

(b) well screened

(c) not earthed

(d) supplied with mains voltage.

18. The equipment at an amateur station should be designed, constructed and maintained so that it

(a) does not cause undue interference with any wireless telegraphy

(b) causes interference within the amateur bands

(c) will transmit callsigns automatically

(d) operates outside the specified bands from time to time.

19. To minimise RF interference in a house not fitted with PME it is wise to

(a) bond the equipment to a water pipe
(b) install antennas in the loft
(c) use an independent RF earth lead
(d) ground the equipment to the mains earth.

20. Earth return circuits should always be

(a) high impedance
(b) highly reactive
(c) low impedance
(d) inductively linked.

21. An external transmitting antenna is always preferred because

(a) it radiates fewer harmonics
(b) it will be subject to less radiation
(c) the coupling to mains wiring is minimised
(d) the transmitted signal is less.

22. The connection between power supplies and RF power amplifiers should be

(a) open wires
(b) AF filtered
(c) RF filtered
(d) well underrated.

23. If the coil in a VFO has no former, then mechanical vibrations

(a) will keep the frequency generated in the band
(b) may take the frequency generated out of band
(c) will have no effect
(d) will improve reception.

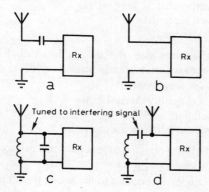

Fig Q5.5

24. Which one of the configurations shown in Fig Q5.5 would be useful in rejecting an unwanted signal at the input to a receiver?

25. The possibility of harmonic radiation should be checked with an absorption wavemeter

(a) on a daily basis
(b) only when a complaint arises
(c) on receiving an interfering signal
(d) from time to time.

Fig Q5.6

26. Fig Q5.6 shows the modulation envelope of a transmitter. Such an envelope should be avoided because

(a) it would be difficult to read
(b) of problems in the PA during the spaces
(c) key-clicks might be produced
(d) the power supply would become unstable.

27. If the accuracy of a digital readout on a transmitter is 10 parts per million, a frequency display of 14.250MHz could be as high as

(a) 14.250001425MHz
(b) 14.25001425MHz
(c) 14.2501425MHz
(d) 14.151425MHz.

28. In order to minimise the risk of self-oscillation in RF circuits

(a) each stage should be well screened
(b) screening should not be used between stages
(c) stages should be connected with open wires
(d) every other stage should be screened.

29. Which one of the following should be used in order to restrict the range of audio frequencies from a microphone?

(a) A high-pass filter.
(b) A resistive divider.
(c) Low-pass filter.
(d) An amplitude limiter.

30. The VFO of a transmitter is subjected to varying room temperatures. This might cause

(a) chirp
(b) drift
(c) band changes
(d) FM.

31. An over-deviated FM transmission will produce

(a) excessive sidebands
(b) one sideband
(c) only two sidebands
(d) complete suppression of sidebands.

32. Stages where harmonic generation occurs should be

(a) sealed in epoxy resin
(b) open to the atmosphere
(c) encased in polystyrene
(d) screened very carefully.

33. Spurious resonances may occur in decoupling circuits due to

(a) the power supply
(b) self-resonance of RF chokes
(c) saturation of the core of RF chokes
(d) the resistive nature of an RF choke.

34. A transmitter is using upper sideband and set to 14.349MHz. It is modulated by audio with a 3kHz bandwidth. This will

(a) be within the allotted allocation
(b) go out-of-band
(c) have zero sidebands
(d) cause over-deviation.

35. The mains transformer in a transmitter is fitted with an internal screen. To minimise the possibility of introducing mains-borne interference it should be connected to
    (a) the chassis and earth
    (b) the VFO output
    (c) the live side of the mains
    (d) nothing.

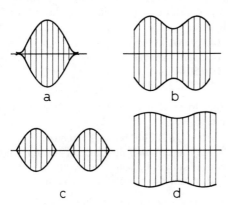

Fig Q5.7

36. Which one of the waveforms shown in Fig Q5.7 represents over-modulation of an AM signal?

37. Over-modulation in an AM signal is likely to cause
    (a) excessive deviation
    (b) 10 sidebands
    (c) minimum interference
    (d) severe splatter.

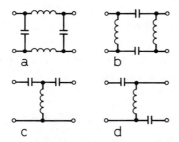

Fig Q5.8

38. Refer to Fig Q5.8. To stop RF going back into the mains cable, which one of the following filters could be fitted in series with the mains lead?

39. If the power output meter of a Class C amplifier shows a small varying reading when it is not being keyed, which one of the following might be the cause?
    (a) Regulated DC.
    (b) Parasitic oscillations.
    (c) Reception of a strong carrier.
    (d) Antenna blowing in the wind.

40. When transmitting on 3.730MHz, the second harmonic will be found at
    (a) 1.865MHz
    (b) 7.460MHz
    (c) 10.190MHz
    (d) 373.000MHz.

41. To keep a shack tidy, an amateur puts all mains cables and RF feeders in a single wiring loom. This
    (a) would represent an ideal situation
    (b) might cause unwanted 50Hz modulation
    (c) might be prone to producing mains borne interference
    (d) will cancel out all interference.

42. Sparks generated at the contacts of a Morse key
    (a) will cause long-range interference
    (b) will cause short-range interference
    (c) produce no interference effects
    (d) provide a perfect signal.

43. Cross modulation is caused by
    (a) the wanted complex signal mixing with itself
    (b) a harmonic mixing with itself
    (c) overdriving an amplifier
    (d) a strong unwanted signal mixing with the wanted signal.

44. A long-wire antenna using a vertical feed line near a house can
    (a) never cause interference
    (b) induce strong unwanted signals into TV coaxial down leads
    (c) cure all interference problems
    (d) produce buzzing on the mains.

45. For best EMC practice, multiplier stages should be
    (a) encased in plastic
    (b) surrounded by long wires
    (c) well screened
    (d) unscreened.

46. To prevent unwanted radiation in the shack, RF connections between units should be made with
    (a) open wire feeder
    (b) good-quality coaxial cable
    (c) bell wire
    (d) good-quality mains cable.

47. When using a digital frequency counter to check the calibration of a transmitter
    (a) connect the counter to the mains transformer
    (b) use a carrier which has no modulation
    (c) key the transmitter at 12 WPM
    (d) use a frequency modulated carrier.

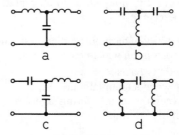

Fig Q5.9

48. Which one of the circuits in Fig Q5.9 would be used in the output of an HF transmitter in order to minimise harmonic radiation?

49. To reduce the risk of parasitic oscillations in a low-power VHF output stage, ferrite beads should be used
   (a) on the emitter lead of the power device
   (b) on the microphone cable
   (c) in series with microphone
   (d) on the loudspeaker lead.

50. To minimise unwanted radiation of sub-harmonics and harmonics, a VHF transmitter should be followed by a
   (a) low-pass filter
   (b) band-pass filter
   (c) high-pass filter
   (d) notch filter.

51. The transmitter should be maintained so that
   (a) it causes no undue interference
   (b) self-oscillation is maximised
   (c) parasitic oscillations are present
   (d) harmonic shielding is minimised.

52. Which one of the following could be used to check for harmonics in a radiated signal?
   (a) An SWR meter.
   (b) An absorption wavemeter.
   (c) A digital frequency meter.
   (d) A dip meter.

53. To minimise frequency changes due to supply voltage variations a VFO should be powered from
   (a) an AC/DC supply
   (b) a varying supply voltage
   (c) a well-stabilised DC supply
   (d) an unstabilised DC supply.

54. If a Class AB linear amplifier is overdriven by an SSB signal it will
   (a) cause splatter on adjacent frequencies
   (b) go into parasitic oscillation
   (c) introduce a carrier wave
   (d) produce a clean signal.

55. When checking the output of an FM transmitter the third harmonic with respect to the carrier should be at least
   (a) −6dB
   (b) −16dB
   (c) −30dB
   (d) −100dB.

56. Which one of the following types of capacitor should be used to RF decouple a loudspeaker lead?
   (a) Ceramic.
   (b) Aluminium electrolytic.
   (c) Tantalum.
   (d) Polycarbonate.

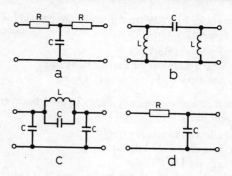

Fig Q5.10

57. In Fig Q5.10 which circuit shows a high-pass filter?

58. A digital frequency counter shows 7.0885MHz when checking a 7MHz transmission. The figure '5' represents
   (a) units of hertz
   (b) tens of hertz
   (c) hundreds of hertz
   (d) thousands of hertz.

59. The simplest piece of equipment used to check the correct harmonic selection in a multiplier stage is
   (a) a multimeter
   (b) a diode probe
   (c) an absorption wavemeter
   (d) a digital frequency counter.

60. A transmitter is amplitude modulated using a carrier frequency of 21.448MHz. The speech bandwidth is 3kHz. The transmission will
   (a) comply with the licence schedule
   (b) cause splatter
   (c) cause harmonics
   (d) exceed the band edge.

61. Which one of the following would be used to minimise the radiation of a specific harmonic?
   (a) Trap in the transmitter output.
   (b) Push-pull output stage.
   (c) High-pass filter in the transmitter output.
   (d) Filter in the receiver lead.

62. Power supply leads in a transmitter should
   (a) be well decoupled at RF
   (b) not be filtered
   (c) be routed via the PA compartment
   (d) have RF oscillations on them.

63. Chirp is a form of frequency instability. It is caused by
   (a) birdies in the receiver
   (b) over-modulation
   (c) over-deviation
   (d) pulling of an oscillator when keying.

64. To obtain high-frequency stability in a transmitter, the VFO should
   (a) be run from a non-regulated AC supply
   (d) be encased in a plastic box
   (c) be powered from a stable DC supply
   (d) change frequency with temperature.

65. Key clicks in a CW transmission are caused by
    (a) VFO instability
    (b) a very stable VFO
    (c) sharp edges to the carrier waveform
    (d) too slow a keying speed.

66. The frequency changing stages in a transceiver should ideally be
    (a) allowed to radiate freely
    (b) frequency modulated
    (c) encased in PTFE
    (d) well screened to minimise unwanted radiation.

67. To check the calibration of a transceiver with a VFO at the band edges, the minimum equipment required is
    (a) a dip meter
    (b) a crystal-controlled, digital frequency meter
    (c) an absorption wavemeter
    (d) an oscilloscope.

68. To minimise interference to adjacent stations on HF, voice frequencies should be kept below
    (a) 500Hz
    (b) 1kHz
    (c) 3kHz
    (d) 5kHz.

69. When making a transmitter VFO, the coil should be
    (a) loosely wound on a ceramic former
    (b) placed in a position as free as possible from temperature variations
    (c) placed next to a fan which cools the PA
    (d) wound as tightly as possible on a stainless steel former.

70. Key-clicks can be reduced by
    (a) slowing down the leading and falling edges of the waveform
    (b) slowing down the leading edge of the RF waveform only
    (c) slowing down the trailing edge of the RF waveform only
    (d) using a vertically polarised antenna.

71. The total bandwidth of an FM transmission is found to be 15kHz. How close to the band edge can a carrier be transmitted in order not to produce out-of-band radiation?
    (a) 0kHz.
    (b) 3kHz.
    (c) 7.5kHz.
    (d) 15kHz.

72. If the bandwidth of a 2m FM transmission is too wide it can be reduced by
    (a) varying the volume control
    (b) adjusting the deviation control
    (c) altering the bias control
    (d) changing the carrier frequency.

73. A VHF/UHF transmitter should ideally be followed by a

    (a) high-pass filter
    (b) crystal filter
    (c) band-pass filter
    (d) mains filter.

74. The presence of harmonics can easily be checked by using
    (a) an absorption wavemeter
    (b) an oscilloscope
    (c) a digital frequency counter
    (d) a diode probe.

75. So as not to cause unnecessary sideband splatter the percentage modulation of an AM signal should be kept below
    (a) 25%
    (b) 50%
    (c) 75%
    (d) 100%.

76. Which one of the following types of mixer keeps unwanted outputs to a minimum?
    (a) Balanced mixer.
    (b) Product detector.
    (c) Single transistor mixer.
    (d) Single diode mixer.

77. Parasitic oscillations can cause interference. This is because they are
    (a) usually the same frequency as the mains supply
    (b) always twice the operating frequency
    (c) not related to the operating frequency
    (d) three times the operating frequency.

78. To stop unwanted radiation from an oscillator, it should be
    (a) enclosed in a metal box
    (b) left unscreened
    (c) not be RF decoupled
    (d) placed in a polythene box.

79. To minimise the risk of unwanted radiation using a matched antenna system, it is wise to
    (a) have a high SWR
    (b) use an ATU or filter
    (c) monitor DC supply voltage
    (d) use a multiband antenna.

80. In order to conserve bandwidth, the frequency components of an audio signal being applied to an amplitude modulator should not exceed
    (a) 500Hz
    (b) 1kHz
    (c) 3kHz
    (d) 6kHz.

81. The output waveform from an SSB transmission is observed on an oscilloscope. The waveform is 'flat topped'. This will produce
    (a) 50Hz modulation
    (b) splatter
    (c) frequency modulation
    (d) phase modulation.

82. If unwanted RF signals are fed back near a VFO this may cause
   (a) rectification
   (b) frequency synthesis
   (c) stabilisation
   (d) frequency instability.

83. Self-oscillation of an amplifier is due to
   (a) poor power supply regulation
   (b) insufficient amplifier gain
   (c) diode switching in the power supply
   (d) coupling between input and output giving a high loop gain.

84. A 144MHz transmitter with no harmonic output causes overloading to a nearby UHF TV. This could best be remedied by placing which one of the following in the TV antenna down-lead?
   (a) Antenna switch.
   (b) Low-pass filter.
   (c) High-pass filter.
   (d) Diode.

85. To minimise harmonic radiation from a single-band UHF transceiver it should ideally be followed by a
   (a) high-pass filter
   (b) low-pass filter
   (c) band-pass filter
   (d) notch filter.

86. The output matching circuit and filter in a Class C amplifier should be
   (a) enclosed in a screened metal box
   (b) put on top of the amplifier to aid cooling
   (c) encased in Perspex so that flashover can be seen
   (d) installed at the top of the mast next to the antenna.

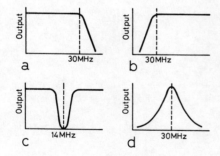

Fig Q5.11

87. Refer to Fig Q5.11. Which one of the filter characteristics would be suitable for following a multiband HF transmitter?

88. An absorption wavemeter is useful for checking
   (a) exact transmission frequency
   (b) frequency drift
   (c) peak modulation index
   (d) harmonic radiation.

89. A harmonic is
   (a) a whole number multiple of a frequency
   (b) a sub-multiple of a frequency
   (c) any frequency greater than the original
   (d) always in the same amateur band as the transmitter.

90. To reduce the risk of self oscillation in a power amplifier, a screen should be used between
   (a) the output and the mains transformer
   (b) input and output circuitry
   (c) the rectifiers and smoothing capacitors
   (d) all resistors.

91. If a transmitter suffers from poor frequency stability it may cause
   (a) electric shocks to the operator
   (b) operation out of the band
   (c) excessive collector dissipation
   (d) excessive power to be drawn from the supply.

92. To cut down radiation from a coil in a tuned circuit, it should be
   (a) enclosed in a plastic screening can
   (b) enclosed in a non-metallic resin
   (c) placed in a metal screening can
   (d) mounted outside the equipment.

93. An SSB transmitter is likely to cause interference to nearby stations if the
   (a) power amplifier is switched off
   (b) PA stage is underdriven
   (c) feeder is well screened
   (d) power amplifier is overdriven.

94. A 'lossy' choke can be used to suppress parasitic oscillations. It is constructed by
   (a) winding thick copper wire on a very-high-value resistor
   (b) making a self-supporting coil of thick copper wire with a silver coating
   (c) winding a coil on a low-value resistor
   (d) using a low-value carbon resistor.

95. If an L-C oscillator is used directly to generate a signal at 14.050MHz in a CW transmitter and drifts by −1%, it will
   (a) stay within the designated band
   (b) go above the top band edge
   (c) go below the bottom band edge
   (d) be rejected.

96. To prevent unwanted mixing products reaching a transmitter output stage, the output of a mixer should be
   (a) followed by resistive coupling
   (b) directly coupled
   (c) followed by a transistor
   (d) well filtered.

97. To prevent RF from a PA stage feeding back to the VFO the DC supply should be
   (a) AF filtered
   (b) well filtered at RF
   (c) hum free
   (d) not filtered at RF.

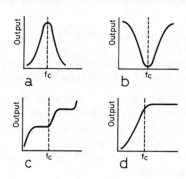

Fig Q5.12

98. Refer to Fig Q5.12. Which one of the diagrams represents a band-pass filter suitable for suppression of harmonics from a single-band transceiver?

99. The digital readout on a transceiver is only accurate to 0.01%. How close can one go to the lower band edge on 10 metres in order to ensure that the carrier is within the band?

    (a) 28Hz.
    (b) 280Hz.
    (c) 2800Hz.
    (d) 28000Hz.

100. To which one of the following bands would a receiver have to be tuned in order to detect the third harmonic from a nearby 7.050MHz transmission?

    (a) 14MHz.
    (b) 21MHz.
    (c) 24MHz.
    (d) 28MHz.

101. Interference is experienced in the 144MHz band from a 432MHz crystal-controlled transmitter which has a crystal oscillating around 12MHz. The most likely multiplication is

    (a) ×2×3×3×2
    (b) ×2×2×3×3
    (c) ×3×3×2×2
    (d) ×3×2×3×2.

102. The reason for placing a small ferrite bead on a transistor lead is to

    (a) screen the lead
    (b) space the transistor above the PCB
    (c) prevent parasitic oscillations
    (d) give matching to 50Ω.

103. Increasing the deviation level of a frequency modulated transmitter will

    (a) improve the speech quality
    (b) increase the speech compression ratio
    (c) overcome FM noise
    (d) widen the RF bandwidth.

104. The minimum equipment for checking the harmonics of a radiated signal is

    (a) a Geiger counter
    (b) an oscilloscope
    (c) a dip oscillator
    (d) an absorption wavemeter.

105. The final frequency in a transmitter is obtained by mixing a VFO with a crystal oscillator. Severe drift occurs in the transmission. This is most likely due to the

    (a) crystal oscillator
    (b) VFO
    (c) mixer
    (d) PA stage.

106. If the carrier in an FM system is over-deviated

    (a) no sidebands are generated
    (b) excessive number of sidebands are generated
    (c) only two sidebands are generated
    (d) only one sideband is generated.

6 Electromagnetic compatibility

AN amateur radio transmitter may affect various types of electronic equipment nearby. There are two possible reasons for this:

(a) *Interference caused by transmitter defects.* The transmitter is emitting harmonics or other spurious signals on frequencies used by other radio services such as broadcasting or some form of communication service such as police, fire service or aircraft. The cure is to reduce the spurious emissions to a sufficiently low level. This topic is covered in Chapter 5.

(b) *Interference caused because a piece of equipment is not able to function correctly in the presence of the strong (legitimate) amateur transmitted signal.* There is no fault with the transmitter or the way in which it is being operated so filtering at the transmitter cannot cure this type of problem. The cause is simply the amount of RF reaching the affected equipment. In many cases, such problems can be solved by filtering or other measures at the affected equipment to improve its immunity. Nevertheless, the amount of the RF generated by the amateur's equipment reaching the affected equipment should be minimised by use of an appropriate type of antenna in an appropriate location.

Clearly, it is of fundamental importance to establish whether (a) or (b) applies. This chapter deals with case (b).

THE MEANING OF ELECTROMAGNETIC COMPATIBILITY

Electromagnetic compatibility (usually abbreviated to 'EMC') is the desirable situation where different types of electrical and electronic equipment are compatible with each other. That is, electronic equipment operates as intended in the presence of signals from nearby radio transmitters and does not cause interference to nearby radio receivers.

So far as amateur radio is concerned, the object is to achieve good EMC performance; that is, not to cause interference to others and to minimise interference to amateur reception. This is, of course, not a simple matter since it involves not only the station but also any radio and electronic equipment operating in the vicinity. The amateur must endeavour to minimise interference caused by his (or her) station and, where appropriate, assist with increasing the immunity of susceptible domestic radio and electronic equipment nearby. Complementary to this is interference to amateur reception. This has always been a problem – amateur stations are often located in urban environments in close proximity to neighbours but the proliferation of computers and digital electronics in modern homes has recently brought it into greater prominence.

In recent years governments have enacted legislation which requires that equipment on sale to the public in the European Union since 1 January 1996 must meet certain EMC standards and carry the CE mark to indicate compliance. These standards fall into two categories:

- *Emission standards.* These specify the maximum level of radio interference which electronic equipment such as computers are permitted to generate.
- *Immunity standards.* These specify the minimum level of immunity which equipment must have to electromagnetic disturbance from outside sources such as signals from radio transmitters.

In the UK the standards are issued by the British Standards Institution, and are harmonised to the common standards of the European Community (EC). In general, EMC standards are framed round a typical radio environment, and fall short of what would be ideal from the radio amateur's point of view. Amateurs tend to generate high field strengths and attempt to receive smaller signals than other radio users in a typical residential area.

Nowadays a typical house may contain a wide variety of electronic devices, any of which might suffer interference from amateur transmissions. In cases where the amateur transmitter is not at fault, the effect is usually called *breakthrough*, emphasising that it is really a limitation of the susceptible equipment which is not sufficiently immune to strong RF signals. Examples of domestic electrical/electronic equipment which may suffer RF breakthrough from amateur signals include:

- Television sets
- Video recorders
- Hi-fi systems
- Telephones
- Passive infra-red (PIR) sensors in security lights

Household electrical appliances with electromechanical switches and controls are unlikely to be affected by amateur signals. Although the use of electronic controls on such equipment is increasing, few breakthrough problems are reported.

Some modes of transmission are more likely to cause breakthrough problems, and it is worth looking at the more frequently used modes from this point of view.

- *SSB.* This is a popular mode, but also the most likely to cause breakthrough, particularly where audio equipment is concerned. This is because the signal amplitude varies at audio frequency and when rectified in the susceptible equipment, is reproduced as a distorted sound.
- *FM.* This is the best mode from the breakthrough point of view, because the susceptible equipment sees only a

constant carrier turned on and off every so often. There should be no rectified audio.

- *CW.* This has two big advantages. First, providing the keying waveform is well shaped, the rectified carrier is not such a problem to audio equipment as SSB. The slow rise and fall gives relatively soft clicks which cause less annoyance than SSB. The second advantage is that it is possible to use lower power for a given contact than with SSB or FM. (There is no doubt that CW has a big advantage over SSB or FM when it comes to the simple criterion of 'getting through' to the other station. Figures up to 20dB are sometimes quoted. However, it must be recognised that this does not take into account the rate of exchanging information or the social aspects of the contact.)

- *Data modes such as packet radio.* These are generally based on frequency-shift keying (FSK) and should minimise breakthrough problems. All data systems involve the carrier being keyed on and off – when going from receive to transmit, and vice versa, and consideration should be given to the carrier rise and fall times just as in CW.

CHARACTERISTICS OF INTERFERENCE EMITTED BY ELECTRICAL AND ELECTRONIC EQUIPMENT

If electrical or electronic equipment causes interference to amateur reception, this may be one of two types:

- *Broad-band RFI.* This can be produced by arcing and sparking, for example in electric motors or vehicle ignition systems. Other broad-band sources include conventional fluorescent lighting and corona discharge from high-voltage overhead power cables. A characteristic of broad-band RFI is that its level does not vary much when tuning across an amateur band.

- *Narrow-band RFI.* This can be produced by oscillators in electronic equipment such as computers, microprocessors and the line timebase in a TV set or computer monitor. Harmonics of such oscillators may fall in amateur bands. For example, if a piece of electronic equipment produces a square wave at 250kHz, harmonics may be heard at multiples of this frequency such as 3500kHz, 3750kHz and possibly up to VHF, eg 144.000MHz, 144.250MHz, 144.500MHz. A TV line timebase which operates at 15.625kHz can produce harmonics across the lower HF bands, eg 3500kHz, 3515kHz, 3531kHz etc. A characteristic of narrow-band RFI is that, when tuning across an amateur band, RFI is found on one or more *spot frequencies* but there is little or no RFI in between them.

If a computer is used in an amateur station and causes RFI, the first thing to find out is whether the RFI is entering the receiver via the antenna or the mains supply. If it enters via the mains supply, it is known as *mains-borne interference.* The sensitivity of a receiver to mains-borne interference from any source can be reduced if the mains transformer in the amateur receiver's power supply has an earthed copper *interwinding screen* between the primary and secondary windings.

If RFI from a computer is picked up by an amateur receiving antenna, there are two main ways of reducing this effect:

- Increase the separation between the amateur antenna and the computer.
- Improve the screening of the computer and its cables.

HOW UNWANTED RF SIGNALS MAY ENTER RADIO AND TV SETS ETC

In order to explain how amateur transmissions may enter a television set, it is useful to outline the principles of a television receiver. Fig 6.1 shows a simplified block diagram of the receiving section of a black and white TV set.

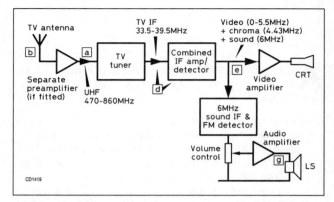

Fig 6.1. Simplified block diagram of the receiving section of a television receiver

The receiver is a superhet, with the RF amplifier and mixer stages contained in a screened box called the *tuner.* The IF output of the tuner is fed to the IF amplifier which amplifies frequencies from approximately 33.5MHz to over 39.5MHz. The output of the IF amplifier is detected to produce the video signal which is amplified and fed to the cathode ray tube (CRT). The video signal contains frequencies up to 5.5MHz and also contains a 6MHz FM sound signal which is fed to the 6MHz sound IF amplifier. This is followed by an FM sound detector, volume control and audio amplifier.

Amateur signals may enter a television receiver, radio receiver or other equipment in a number of ways.

(a) Entry via the RF stages

This may cause blocking or cross-modulation, both of which are likely to affect all channels.

Cross-modulation occurs when a strong RF signal such as an amateur's transmission enters a stage in a receiver such as the RF amplifier stage in a television set. This causes the gain of the affected stage to vary (usually it is reduced). Variations in the amplitude of the amateur signal – such as occur when transmitting SSB, AM or even CW (A1A mode) – are therefore transferred to the TV signal. This can be very disruptive and cause fluctuating dark and light horizontal bars across the picture. This effect is less noticeable where the transmission amplitude is constant (eg FM and data modes). Nevertheless, FM transmissions may still cause blocking.

Blocking or *desensitising* means that the presence of a strong amateur signal reduces the gain of the RF stages of a TV set. This causes the picture to become weak and noisy, and in severe cases, the screen may go completely blank.

(b) Entry via a TV antenna amplifier (if fitted)

If a mast-head preamplifier or set-back preamplifier is used, blocking or cross-modulation may occur in the preamplifier rather than in the RF stages of the TV set. If this occurs, filtering is required at the *input* of a preamplifier.

(c) Harmonic generation

This effect is similar to that caused when the amateur signal itself contains harmonics and typically only affects one TV channel. The important difference is that the harmonics are generated *inside the affected equipment* and are not being produced by the transmitter. Harmonic generation in a receiver normally requires a fairly high level of unwanted signal in the affected stages, ie sufficient to over-drive the circuit so that it becomes non-linear. Harmonics can be generated in RF and IF amplifiers, mixers etc, and particularly in TV and radio tuner stages or TV preamplifiers.

(d) Entry via the IF stages

Amateur signals may break through into an IF amplifier, particularly if the IF amplifier is not well screened. A symptom of IF breakthrough is that signals on one particular amateur band affect all TV channels or all FM stations. This is because whichever TV channel or FM station is being received, the receiver always converts it to the same IF. Examples of IF breakthrough include the following:

- FM broadcast receivers normally use a 10.7 MHz IF. A strong 10.1MHz amateur signal may be close enough to 10.7MHz to cause breakthrough. There is also some possibility that strong third harmonics from the 3.5MHz band could affect the 10.7MHz IF stages in an FM radio.
- If an amateur signal on 18.1MHz breaks through into a TV IF amplifier, it may be doubled to 36.2MHz (see '(c) Harmonic generation' above). The pass band of a TV IF amplifier is from 33.5 to over 39.5MHz so the unwanted 36.2MHz signal is amplified and causes interference such as patterning, loss of colour and poor synchronisation (picture rolls). Another possibility is that the 18MHz band amateur signal has an excessive level of second harmonic, which could break through into the TV IF amplifier.

(e) Direct reproduction

Certain stages such as video amplifiers in TV sets and video recorders have a wide bandwidth and can amplify amateur signals in the 1.8, 3.5 and even the 7MHz bands. If the amateur signal enters one of these stages, it is simply added to the wanted signal. This often causes finely spaced diagonal bars on the picture. If a 3.5MHz transmission enters the colour circuits centred on 4.43MHz, the picture sometimes reverts to black and white. Note that in many cases a relatively low level of unwanted signal flowing in the circuit may produce a significant amount of interference.

(f) Rectification (detection, demodulation etc)

As with (a), (b) and (c), non-linearities are responsible. Any type of electronic equipment contains semiconductors and the PN junctions in these devices can rectify the unwanted RF signal. The rectified signal may then be amplified by other semiconductors. The overall effect depends on the type of equipment. It may be disturbances of the vision on TVs or sound on entertainment systems. In the case of control devices, the rectified signal may upset the logic and cause totally unpredictable results. Alarm systems which use sensors with semiconductor components – and most do somewhere in the system – can be susceptible to this sort of problem.

(g) Entry via the audio stages

This is a specific example of (f). RF can enter the audio amplifier of a television receiver (or other type of equipment) due to pick-up on the loudspeaker cable or elsewhere. This is more likely to occur with TV sets which have external loudspeakers. If breakthrough is still present when the volume control is turned down to minimum, this indicates that the RF is entering the audio power amplifier directly rather than the earlier stages before the volume control.

(h) Entry via mains wiring

If RF signals from a transmitter are conducted into other electronic equipment via the mains wiring, this is called *mains-borne interference*. Clearly, the amount of RF which is coupled onto the mains wiring should be minimised by good station design as described below. The affected equipment is likely to be more immune to mains-borne interference if it has an earthed interwinding screen in its mains transformer.

IMPROVING RF IMMUNITY OF DOMESTIC EQUIPMENT

Frequencies used for radio and TV in relation to amateur bands

Fig 6.2 overleaf shows where amateur bands lie in relation to frequencies used by other services such as FM radio broadcasting (88–108MHz) and UHF TV (470–860MHz). If either the transmitted or received signals require additional filtering, it gives an indication of which type of filter might be suitable.

If amateur transmissions affect radio, TV or other equipment which uses radio in some way, the first thing to check is whether the cause is a harmonic or spurious emission from the transmitter. Consider the frequency on which the amateur transmitter is operating, and the frequency on which the radio or TV is suffering interference. If the frequency of the broadcast radio or TV signal is close to two, three, four or five times the frequency of the amateur transmission, then it is very likely that the problem is due to a harmonic of the transmitter. Transmitter design which minimises harmonic and other unwanted outputs is dealt in Chapter 5. There is, however, also a possibility that a harmonic is being generated in the affected equipment (see '(c) Harmonic generation' above on this page).

Because the higher harmonics usually fall off in level (see Fig 5.1), the UHF harmonics which are radiated by a well-designed HF transmitter are rarely responsible for television interference (TVI). Much greater attention must be paid to VHF and UHF amateur transmissions, however. For example, some harmonics of the 144–146MHz band fall within certain UHF TV channels:

- The fourth harmonic falls within channel 34 (575.25MHz vision, 581.25MHz sound)
- The fifth harmonic falls within channels 52 (719.25/725.25MHz) or 53 (727.25/733.25MHz).

However, unless the harmonics are particularly strong, this problem is likely to be apparent only in those areas where one of these channels is actually used for TV broadcasting.

The FM radio band (87.5 to 108MHz) may suffer from certain harmonics:

- The second harmonic of the 50–52MHz band falls between 100 and 104MHz.
- The high frequency end of the 28.0–29.7MHz band has a third harmonic which falls between 87.5 and 89.1MHz.

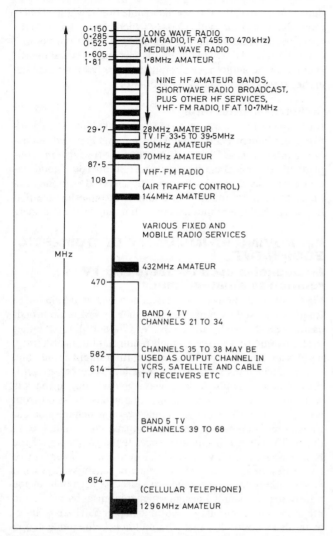

Fig 6.2. Frequencies of amateur bands in relation to those used by other services

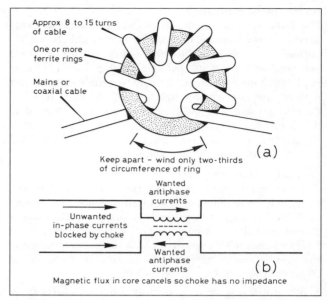

Fig 6.3. (a) Winding details of a ferrite ring choke for use as a mains filter or as a braid-breaker in a coaxial cable. (b) How it behaves electrically

Use of ferrite ring (toroidal) chokes and filters

The ferrite ring (toroidal) choke is probably the most useful item in the EMC armoury. It is used at the transmitting station to limit unwanted RF currents on various leads, including coaxial antenna feeders. It may also be used to increase the immunity of susceptible equipment by reducing the entry of unwanted RF by 'choking' the external leads. Ferrite ring chokes can be fitted to coaxial cables, loudspeaker leads or other cables to impede *in-phase* or *common-mode* signals. In relation to a loudspeaker cable, this means that there is RF on *both wires together* relative to earth. In relation to a coaxial cable, it means that there is RF on both the braid *and inner* relative to earth.

For EMC use, it is important to use a ferrite core with the right characteristics if optimum performance is to be achieved (these are given in the *RSGB Guide to EMC* and the *RSGB Yearbook*). Ferrite cores must sufficiently have high permeability at the interfering frequency to give high inductance. At the same time they should have sufficient loss at radio frequencies to avoid unwanted resonance. At radio frequencies

the choke behaves as an ideal (lossless) choke in series with a 'loss' resistance.

Fig 6.3(a) shows how a choke is constructed. The main requirement is to have a high inductance at the interfering frequency. This can be achieved by winding sufficient turns on to the core. The inductance is proportional to the thickness of the core, so that winding the wire onto two cores 'stacked' gives double the inductance. The inductance is proportional to the *square* of the number of turns, so that doubling the number of turns gives *four times* the inductance. Capacitance across the winding effectively shunts the choke, so that the end of the windings should be kept apart. Filling the core about two-thirds full of turns is a good rule of thumb. Information on winding chokes will be found in the *RSGB Guide to EMC* and the *RSGB Yearbook*.

There are alternative forms of ferrite choke, such as a two-part core and clamp, or ferrite rod. A ferrite rod choke will require many more turns and is not particularly effective on the lower HF bands. The advantage of a ring-shaped core is that it has a closed magnetic circuit, which greatly increases the effective permeability.

▶Differential and common-mode currents

To understand why ferrite chokes are such useful components it is necessary to appreciate the significance of differential and common-mode currents. When a load is connected to a generator, the wanted current flows from the source on one wire and back to the source on the other. This is *differential* current flow. If the wires are close together, a twisted pair for instance, the magnetic fields cancel almost completely (because they are equal and opposite). If such a pair of wires is wound on a ferrite core there is no magnetic field to interact with the core and the flow of wanted current is unaffected. If a pair of wires is in an electromagnetic field – in effect acting as an unwanted antenna, then the current flows on both wires in the same direction as if the pair were one wire. This is called *common-mode* or *in-phase* current (Fig 6.3(b)). When the pair of wires are wound on a ferrite core, there is no magnetic field cancellation and the core 'sees' the magnetic field of the common-mode current. Consequently it exhibits a high inductance so far as these common-mode currents are concerned and

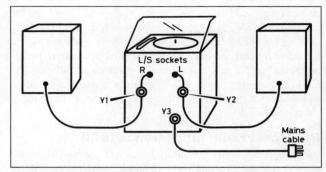

Fig 6.4. Fitting ferrite ring chokes to an audio system

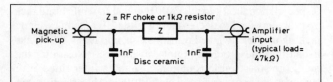

Fig 6.5. A low-pass filter used to cure RF breakthrough into an audio input such as a magnetic pick-up cartridge.

acts as a choke. A good example would be a ferrite choke on a hi-fi speaker lead. The differential audio currents to the speaker are unaffected, while any unwanted common-mode currents (from a nearby transmitter, for instance) are severely attenuated.◄

Audio equipment

Audio hi-fi equipment often suffers from RF breakthrough, whether it incorporates a radio tuner or not. As with other domestic equipment, breakthrough to such devices should become less of a problem as older equipment is replaced by products complying with the EMC regulations. Audio amplifiers are easily driven into non-linearity by high-level RF signals, and rectification occurs. When AM (A3E) transmission was popular, the hi-fi owner would normally hear every word transmitted, and possibly at considerable volume. With SSB however, only the characteristic 'quack quack' will be heard. With FM, there may only be a click when the transmission starts and finishes, and this may often go unnoticed. However, in cases of serious overload, the audio volume may decrease, or even be totally silenced.

In stereo systems, the loudspeaker leads are frequently the cause of the trouble. They form a dipole antenna which is only too efficient at picking up radio transmissions, and may even resonate on some amateur bands. Strong RF currents are fed through the audio amplifier, where they are detected and the resulting audio comes out of the speaker sockets. A characteristic of this effect is that the breakthrough is still present when the volume is turned down to minimum. If the breakthrough disappears when the speakers are unplugged and headphones are used, this confirms that the RF is being picked up in the speaker cables.

A ferrite ring choke should be inserted into each speaker cable close to the amplifier speaker output socket as shown by Y1 and Y2 in Fig 6.4. This is often very successful although, in some cases, an additional ring may be required on the mains cable at Y3. Alternatively, the use of screened loudspeaker cables can be effective in some cases.

If turning the volume down causes the breakthrough to disappear, this indicates that the RF is being detected in a stage *before* the volume control such as a preamplifier. Where the audio equipment consists of separate units, it is usually possible to filter the interconnecting leads but, when it is one integrated system, such possibilities are limited. Where the leads are accessible, using the ferrite ring choke

technique to block common-mode unwanted RF currents is often effective.

In some cases, RF breakthrough occurs in a high-gain audio stage handling low-level signals such as from a magnetic pick-up cartridge. If the audio equipment consists of separate units, the filter circuit shown in Fig 6.5 may be used near the input socket of the preamplifier.

Interference to television (TVI)

In the UK, TV is only broadcast at UHF (470 to 860MHz). These days, interference is rarely due to a serious technical shortcoming in the amateur transmitter. It is more likely to be due to the inability of the equipment suffering the interference to withstand the presence of the strong amateur signal.

A UHF TV antenna is too short to pick up much signal on the HF amateur bands (ie below 30MHz). On the HF bands, it is much more common for pick-up to occur on the braid of the TV antenna downlead as shown in Fig 6.6, particularly if the transmitting antenna is vertically polarised. The coaxial downlead acts rather like a receiving antenna operating against earth. (There may be no earth connection, but the mains wiring and the capacitance of the equipment to earth has the same effect.). RF currents are picked up on the braid as common-mode signals, flow into the set via the antenna socket and pass through the set into the mains wiring. Almost any part of the circuit may be affected.

A conventional high-pass filter, fitted in the coaxial socket at the TV set antenna input, filters only those signals which are picked up on the antenna itself, and travel down the inside of the coaxial cable, so it will probably be ineffective. However, if a ferrite ring choke or another type of braid-breaker (see below) is fitted at point X in Fig 6.6, this is much more likely to be successful. Occasionally a ferrite ring choke may be needed on the mains lead at point Y in Fig 6.6.

At frequencies above about 30MHz, the TV antenna becomes an increasingly efficient receptor of unwanted signals

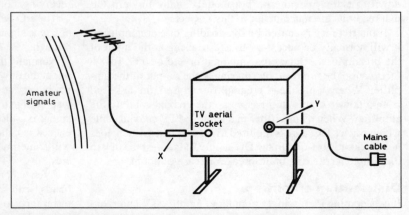

Fig 6.6. Pick-up of HF signals by the braid of a coaxial cable.

(especially on the 144 and 432MHz bands), while braid pick-up problems tend to decrease. If it is the TV antenna which is picking up the unwanted transmission, and it has been established that the problem is not caused by a transmitter harmonic or other spurious output, a suitable filter fitted at the antenna socket of the TV set should always be effective, provided that it has sufficient rejection on the unwanted frequency, for example:

- 50MHz breakthrough on UHF TV requires a high-pass filter at the TV
- 432MHz breakthrough on UHF TV requires a high-pass filter with sharp cut-off at the TV

For operation on any band up to and including the 432MHz band the best choice is probably a good-quality UHF high-pass filter which has a sharp cut-off below 470MHz. However, if interest is concentrated on a particular band, a band-stop filter could be used. Fig 6.9 on p106 shows a simple circuit which is easy to construct and which can be aligned without test equipment.

Video cassette recorders (VCRs)

These have problems in addition to those suffered by TV sets. Most recorders incorporate a wide-band antenna preamplifier which covers all UHF (and possibly VHF) TV bands. This may be susceptible to overloading by strong amateur signals (especially VHF and UHF). On replay, the high-gain video circuits which amplify the weak signals delivered by the heads may suffer from the lower frequency bands – particularly 1.8, 3.5 and 7MHz. Note that filters and braid-breakers may have to be fitted both to the antenna lead and the RF lead to the TV set. An increasing number of installations use a SCART lead to connect the VCR to the television set. This is good practice, and removes one possible pick-up route provided the lead is well screened.

Masthead preamplifiers

These are sometimes used in areas of poor reception of TV and FM radio. They are normally fitted directly at the antenna, and powered via the coaxial downlead. Some TV preamplifiers only cover the UHF TV band or part of it while others are broad-band VHF/UHF types covering 40–860MHz. The VHF/UHF type can be particularly susceptible to blocking or cross-modulation by amateur VHF signals. Some older types are not screened and may also respond to HF signals down to a few megahertz. Fortunately many modern CE marked units are much better in this respect.

If interference is caused by overloading of a preamplifier, it will normally be necessary to add filtering at the input of the preamplifier. Once cross-modulation etc occurs, its effects cannot be removed by filtering at the output of the amplifier. Where a masthead preamplifier is used, the DC feed from a power supply unit passes up the coaxial cable to the amplifier. When using a filter in a length of TV coaxial cable which carries DC, care is required to select a filter which does not block or short-circuit the DC supply. It is safest to stick to the simple ferrite ring braid-breaker in case of doubt.

Distribution amplifiers

It is becoming increasingly popular to amplify TV and radio signals, and then split them to feed several rooms in the house.

As with masthead units, some systems are wide-band and are easily overloaded if amateur signals reach the input. Again, as with masthead amplifiers, units are now available which are tuned for certain bands. Generally breakthrough remedies as applied to TV sets can be used with such amplifiers. The EMC regulations apply to TV amplifiers and the situation should start to improve over the next few years as older models are replaced.

Broadcast radio interference (BCI)

Nowadays most cases of interference to broadcast radio reception are due to some form of breakthrough rather than a transmitter problem, although there are occasional cases of interference to the VHF broadcast band (Band 2) due to harmonics from HF transmitters. These are easily traced by consideration of the frequencies involved. Breakthrough can be caused by any of the mechanisms discussed above, and the remedy is to prevent the unwanted signal entering the susceptible equipment. When a receiver operating on the VHF band (Band 2) has external leads (eg antenna, coaxial cable, mains or ancillary leads), then a ferrite choke or ferrite braid-breaker is appropriate. In some instances a filter in the antenna coaxial cable may be required, for example:

- 144MHz breakthrough on FM radio broadcasts requires a low-pass (or band-pass) filter at the FM receiver.
- 14MHz breakthrough on FM radio broadcasts requires a high-pass filter at the FM receiver.
- 50MHz breakthrough on FM radio broadcasts requires a high-pass filter at the FM receiver.

In the case of portable receivers, most modern types have an internal ferrite rod antenna for medium wave and a telescopic rod antenna for VHF. In most cases there is not much that can be done to alleviate breakthrough except to move the set to a location where the interference is at its lowest level. If breakthrough occurs when the set is operated from the mains and not when it is working on batteries, a ferrite choke in the mains lead will probably cure the problem.

An interesting cause of interference to medium wave receivers is image interference (see Chapter 4) from 160m transmissions. This is caused by an amateur signal being on the image frequency, that is, an unwanted frequency which produces the correct intermediate frequency (IF), which is usually 455kHz. The *image frequency* is spaced from the wanted frequency by twice the IF. The following example relates to receiving a broadcast station on 1053kHz:

The LO would be on 1053 + 455 kHz = 1508kHz and an amateur signal on 1963kHz would beat with the LO to give 455kHz.

Normally the tuned ferrite rod antenna of the receiver would reject the unwanted signal at 1963kHz, but if the amateur signal is very strong, it may well be reproduced along with the wanted signal. The ability of a receiver to reject this unwanted signal is called *image rejection*. In the past, image interference was called *second-channel interference*, and this term will sometimes be found in old textbooks and technical articles.

Even when operating on the higher-frequency amateur bands, with some receivers there is still the possibility of interference to medium-wave reception (rarely to the long-wave). The receiver local oscillator often contains so many harmonics (in any case these will be produced in the mixer stage) that each time one falls 455kHz away from an amateur signal, a 455kHz IF is produced.

Telephone equipment

Many modern telephones are much more susceptible to strong RF fields than their traditional non-electronic counterparts. The problem stems from the use of semiconductor devices in both telephones and other related equipment such as answering machines. RF may be picked up on overhead telephone wires, indoor telephone wiring or in the telephone itself. The problem is compounded by the fact that most households now have several handsets connected to the master line jack by relatively long lengths of cable. Telephone equipment comes under the new EMC regulations and an improvement in immunity of devices on sale to the public is becoming evident.

Proprietary filters are available which plug into the telephone socket to reduce RF signals reaching the telephone from the line. Such filters must be approved for fitting to telephone installations and it is not generally permissible to fit home-constructed filters or to modify telephone equipment internally. The only other step which an amateur can take is to fit ferrite ring chokes to the leads of affected equipment.

Alarm systems and security lights

Passive infra-red (PIR) sensors used in security lighting and intruder alarms contain high-gain amplifiers which can be susceptible to RF triggering by any mode of transmission including CW. In many cases, there is little which can be done to improve the immunity using external filtering so it is necessary to change the sensor for a more immune type.

CHARACTERISTICS OF FILTERS

The purpose of a filter is to pass the wanted frequencies and reject the unwanted. All filters introduce some *insertion loss* at the frequency of the wanted signal and it is important that this loss is acceptably low (less than 1dB if possible). The frequency at which the loss of a filter starts to increase is called the *cut-off frequency*. In the case of a low-pass filter, frequencies below the cut-off frequency are in the *pass band* where the loss is low (ideally zero). Frequencies above the cut-off frequency are in the *stop band* where loss progressively increases.

It is important to realise that a low-pass filter does not completely block all frequencies above the cut-off frequency. For any filter, the sharpness of the transition between the pass band and the stop band (and how well it rejects an unwanted signal which is close to the wanted) depends on the complexity of the circuit. In a simple filter, the loss only increases gradually above the cut-off frequency. If a sharp cut-off is required it is necessary to add more sections to the filter. For example, if the simple HPF circuit of Fig 6.7(b) had a cut-off frequency (f_c) of 470MHz (for passing UHF TV signals), it would give little rejection of transmissions on 432MHz.

Another important filter parameter is its *characteristic impedance*. This is particularly important for filters used at the output of a transmitter. A filter inserted in a 50Ω feeder should, inside its pass band, appear simply as another piece of 50Ω feeder, ie it should match the feeder characteristic impedance. The match may not be perfect, but a good filter will exhibit a low SWR, ie 1.2:1 or less. A mismatched filter will have a

high SWR, increased insertion loss and often a degraded stop band.

Various types of filter such as high-pass, low-pass, band-stop and mains filters may be used for amateur radio EMC purposes. The type most suitable for a particular application may be determined from the spectrum chart shown in Fig 6.2.

'T' and 'pi' low-pass filters and their response

Fig 6.7(a) shows a simple 'T' and 'pi' type L-C low-pass filter and its response. An L-C low-pass filter has one or more inductors *in series* with the signal path and one or more capacitors *shunting* the signal to ground. At high frequencies, the inductors introduce a high impedance in series with the signal path and the capacitors introduce a low impedance from the signal path to ground.

'T' and 'pi' high-pass filters and their response

Fig 6.7(b) shows a simple 'T' and 'pi' type L-C high-pass filter and its response. An L-C high-pass filter has one or more capacitors *in series* with the signal path and one or more inductors *shunting* the signal to ground. At low frequencies, the capacitors introduce a high impedance in series with the signal path and the inductors introduce a low impedance from the signal path to ground.

Band-stop (notch) filters

Fig 6.8 shows two types of band-stop or *notch* filter and their response. Filter (a) uses a series L-C resonant circuit between the signal path and ground. At its resonant frequency, the series resonant circuit presents a low impedance which shunts most of the signal to ground. Filter (b) uses a parallel L-C resonant circuit in series with the signal path. At its resonant frequency, the parallel resonant circuit presents a high impedance which prevents most of the signal from passing through.

The filter shown in Fig 6.9 is a combination of a high-pass and notch filter which gives increased rejection of a particular band of interest – in this case 144MHz.

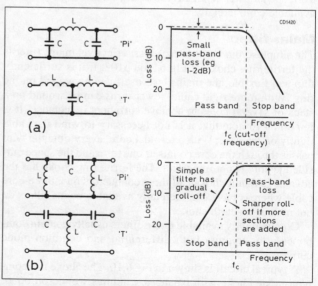

Fig 6.7. (a) 'T' and 'pi' low-pass filters and their response. Note the small pass-band loss, eg 1–2dB. (b) 'T' and 'pi' high-pass filters and their response. The dotted line shows the sharper roll-off if more sections are added to the filter

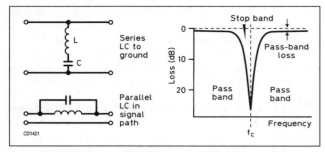

Fig 6.8. Band-stop (notch) filters and their response

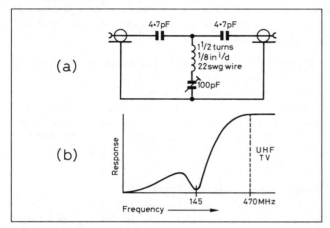

Fig 6.9. A high-pass filter with increased rejection of a particular band of interest – in this case 144MHz

Band-pass filters

An example of a band-pass filter for use in an amateur radio EMC situation is an 88–108MHz filter for use at the antenna input of an FM radio receiver. Such a filter would require a bandwidth of 20MHz and would reject amateur transmissions above and below the FM broadcast band. In practice, however, such a filter is not easy to construct although some are available commercially.

Mains filters

The simplest, but by no means least effective, mains filter is the ferrite ring choke of Fig 6.3 on p102. If it is sufficiently thin and flexible, the mains lead itself can be wound on the ring. With more rigid cable, fewer turns can be wound on a stack of several cores to achieve sufficient inductance. It is important to note that it is not necessary to wind the cable tightly on the core. With a toroidal core, every time the wire passes through the core counts as one turn, and the space outside the core is not important. The ferrite ring choke has the advantage that it chokes all three conductors on a three-core cable whereas most commercially available mains filters do not include an earth choke.

Commercially available mains filters usually contain components to suppress both differential and common-mode currents.

A typical circuit is shown in Fig 6.10. The choke is a common-mode choke with balanced windings wound on opposite sides of the core, because they have the mains voltage between them. The choke works in conjunction with the capacitors Cy in Fig 6.10 to suppress common-mode currents.

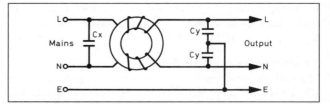

Fig 6.10. The circuit of a typical mains filter

Capacitor Cx reduces high-frequency differential currents. Some commercial units also include additional semiconductor components to suppress spikes between live and neutral. The capacitors Cy are safety critical and special 'Class Y' capacitors are required. It is therefore recommended that only commercially produced mains filters should be used.

Braid-breakers

This is the colloquial term for any component which reduces the flow of unwanted current on the screen of a coaxial cable. A simple braid-breaker can be made by winding thin coaxial cable onto a ferrite ring. The wanted signals flow along the inner conductor of the coaxial cable and return inside the braid so they are not affected by the presence of the ferrite. The unwanted currents flow on the outside of the braid and return via earth so they 'see' a substantial impedance due to the choke. This is not a true braid-breaker, however, as it does not break the braid at DC.

Fig 6.11 shows another method of braid-breaking using a 1:1 ratio RF transformer which allows the wanted *differential mode* or *anti-phase* signals to pass through with low loss. This is not designed as a filter, however, and some types pass all frequencies above about 10MHz. The important point is that the common-mode or in-phase signals are blocked. This is a true braid-breaker as it actually breaks the braid at DC. It therefore requires a high-value resistor to discharge any build-up of static electricity on the TV antenna.

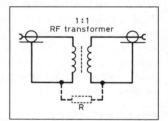

Fig 6.11. Braid-breaking using a 1:1 RF transformer which can only pass the wanted differential currents. R is a static discharge path – 10kΩ or more

One method of construction is to use two tightly coupled windings (usually twisted together) on a small ferrite bead or a two-hole ferrite core. Another is the *Faraday loop* method, using two loops of coaxial cable taped together. However, great care must be taken to prevent excessive signal loss at higher frequencies. Home-constructed units will probably be unsuitable for UHF TV.

High-pass filters combined with a braid-breaker are available commercially, and these make a neat and convenient way of improving the immunity of the TV installation.

A combined high-pass filter and braid-breaker

Fig 6.12 shows a simple high-pass filter which also doubles as a capacitive braid-breaker. This can be effective against breakthrough from the HF bands and 50MHz but has limited effect on the 144MHz band. As this is a balanced high-pass filter used in an unbalanced coaxial feeder, it is not a particularly

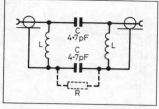

Fig 6.12. Combined UHF TV high-pass filter and braid-breaker. This filter also attenuates interfering signals picked up on the antenna below 470MHz. L is 4 turns 22 SWG 5mm ID. R is a static discharge path – 10kΩ or more

satisfactory solution. As television signals have become more complex with the introduction of teletext, NICAM stereo sound and digital broadcasting, the home construction of filters for TV has become more exacting. If there is a serious mismatch to the wanted signal, this can cause reflections which may adversely affect teletext or NICAM sound. The simple ferrite choke braid-breaker shown in Fig 6.3 has negligible effect on the wanted signal but if anything more sophisticated is required, it may be necessary to purchase one of the commercially available filter/braid-breaker combinations. See the *RSGB EMC Guide* and the *RSGB Yearbook* EMC section.

Bypassing of RF signals in audio amplifier stages

In some cases of breakthrough into audio equipment, particularly at VHF, external filtering cannot be applied or is not effective. In such cases, it may be necessary to apply internal filtering. Although radio amateurs are strongly advised not to perform internal modifications to neighbours' equipment, the following information may be useful to allow a service engineer to perform such modifications. The base-collector junction of an NPN or PNP transistor in an audio amplifier is reverse biased, so it does not rectify RF. The base-emitter junction is forward biased, however, and, if sufficient RF reaches this junction, operates as an unwanted AM detector diode. This causes any amplitude modulation on the RF signal to be fed into the audio amplifier where it is amplified.

This type of breakthrough can be tackled by preventing the RF from reaching the base-emitter junction. This can be done in several ways, as shown in Fig 6.13. A capacitor of about 1nF between base and emitter acts as an RF bypass capacitor, preventing the RF from reaching the junction as shown in Fig 6.13(a). This capacitor should not affect the wanted audio signal significantly. A disc ceramic type of capacitor is most suitable as it has good performance up to VHF provided the leads are as short as possible. Another approach is to fit a ferrite bead in series with the base, as shown in Fig 6.13(b) and (c). This forms an RF choke and is likely to be more effective if combined with a capacitor as shown in Fig 6.13(d).

AMATEUR STATION DESIGN FOR IMPROVED EMC

Because the amateur station is likely to be in close proximity to domestic electronic equipment, it is in the radio amateur's interest to minimise the possibility of EMC problems. The amateur must obviously ensure that the levels of unwanted emissions from his or her station are acceptably low. Nevertheless, it is the purpose of a transmitting station to generate and radiate RF fields so it is inevitable that these fields will be fairly strong in the immediate vicinity of the station. The amateur can help to reduce the impact of the problem by careful design of the station. In particular, the antenna should be sited to minimise the strength of RF fields in neighbouring

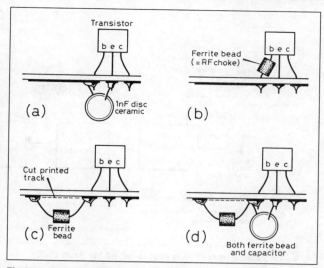

Fig 6.13. Examples of internal filtering sometimes needed to cure stubborn cases of breakthrough – especially from VHF and UHF transmissions. High-gain, low-level audio stages are particularly vulnerable

property, while maximising the useful radiation which clears the immediate vicinity and goes on to reach the distant receiving stations. While this is not always easy, it has a number of benefits. It minimises the chance of interference to domestic equipment, and of the station picking up noise from domestic equipment. It also improves the performance of the station – high field strengths in adjacent premises not only give rise to EMC problems but also waste power that should really be going out to distant parts of the globe! Particular attention should be paid to the type and location of the antenna, its feeder and how the station is earthed.

Fig 6.14 shows an amateur station designed for good EMC. Many of the points illustrated are considered in more detail below.

RF grounding

From the EMC point of view, the purpose of an earth is to provide a low-impedance path for RF currents which would otherwise find their way into house wiring, and hence into susceptible electronic equipment in the vicinity. Usually, the RF earth is effectively in parallel with the mains earth path. Good EMC practice dictates that any earth currents should be reduced to a minimum by making sure that antennas are balanced as well as possible.

The minimum requirement for an RF earth for HF operation is several copper pipes 1.5m long or more, driven into the ground at least 1m apart and connected together by thick cable. The connection to the station should be as short as possible using thick cable or alternatively flat copper strip or braid. This is easy when the shack is on ground level, which is the preferred location at HF.

Where the shack is installed in an upstairs room, the provision of a satisfactory RF earth is a difficult problem, and sometimes it may found that connecting an RF earth makes interference problems worse. In such cases it is probably best to avoid the need for an RF earth by using a well-balanced antenna system but don't forget to provide lightning protection.

Key points about RF grounding of an amateur HF station are as follows:

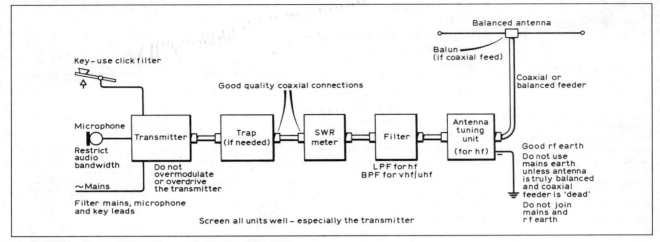

Fig 6.14. Example of station layout required for good EMC

- The outer conductor of the coaxial cable feeding a transmitting antenna should be RF grounded at the point where it enters/leaves the building.

- An independent RF earth with a short lead should be used.

- Mains earth, water pipes or central heating pipes should not be used as an RF earth.

- An inductively coupled ATU (see below) has the advantage of isolating RF earth from mains earth.

Safety reminder

Precautions with mains supplies using protective multiple earthing (PME)

Throughout this chapter and Chapter 2, various recommendations are made concerning earthing of equipment. These techniques have been used for many years in houses wired in the conventional way where the neutral and earth are separate. In recent years increasing use has been made of a system known as *protective multiple earthing* (PME). In a PME system the neutral and earth are connected together when they enter the customer's premises. For safety reasons special regulations apply to the connection of additional earths to such systems, and also to conductors such as antennas which go outside the house. Failure to comply with these regulations could lead to a serious accident. Anyone who is in doubt about PME or any aspect of electrical safety should contact their supplier for advice. At the time of writing this is the Regional Electricity Company (REC) whose telephone number can be obtained from your electricity bill. The RSGB has published a leaflet on PME which is available on receipt of a stamped self-addressed envelope from RSGB headquarters. You do not have to be an RSGB member to obtain one.

See also 'Safety' in Chapter 2.

Mains filtering

A mains filter should be used in the supply to an amateur station to prevent RF energy being fed back via the mains supply. The disadvantage of a conventional mains filter shown in Fig 6.10 on p106 is that it does not filter the earth wire. This can be overcome by winding the mains lead supplying the transceiver and its ancillaries onto a stack of ferrite cores as described previously for breakthrough reduction.

Filtering and screening

At HF, where operation usually takes place on several bands in the range 1.81 to 29.7MHz, a low-pass filter (LPF) with a cut-off frequency of around 30–35MHz is often inserted in the feed to the transmitting antenna to reduce harmonics of a multiband HF transmitter. While this will not reject unwanted signals below 30MHz, it does protect the VHF radio band and other services which might be affected even by low levels of unwanted signals. A few milliwatts at VHF can cause a surprising amount of interference over a wide area.

At VHF and UHF, although a few transmitters do cover more than one band, each band usually has its own antenna and feeder. While low-pass filters could be used, it is just as convenient to use a band-pass filter for each band. This will remove unwanted transmitter outputs either side of the amateur band. It will also help on reception where very strong radio transmissions from other services sometimes cause overload problems to sensitive amateur receivers. This has become a common problem in recent years where relatively high power transmitters such as paging systems are operating on VHF at frequencies quite close to the amateur bands.

The *trap* shown in Fig 6.14 is not always necessary but, if used, it can be a simple stop or notch filter, often consisting of a single resonant circuit. It is therefore simple to make and to tune to the correct frequency. It can provide an additional 20 to 30dB of attenuation over a relatively narrow bandwidth – often very useful when a particular transmitter harmonic might cause a problem, such as the second harmonic of 50MHz. At VHF and UHF, a tuned coaxial *stub* (usually a quarter-wavelength long) is often used. Unless it is compensated, a trap may cause some mismatch. This is usually small, but to prevent a permanently high SWR reading, it is best to locate it before the SWR meter.

The effectiveness of additional filtering can be seriously impaired if unwanted signals such as harmonics are allowed to leak out of a transmitter or RF power amplifier. While the signal which is fed to the antenna may be 'clean', the signals which leak out may cause persistent, and apparently incurable, interference problems. Serious attention should be paid to the effectiveness of the screening inside the transmitter and of the case, and of the decoupling and filtering of the power, key, microphone and any other leads connected to the transmitter.

These must not be allowed to carry RF energy from inside the case and then allow it to be radiated.

OUTPUT POWER AND FIELD STRENGTH
SWR/power meter

The SWR meter is described in Chapter 8. With some designs, the sensitivity varies with frequency. With others, it is essentially constant over a wide frequency range, and this type is usually calibrated to measure RF power. Some meters will read peak envelope power (PEP) and are convenient for SSB measurements. The SWR meter enables the impedance match of the antenna and feeder system to be checked, or for the ATU (if used) to be adjusted for minimum SWR at its input, thereby presenting the correct load impedance at the transmitting frequency. The positions of the SWR meter and filter in Fig 6.14 could be interchanged but, as the meter uses diodes to rectify a sample of the RF signal passing through it, these may generate some low-level harmonics. It is therefore good practice to place the filter after the SWR/power meter in order to remove any harmonics.

▶**Field strength**

It is possible to calculate the electric field strength generated near a transmitting antenna. The electric or E-field strength at a certain distance is given by the equation below which assumes far-field 'free space' conditions.

$$E = \frac{\sqrt{49.15 P_d}}{d}$$

where E is the electric field strength in volts/metre, d is the distance from the antenna in metres, and P_d is effective radiated power (ERP), ie the input power to the antenna multiplied by the gain of the antenna relative to a dipole.

For example, if a particular TV receiver is immune to a field strength of 1.78V/m, the above formula shows that an ERP of only 6.43W is required at a distance of 10m to produce this field strength.◀

The use of the minimum transmitted power necessary

The maximum available power should not be used at all times. For a particular contact, the power used should be no more than necessary. This reduces the chance of EMC problems and also allows other amateurs to use the same frequency some distance away.

ANTENNA TUNING UNIT (ATU)

Antenna tuning unit is the traditional name for the device which matches the antenna to the transmitter (see Chapter 7). It is also sometimes known as an *antenna matching unit* (AMU), a *transmatch* or *antenna system tuning unit* (ASTU). In fact the ATU may both tune and match the antenna depending on circumstances so the traditional name is as good as any other, and will be used in this chapter. Opinions differ as to whether an ATU is necessary in situations where the antenna and feeder system presents the correct 50 or 75Ω impedance required by the transmitter, SWR meter and filter. However, the 30MHz low-pass filter in an HF station will not remove those transmitter harmonics which fall inside its pass band, eg when operating on 14MHz and below. It is unlikely that the harmonic suppression of the transmitter alone will exceed 50dB. Depending on the type of circuit used, an ATU can provide some useful band-pass filtering which gives

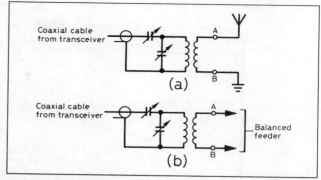

Fig 6.15. Inductively coupled ATU (Z match) isolates RF from mains earth.

additional attenuation of harmonics and other unwanted outputs.

Certain types of ATU also have the advantage that they allow the earth system of the antenna and feeder to be isolated from the rest of the station equipment if required. Fig 6.15 shows the principle of an inductively coupled ATU circuit such as a *Z match*. In Fig 6.15(a), the RF currents flowing via the RF earth cannot reach the mains earth because the two earth systems are completely separate.

In Fig 6.15(b), an inductively coupled ATU is used to drive a balanced feeder. The ATU therefore performs the function of a balun (see below).

LOCATION OF AMATEUR ANTENNAS AND MASTS

Amateur antennas and masts should be located as far as possible from buildings, wiring, TV antennas and overhead telephone or electricity cables. Increasing the separation reduces the coupling very rapidly. Amateur transmitting antennas should not be located in a loft or indoors as this causes close coupling to mains wiring etc. If there is no choice but to have antennas very close to the house or even in the loft, then it will almost certainly be necessary to restrict the transmitted power and/or to use more 'EMC friendly' modes of transmission.

TYPES OF AMATEUR ANTENNAS

Where breakthrough is likely to be a problem, HF transmitting antennas should be:

- *Horizontally polarised*. House wiring and radio and TV down leads tend to act as crude earthed vertical antennas and hence tend to be more susceptible to vertically polarised radiation.
- *Balanced*. A dipole fed via a balun is an example of a balanced antenna. If an antenna is not balanced, this causes out-of-balance currents on feeders, giving rise to radiation which has a large vertically polarised component. This can be a particular problem with end-fed antennas which are generally unsatisfactory from the EMC point of view and are best kept for portable and low-power operation.
- *Compact*. Physically small antennas tend to have less extensive near fields, and so make for reduced coupling to other conductors. In most gardens, a dipole for a low-frequency band such as 3.5MHz is almost bound to have one end near the house and a compromise is inevitable. There

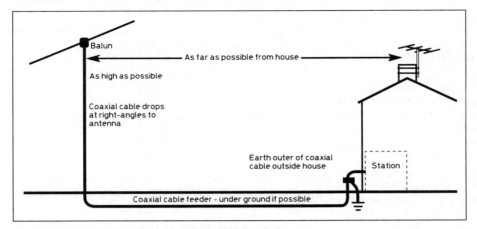

Fig 6.16. Antenna and feeder system with EMC in mind

are possibilities for compact antennas for lower frequencies, such as magnetic loops and loaded verticals. It is not possible to be dogmatic – every situation is different. At low frequencies it may be better to use a vertical antenna because by doing so it is possible to get the whole antenna much further from the house.

An antenna system planned to minimise unwanted local fields will also pick up less radio frequency interference (RFI) when used for reception. Most problems of RFI are caused by fields radiated from nearby conductors such as mains wiring. All the techniques which minimise coupling to such sources will be beneficial.

An example of an HF antenna and feeder system with EMC in mind is shown in Fig 6.16.

The dipole is fed by coaxial cable with a balun at the feed point. The coaxial cable drops at right-angles to the antenna so that there is equal capacitance from each side of the dipole to the braid of the cable. The feeder should not be routed so that it is nearer to one half of the dipole than the other, as this makes the dipole unbalanced. Similarly, if one half of the dipole is close to a building, wiring or pipes this also makes the dipole unbalanced. In either case, an unbalanced dipole causes unwanted RF currents to flow on the outside of the braid of the feeder.

Yagi

The directional characteristics of a Yagi can be used to advantage by pointing the beam away from neighbouring properties and minimising the field strength generated in those properties. With a high-gain VHF Yagi antenna system, however, it is possible to generate very high field strengths in the direction of the beam.

▶For instance, the equation in the 'Field strength' section above shows that 100W fed to a dipole antenna would give a field strength of about 4.67V/m at a distance of 15m. The same transmitter, if fed into a high-gain VHF beam with a gain of 20dB relative to a dipole, would give a field strength, in the direction of the beam, of 46.7V/m at the same distance. Again, it comes down to the fact that if you want to run high power to a high-gain beam, the antenna must be kept as far from neighbouring houses as possible and of course, as high as practical.◀

Long wire

Antennas which use the earth as part of the radiating system, ie antennas tuned against ground, should be avoided if

possible since these inevitably involve large RF currents flowing in the earth system. If this type of antenna must be used, arrange for it to be fed through coaxial cable so that the earth, or better still some form of counterpoise, can be arranged at some distance from the house.

Fig 6.17 shows an unsatisfactory way of feeding a long-wire antenna. The section nearest the ATU carries the highest current and therefore radiates most strongly. The whole antenna current has to flow into the RF earth and as the RF earth wire is relatively long, it also causes strong radiation into the house.

Fig 6.18 shows an improved arrangement where a long wire is fed from the far end. Multiband operation can be achieved using a remote ATU or a trap. The earth lead is short and the section of antenna nearest the ATU which radiates most strongly is furthest from the house. Nevertheless, the end of the wire which is furthest from the ATU carries a high RF voltage so it should not be too close to the house. The braid of the coaxial cable from the transmitter to the ATU should be earthed.

USE OF SCREENED FEEDER CABLES, BALANCED LINES AND BALUNS

From an EMC point of view, coaxial feeder is preferable to unscreened balanced feeder or an open-wire feeder. If

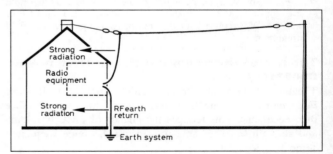

Fig 6.17. Typical end-fed antenna (often used by short-wave listeners). This results in strong radiation into the house and can cause problems when transmitting.

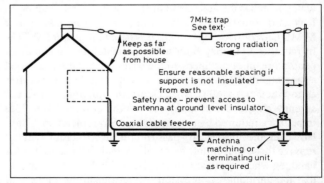

Fig 6.18. An end-fed antenna with improved EMC characteristics. Although less convenient than Fig 6.17, this method causes far fewer interference problems

balanced feeder is used, it should be fed from a source with a balanced output such as some types of ATU. The balance of the feeder will be impaired if one side of the feeder is closer to any conductive object than the other. This problem can be overcome by using a screened balanced feeder made from two parallel lengths of coaxial cable, as shown in Fig 6.19. The characteristic impedance of the screened balanced feeder is twice the characteristic impedance of the coaxial cable used. Hence two lengths of 50Ω cable form a 100Ω balanced feeder. The screens of the two cables should be joined at both ends and should be connected to RF earth at the source end.

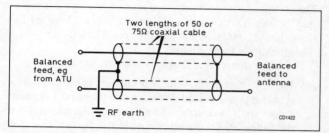

Fig 6.19. A screened balanced feeder made from two lengths of coaxial cable

A *balun* (balanced to unbalanced) transformer should be used where a coaxial feeder feeds a dipole. Baluns are available with various impedance ratios such as 1:1 or 1:4. Fig 7.8 shows the arrangement of windings in a 1:1 balun transformer.

METHOD OF APPROACH TO EMC PROBLEMS
Test transmissions

On obtaining an amateur licence, radio amateurs would be extremely unwise to start making transmissions at the maximum permitted power level without having due regard to the amount of interference which might be occurring. They should not adopt the attitude that they are licensed to run full legal power and can do so regardless of the consequences. Their first concern should be to find out the extent of any problems, and the best place to start is their own home.

The Amateur Licence (BR68) states that interference tests should be carried out "from time to time". It is a good idea to do tests, particularly when changes are made to the station equipment or antenna system, or when different bands are operated. This obviously includes putting the station on the air for the first time. In order to minimise possible annoyance, initial tests should be at low power and of short duration, preferably at times when neighbours are unlikely to be affected. If relationships are favourable, you may feel it is appropriate to inform them of these tests so that they can report any signs of interference without delay. On the other hand, care should be taken not to cause unnecessary alarm about a problem which may be less severe than anticipated. The licence conditions state that the periods of test transmissions should be logged; 'EMC test' is a suitable entry. It is useful to record in some detail the test conditions, such as the transmitter and other equipment used, power output, antenna system, interference observed, effectiveness of filtering etc. If the station is inspected by the RA, this will show that you have tried to avoid "undue interference" as required by the licence.

Be prepared

You should solve any breakthrough problems with your own TV, radio, hi-fi etc. This may seem unnecessary if you live alone, but it is a useful exercise for two reasons. First, it provides a very convincing demonstration to a neighbour in the event of a complaint. Secondly, it provides useful experience of how to solve a problem. A few EMC filters and ferrite rings should also be available so that any problems with breakthrough on neighbours' equipment can be tackled promptly.

Leaflets on a variety of EMC-related topics can be obtained from the RSGB on receipt of an A4 SAE. The RA also produces a series of leaflets on EMC and the radio amateur, as well as a useful booklet entitled *Guidelines for Improving Television and Radio Reception* (RA323).

Dealing with a complaint

If a neighbour has started to experience interference, then their reaction may be reasonably friendly provided that the transmissions have only been for short periods. However, they are unlikely to know anything about interference problems and will expect the amateur to 'put a stop to it'. It is at this point especially that you are advised to conduct yourself with the greatest diplomacy and tact. Good neighbourly relationships can suddenly turn sour and develop into protracted confrontation. This must be avoided at all costs.

The assistance of the RA can be requested by either party, as described below, but only the neighbour can request a visit to their own property. In the case of supposed interference by an amateur station a radio amateur should not ignore the complaint and should not refer the complainant to the RA immediately. It is in everyone's interest to co-operate to solve the problem and avoid the delay and expense of going through the official channels. This will probable involve you visiting the neighbour who has the problem. Visits should not be protracted, but carried out in an efficient, business-like manner. You should not say that the affected equipment is at fault or of poor quality. The assistance of another radio amateur is helpful. If possible, a selection of filters and other devices should be taken.

Test transmissions, conditions and results (successful or otherwise) should be made and recorded in the log.

It must be stressed that you should fit filters only if the complainant is perfectly happy for you to do so. Even if you are technically qualified, you are advised not to make modifications to equipment belonging to someone else. If things go wrong, you could be thought responsible for subsequent faults which occur in the equipment, or worse, held responsible in case of an accident.

Having demonstrated that a filter provides a satisfactory cure, you are not obliged to provide one free to the complainant. However, as the cost is probably quite low, it is a good idea to lend the filter to the neighbour for as long as it is needed. If the problem cannot be solved immediately, for example because a particular filter needs to be obtained, it would be reasonable for you to agree to stop transmitting on the band or bands which cause the problem but only for a temporary period such as one to four weeks.

RA involvement

In the UK the Authority governing the use of all types of radio is the Radiocommunication Agency (RA). So far as radio amateurs are concerned the function of the Agency is described in the *Terms, Provisions and Limitations* booklet BR68 that accompanies the amateur licence. BR68 is updated from time to time.

BR68 sets out the obligations in the amateur licence in regard to the avoidance of interference. It refers to both spurious emissions and to "excessive field strength". The former refers to interference caused by transmitter defects and the latter refers to interference caused by using excessive power in inappropriate conditions. A neighbour can report a suspected source of interference by filling in Part A of form RA179, which is obtainable on request from the RA. Likewise a radio amateur can ask the RA to inspect his or her station. In either case the officers of the RA will inspect the station at their discretion, and no charge is payable. If the problem is due to spurious emissions the RA may instruct the amateur to cease operation until the situation is rectified. If the problem is deemed to be excessive field strength then they may recommend that the amateur takes steps to reduce the field strength in the affected area. If the amateur does not comply then the recommendations could be made obligatory by the issuing of a change to the licence conditions for that station, known officially as a *Notice of Variation* or NoV. Fortunately this action is rarely resorted to.

In many cases the RA have inspected an amateur station on receipt of a complaint from someone in the neighbourhood, and have found the station to be satisfactory. In such cases they would advise the complainant accordingly. If someone wishes the RA to visit their property to investigate a case of interference, and recommend solutions, then Part B of form RA179 must be filled in by the person concerned. In this case, a fee must be paid which includes the cost of any filters fitted by the RA. Certain conditions must be fulfilled before the RA will undertake to investigate a problem, and these are set out in form RA179.

Summary

In order to deal with any EMC problems promptly and effectively, you should:

- make test transmissions and solve any problems in your own home.
- keep a small stock of filters and ferrite rings.

On receiving a complaint of breakthrough from a neighbour, you should:

- do tests to establish the cause (it is useful to enlist the help of another radio amateur).
- co-operate with the neighbour and help to find a solution.

On receiving a complaint of breakthrough from a neighbour, you should NOT:

- ignore the complaint.
- refer the complainant to the RA immediately.
- say that the neighbour's TV etc is at fault.
- modify the affected equipment.
- agree to stop transmitting permanently.

EMC CONSIDERATIONS FOR MOBILE INSTALLATIONS

Amateurs who have experienced EMC problems at their home station may decide to operate mobile to escape such difficulties.

However, with modern cars having an increasingly high number of on-board electronic systems, mobile operation itself can be somewhat hazardous if certain basic precautions are not followed. Advice given by the car manufacturer should always be followed, as failure to do so could invalidate the warranty in the event of RF interfering with any vehicle electronic equipment. Attention must be paid to the location of the transceiver in the car, the connection to the power supply, the routing of any cables and the position and grounding of antennas.

Location of transceiver

The instruction manual provided with an amateur transceiver may contain a section on mobile installation. These instructions should be followed unless they conflict with the vehicle manufacturer's instructions.

A mobile transceiver should be located so that:

(a) The risk of injury to vehicle occupants in the event of an accident is minimised. If the fascia, glove pocket and/or parcel shelf is designed to collapse under impact, then the fitting of a transceiver should not prevent this from happening.
(b) All necessary controls are within easy reach of the driver (if the driver is the prime user) but not in such a way as to distract attention from the road.
(c) Hot or cold air does not blow directly onto the unit which should not be subjected to large temperature variations.
(d) It does not obstruct the inflation of an air bag (if fitted).

Connection to the 12V supply

The 12V supply to the transceiver should be via positive and negative cables which are connected directly to the battery terminals via the tags or clamps which connect to the battery pillars. It should not be plugged into a cigar lighter socket.

Both the positive and negative cables should be fitted with a fuse as close as possible to the battery. The fuse rating should be as recommended by the transceiver manufacturer. The reason for fitting a fuse to the negative cable is that under certain fault conditions, the return current for the starter motor could flow via the transceiver negative cable and the braid of the antenna feeder.

If a moulded twin-core supply cable is not used, both the positive and negative supply cables should be twisted together along their length in order to reduce noise and interference induced by other wiring.

If it is necessary to control the 12V supply to the transceiver via the ignition switch, a relay should be fitted as shown in Fig 6.20. Suitable relays are sold as 'accessory relays' by car accessory shops and may incorporate a fuse.

Routing of DC supply cables

The transceiver DC supply cables should be routed so that:

(a) they avoid sharp edges or abrasion. Wherever a cable passes through a bulkhead, a grommet must be used.
(b) they are clear of vehicle wiring looms or electrical/electronic units particularly the engine control unit (ECU) and ignition coil. This is to minimise possible interference to or from vehicle electrical or electronic systems.
(c) if they need to cross from one side of the car to the other, they are routed along the side and front of the engine compartment.

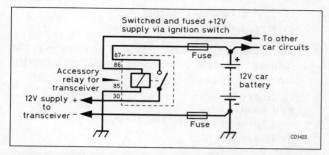

Fig 6.20. Installation of a relay near the car battery so that the ignition switch controls the supply to the transceiver

(d) they are kept clear of fuel pipes, brake pipes, hot components or moving parts.

(e) they approach the battery so that if removed, they cannot accidentally be reconnected the wrong way round. This can be done by making one wire shorter than the other.

Antenna location and grounding

If possible, a permanently mounted antenna should be used. The preferred location is in the centre of the roof, as this provides the most effective ground plane. Ideally, a hole should be drilled, as this provides the best grounding provided paint is removed inside the panel. If there is a sun roof, the antenna should be located approximately midway between the sunroof opening and the rear window. If an alternative method of mounting is used, for example a gutter mount or roof rack mount, it is important to ensure that the braid of the coaxial cable is well grounded to the vehicle body shell at the antenna mounting point. If this is not possible, the braid of the cable should be grounded as close as possible to the point of entry to the vehicle using a short, wide length of copper braid. Some cars have threaded inserts in the body shell above the doors; these are intended for fixing a roof rack but can also be used for mounting or grounding an antenna.

An alternative location for an antenna on a saloon car is in the centre of the rear boot lid. In this case, it is advisable to fit short copper grounding braids at least 12mm wide to ground the boot lid to the car body shell. The purpose of these is to ensure adequate RF grounding which the hinges alone may not provide.

Mounting a VHF antenna on the front or rear wing of a car is likely to give a distorted radiation pattern. If a wing-mounted antenna is used, it should be located well away from electronic modules in the engine compartment to avoid subjecting such modules to excessively high field strengths which could cause malfunction.

On a vehicle with panels made of fibreglass or other non-conductive material, the antenna ground connection should be attached to a ground plane consisting of thin sheet metal fitted inside the panel. For maximum effectiveness at VHF, the antenna should be at least a quarter-wavelength from any edge of the metal sheet.

If a magnetic mount antenna is the only option, it should be located as for a permanently mounted antenna. A magnetic mount antenna can be useful for test purposes to check for possible unwanted effects on vehicle electronics before fitting a permanent antenna.

'Glass mount' antennas are available for amateur UHF and possibly VHF mobile operation. Such antennas work by capacitive coupling through the glass and have no direct electrical connection to the radiating element. These are not recommended from an EMC point of view but, if used, a glass-mounted antenna should be located well clear of any heating elements in the glass to avoid coupling of RF signals into the vehicle's electrical system.

For a long HF mobile antenna, the rear bumper may be the only feasible location. If the bumper is non-conductive, the antenna ground connection should be attached to the vehicle body shell via the shortest possible length of copper braid. If any tuning network is used with an antenna, this should be shielded and close to the antenna but clear of vehicle electronics and wiring.

Routing of antenna cables

Good-quality coaxial cable should be used with at least 95% shield coverage. Nevertheless, some RF may still be present on the outside of the cable due to imperfect shielding, antenna mismatch or poor antenna grounding. To minimise the possibility of unwanted interaction with vehicle electronic systems, the antenna cable should be routed well away from any vehicle wiring or electronic modules, particularly the engine management system.

Testing

After installing the transceiver and fitting and adjusting the antenna, it is advisable to perform some tests to check for possible effects of RF on vehicle electronic systems. With the vehicle stationary and the engine running the following should be checked while the transmitter is being operated at its maximum power:

(a) there is no apparent engine misfiring;
(b) no warning lights flicker or come on;
(c) the direction indicators flash at the normal rate;
(d) the windscreen wipers operate normally; and
(e) there are no unwanted effects on other electronic systems, such as central locking or air bags.

If any unwanted effects occur, it will be necessary to relocate the antenna, reduce transmitter power or both.

It should be noted that not all possible adverse effects can be detected when the vehicle is stationary, for example, anti-lock braking, cruise control, automatic transmission, electric power assisted steering. It is therefore advisable to test drive the vehicle in a suitable location off the public highway. If any effect such as engine misfiring is noted when the transmitter is operated, transmission should cease immediately.

Further reading

If you would like to have more information on this subject, the MPT1362 (1997 edition), *Code of Practice for installation of mobile radio equipment in land based vehicles,* is available from the Radiocommunications Agency.

PRACTICE QUESTIONS FOR CHAPTER 6

1. A neighbour's hi-fi system is suffering RF breakthrough. One possible cure would be
    (a) a ferrite bead on the transmitter lead
    (b) a capacitor across the transmitter lead
    (c) screened loudspeaker leads
    (d) open wire feeder for the transmitter lead.

2. Which one of the following is most likely to produce continuous broad-band interference?

   (a) An electric light switch.
   (b) An incandescent bulb.
   (c) A microwave transmitter.
   (d) Poor commutation in an electric drill.

3. The sensitivity of a receiver can be affected by

   (a) strong RF signals on a nearby frequency
   (b) removing all crystals
   (c) good AF filtering
   (d) incorrect adjustment of the volume control.

4. Rectification of an RF signal in an audio amplifier is likely to occur

   (a) in a tantalum capacitor
   (b) at a base-emitter junction
   (c) at the junction of two resistors
   (d) in a copper wire.

5. All equipment carrying RF currents should be

   (a) not earthed at all
   (b) connected to the mains
   (c) screened as well as possible
   (d) left 'floating'.

6. When living in a densely populated area and transmitting during evening TV hours it is advisable to

   (a) always use maximum transmitter output
   (b) use only sufficient power to maintain communications
   (c) use bands that are known to cause TVI
   (d) lower the antenna below roof height.

7. A braid-breaking choke in a TV antenna downlead will block

   (a) all AC signals
   (b) out-of-phase interfering signals
   (c) in-phase interfering signals
   (d) mains hum.

8. Capacitors used in RF filters should be

   (a) aluminium electrolytics
   (b) tantalum electrolytics
   (c) ceramic
   (d) polycarbonate.

9. A typical wide-band TV preamplifier may be susceptible to

   (a) mains hum
   (b) DC supply variations
   (c) overloading from a distant transmitter
   (d) overloading from a nearby transmitter.

10. The third harmonic from a 29MHz transmission lies in

    (a) a UHF band
    (b) the FM broadcast band
    (c) a PMR band
    (d) another amateur band.

11. Unwanted RF pick-up in the IF stage of a TV set usually results in

    (a) problems with the TV picture
    (b) poor power supply regulation
    (c) random channel changing
    (d) no audio output.

12. Which one of the following should be fitted to a TV antenna downlead to reduce strong signals from a 21MHz transmitter?

    (a) High-pass filter.
    (b) Low-pass filter.
    (c) UHF amplifier.
    (d) Band reject filter.

13. If an antenna runs close and parallel to an overhead 240V AC power line, there may be the possibility of

    (a) obtaining cheap power
    (b) harmonics being generated
    (c) producing mains borne interference
    (d) 50Hz modulation on all signals.

14. Instead of a braid-breaking choke to stop TVI it might be possible to use

    (a) resistors
    (b) a mains auto transformer
    (c) an RF isolation transformer
    (d) no screening.

15. The use of an indoor transmitting antenna

    (a) should always be encouraged
    (b) will never cause coupling with the mains
    (c) may cause coupling into the mains
    (d) gives more long-distance contacts.

16. The type of transmission most prone to causing interference to an audio amplifier system is

    (a) frequency modulation (FM)
    (b) frequency shift keying (FSK)
    (c) amplitude modulation (SSB)
    (d) Morse code (CW).

17 A 435MHz high-gain antenna points straight into a UHF TV receiving antenna. This could cause

    (a) problems with the 435MHz receiver
    (b) overloading of the TV front end
    (c) self-oscillation of the 435MHz transmitter
    (d) melting of the TV antenna coaxial cable.

18. The medium waveband is prone to image interference from

    (a) UHF transmitters
    (b) VHF transmitters
    (c) 28MHz transmitters
    (d) 1.8MHz transmitters.

19. A corroded connector on a neighbour's TV receiving antenna may cause

    (a) unwanted mixing products due to it exhibiting diode properties
    (b) rectification of the mains supply
    (c) general reception of foreign stations
    (d) increased amplification of the signal.

20. A transmitter is connected by a short coaxial cable to a collinear antenna with 6dB gain. When the output power to the antenna is reduced to 5W no more interference is

caused to a neighbour's hi-fi system. This corresponds to an effective radiated power of

(a) 1W
(b) 10W
(c) 20W
(d) 30W.

21. One way of eliminating RF interference in an audio power amplifier is to fit a disc ceramic capacitor

(a) across the base-emitter junction of the audio power transistor
(b) across the base-collector junction of the audio power transistor
(c) between ground and emitter
(d) between the collector and emitter leads of the audio power transistor.

22. If a neighbour complains of breakthrough, the immediate response should be to

(a) imply the neighbour's equipment is at fault
(b) tell them it is not your responsibility
(c) politely arrange to do tests
(d) inform RSGB and DTI immediately.

23. Which one of the following combinations of components is used to make an RF filter?

(a) Diodes and resistors.
(b) Zener diodes and inductors.
(c) LEDs and capacitors.
(d) Inductors and capacitors.

24. The insertion loss in the pass band of a passive high-pass filter for a TV download should be in the range

(a) −6 to 0dB
(b) 0 to 6dB
(c) 12 to 18dB
(d) 24 to 30dB.

25. The impedance of a filter to be used in a UHF TV download is normally

(a) 0Ω
(b) 25Ω
(c) 50Ω
(d) 75Ω.

26. Interference is caused to a TV when an amateur is operating on HF. The signal will most likely be entering the TV

(a) via the earth lead
(b) through the transmitter power supply
(c) via the antenna coaxial cable screen and/or IF stages
(d) by frequency multiplication in free space.

27. An amateur lives in a terraced house. To minimise the possibility of interference, the best position for an HF wire antenna is

(a) attached to a joint chimney stack next to the TV antenna
(b) along the row of houses at gutter height
(c) at right-angles to the row of houses and going away from them
(d) within the roof space.

28. The second harmonic of a 435MHz transmission lies

(a) in a police band
(b) between 1GHz and 10GHz
(c) in a UHF TV band
(d) below 144MHz.

29. When operating on VHF a neighbour who is using a TV set-top antenna complains of interference. One way of eliminating the problem would be to suggest

(a) better coaxial cable on their antenna
(b) the use of a masthead amplifier
(c) the use of an external TV antenna
(d) replacement of the TV receiver.

30. To minimise the risk of interference the feeder used for a transmitting antenna should

(a) be made up of long wires
(b) use unscreened feeders near the building
(c) use only screened feeders near the building
(d) not be earthed in any part of the feeder.

31. No interference is caused when operating a mobile HF set at home from a battery supply and using the base antenna. When using the same arrangement with an earthed battery charger connected, interference occurs on an electronic organ. The possible cause is

(a) the production of sub-harmonics at the transmitter
(b) very strong received signals
(c) poor RF earthing
(d) that the RF earthing is too good.

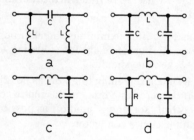

Fig Q6.1

32. A 432MHz amateur station causes interference to a nearby TV receiver. Which one of the filters shown in Fig Q6.1 could be fitted in the TV download in order to minimise the interference problem?

Fig Q6.2

33. Fig Q6.2 shows a former on which a cable is wound to make a mains filter choke. The former would be made of

(a) plastic
(b) steel
(c) ferrite
(d) paramagnetic.

34. The type of interference generally caused by a transmitter can be classified as
    (a) broad-band
    (b) wide-band
    (c) white noise
    (d) narrow-band.

35. If the mains earth is used as an RF earth, it could cause
    (a) mains hum
    (b) parasitic oscillations
    (c) mains-borne interference
    (d) self-oscillation.

36. How far should a TV antenna be placed from a transmitting antenna in order to reduce the risk of interference?
    (a) As far as possible.
    (b) As close as possible.
    (c) 1.098 metres.
    (d) Half a wavelength away at 432MHz.

37. A TV receiver still under guarantee suffers interference from a nearby transmitter. The transmitter output is proved to be 'clean' and the provision of a filter in the TV downlead has little effect. A sensible approach might be to
    (a) suggest that the TV is not used
    (b) suggest the TV user returns the set to the shop and asks for a more immune model
    (c) send the TV set to the consumer unit for assessment.
    (d) get the TV user to fit filters in the transmitter output lead.

38. When making a filter to minimise breakthrough and cutting the coaxial cable ready for soldering to the connecting socket, one should
    (a) cut as much screening braid off as possible
    (b) short the screening braid to the centre conductor
    (c) cut as little screening braid off as possible
    (d) earth the centre conductor.

39. The insertion loss of a high-pass filter in a TV downlead is measured in
    (a) decibels
    (b) watts
    (c) ohms
    (d) angstroms.

40. A strong RF signal is induced into the IF stage of a neighbour's broadcast receiver. This is known as
    (a) intermediate pick-up
    (b) frequency pick-up
    (c) Faraday pick-up
    (d) direct pick-up.

41. Attempts at reducing interference caused on a TV by a nearby amateur transmitter have failed. The next step should be to
    (a) ask the RSGB EMC Committee to look at the TV set
    (b) ask the local office of the RA to investigate further
    (c) send the transmitter to the DTI
    (d) open the back of the TV receiver.

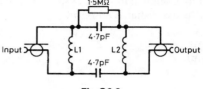

Fig Q6.3

42. The filter shown in Fig Q6.3 is a
    (a) band-stop filter
    (b) notch filter
    (c) braid-breaker and high-pass filter
    (d) low-pass filter only.

43. A TV picture suffers from herringbone patterning. The most likely cause is
    (a) poor commutation in an electric vacuum cleaner
    (b) a nearby radio transmitter
    (c) a facsimile receiver
    (d) a model train set.

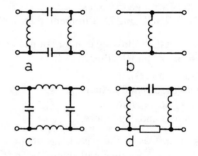

Fig Q6.4

44. Refer to Fig Q6.4. To minimise RF going back into the mains, which one of the following could be fitted in the mains input of a piece of equipment?

45. A neighbour complains of interference to a television receiver but the interference disappears when the antenna is disconnected. This coincides with the amateur's transmission times. As a first step
    (a) try a mains filter
    (b) suggest they use a set-top antenna
    (c) try a filter in the TV downlead
    (d) renew the antenna cable.

46. The main cause of intermodulation products in a receiver is
    (a) the receiver being tuned off-channel
    (b) a crystal filter being used
    (c) non-linearity in the RF stages
    (d) a good preselector being used.

47. In fitting a filter in a TV downlead which one of the following combinations is correct?

	Impedance	Insertion loss
(a)	3Ω	75dB.
(b)	25Ω	60dB.
(c)	50Ω	−75dB.
(d)	75Ω	3dB.

48. Which one of the following filters should be used in order to attenuate 21MHz signals on a TV downlead?

   (a) Low-pass filter.
   (b) High-pass filter.
   (c) Band-reject filter at the TV frequency.
   (d) Band-pass filter at 21MHz.

49. Interference is only caused on a hi-fi system when the audio cassette deck is in use. This might be eliminated by

   (a) a ceramic capacitor across a base-emitter junction in the cassette player preamplifier
   (b) an electrolytic capacitor across a base-emitter junction in the cassette player preamplifier
   (c) additional power supply smoothing
   (d) a 1MΩ resistor across a base-emitter junction in the cassette player preamplifier.

50. Severe interference on a radio receiver is experienced when a PCB with digital circuits is running on the bench. This interference might be reduced if the PCB was

   (a) put in a plastic box
   (b) encased in epoxy resin
   (c) placed in an earthed wooden box
   (d) placed in a screened copper box.

51. A baby alarm is connected by a long length of twin flex. It is prone to interference from a nearby transmitter. One way to minimise unwanted pick-up would be to

   (a) double the length of flex
   (b) use screened connecting cables
   (c) use a double twin flex
   (d) split the twin flex and reroute.

52. When transmitting in the 1.81–2.0MHz band, image interference problems may occur on the

   (a) UHF TV band
   (b) FM broadcast band
   (c) long waveband
   (d) medium waveband.

53. It is found that interfering signals from a 144MHz transmitter are being induced on the braid of an antenna downlead to a domestic FM broadcast receiver. One possible method of reducing the interference is

   (a) to fit a braid-breaker
   (b) remove the 144MHz earth connection
   (c) cut back the braid on the downlead
   (d) fit the 144MHz transmitter with a low-pass filter.

54. A 435MHz transmitter/antenna system gives 1kW ERP and points straight at a neighbour's TV antenna. This could cause

   (a) problems with the 435MHz receiver
   (b) problems with the 435MHz transmitter
   (c) self-oscillation of the transmitter
   (d) overloading of the TV front-end.

55. To remove a narrow band of frequencies that may cause interference, it might be possible to use a

   (a) notch filter
   (b) mesh filter
   (c) resistor
   (d) band-stop filter.

56. Which one of the following devices is prone to causing wide-band noise?

   (a) Home computer.
   (b) 1kHz tone generator.
   (c) RF generator set to 90MHz.
   (d) 28MHz transmitter.

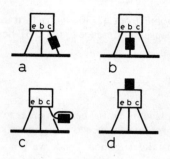

Fig Q6.5

57. Refer to Fig Q6.5. If a ferrite bead is to be fitted on a transistor lead to reduce an interference problem, which arrangement is most likely to produce a cure?

58. RF interference is found to be entering a TV by the IF lead. It is impractical to remove the lead from the tuner. What type of capacitor could be placed between the screen and the centre of the lead to effect a cure?

   (a) 10µF electrolytic
   (b) 10nF disc ceramic
   (c) 2pF polystyrene
   (d) 1µF polycarbonate.

59. The coaxial cable from a transmitter feeds a balanced half-wave dipole. The cable runs vertically next to the house and causes some interference. To minimise this problem it would be wise to

   (a) replace coaxial cable with a single wire feeder
   (b) put intermittent loops into the coaxial cable
   (c) put the coaxial cable in a plastic pipe
   (d) feed the dipole via a balun.

60. A transmitter has a fixed power output and fixed length of cable to the antenna. To keep the ERP reasonably low without adversely affecting the receive capability one should

   (a) put resistors in series with the coaxial cable
   (b) put chokes in series with the coaxial cable
   (c) use an antenna with low gain
   (d) use plastic antenna elements.

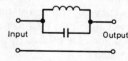

Fig Q6.6

61. The filter shown in Fig Q6.6 is a

   (a) band-stop filter
   (b) low-pass filter
   (c) high-pass filter
   (d) resistive pad.

62. If interference is caused to a government wireless station there can be an oral demand to close down. This is followed initially by
    (a) confirmation in writing
    (b) a visit from the police
    (c) confiscation of equipment
    (d) licence restrictions.

63. The harmonic from a 430–440MHz transmitter most likely to cause interference to the UHF band is the
    (a) second
    (b) third
    (c) fourth
    (d) fifth.

64. The best place for an HF beam in order to minimise the possibility of interference to a neighbour's equipment is
    (a) against the neighbour's side wall
    (b) overhanging the neighbour's roof space
    (c) as high and as far away as possible
    (d) as low and as near the house as possible.

65. To improve an amateur station design with regards to EMC one could
    (a) bond the transmitter to the water pipe in the house
    (b) provide a good RF earth for all the equipment
    (c) remove all earth connections
    (d) connect to the incoming Alkathene water pipe.

66. A buzz occurs on TV sound along with white 'tadpoles' across the screen. The interference is most likely to be caused by
    (a) a taxi transmitter
    (b) a vacuum cleaner
    (c) a clockwork brush
    (d) an audio signal generator.

67. When transmitting fast-scan TV, the picture appears on a neighbour's TV. To remedy the situation one could
    (a) select suitable pictures
    (b) reduce power output to a minimum
    (c) increase modulation depth
    (d) increase picture contrast.

68. If two transmissions are received in a non-linear device
    (a) they will cancel each other out
    (b) neither will be received
    (c) they must be transformer coupled
    (d) intermodulation products are produced.

69. On an amateur receiver, unwanted signals are found approximately every 15.625kHz. This is probably due to
    (a) a low-frequency government station
    (b) unwanted radiation of a TV line timebase
    (c) wanted radiation of a TV line timebase
    (d) a military beacon.

70. If it is proved that interference is getting into equipment via the mains, it is necessary to
    (a) inform the CEGB
    (b) fit a mains filter
    (c) swap over the line and neutral connection
    (d) disconnect the earth and re-route mains cable.

71. To reduce the possibility of interference, the power used should be
    (a) the minimum to maintain reliable communication
    (b) the maximum permissible
    (c) always less than 1W but greater than 500mW
    (d) half the maximum permissible.

72. When using a PCB drill, interference is experienced on the 14MHz band. The interference the drill generates is classified as
    (a) boring
    (b) saw-like
    (c) broad-band
    (d) narrow-band.

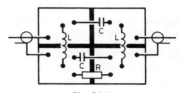

Fig Q6.7

73. Refer to Fig Q6.7. The resistor R is used to
    (a) stop static build-up
    (b) provide static
    (c) damp oscillations
    (d) stop parasitics.

74. When visiting a neighbour's house to check for TVI as a first step
    (a) remove the TV mains plug and check the picture
    (b) remove the TV antenna lead to see if the interference still persists
    (c) switch the TV off
    (d) take the back off the TV and earth the chassis.

75. So as not to invalidate the car's warranty, which one of the following should always be followed before installing a mobile transceiver?
    (a) The RSGB mobile installation guidelines.
    (b) Advice from the car salesman.
    (c) The car manufacturer's instructions.
    (d) Amateur equipment manufacturer's instructions.

76. A mobile transceiver should be located so that
    (a) it is near the ventilator/heating system
    (b) it falls off the dashboard on impact
    (c) the leads reach the cigar lighter socket
    (d) all controls are easily accessible.

77. The preferred location for a VHF mobile antenna is
    (a) on the dashboard
    (b) in the centre of the roof
    (c) on the back bumper
    (d) on the front wing.

78. To minimise the risk of interaction with vehicle electronic systems the antenna cable should be
    (a) strapped to the vehicle wiring harness
    (b) kept as long as possible
    (c) routed well away from any wiring
    (d) routed round the inside of the engine compartment.

Check your answers using the key in Appendix 4.

7 Propagation and antennas

RADIO communication depends on the radiation of electromagnetic waves from the transmitting antenna. The electromagnetic waves are created by the alternating RF currents in the antenna which are produced by the output of the transmitter.

▶The transmitted signal may be regarded as a succession of concentric spheres of ever-increasing radius, each one a unit of one wavelength apart, formed by forces moving outwards from the antenna. At great distances from the transmitter these hypothetical spherical surfaces, called *wave-fronts*, approximate to plane (flat) surfaces.◀

There are two inseparable fields associated with the transmitted signal, an *electric field* (E) due to voltage changes and a *magnetic field* (H) due to current changes, and these always remain at right-angles to one another and to the direction of propagation as the wave proceeds. The oscillations of each field are in phase and the ratio of their amplitudes remains constant. The lines of force in the electric field are parallel to the plane of the transmitting antenna. The electric field is measured by the change of potential per unit distance, and this value is termed the *field strength*.

The two fields are constantly changing in magnitude and reverse in direction with every half-cycle of the transmitted carrier. As shown in Fig 7.1, successive wave-fronts passing

a suitably placed second antenna induce in it a received signal which follows all the changes carried by the field and therefore reproduces the character of the transmitted signal. The field strength at the receiving antenna may range from less than 1µV/m to greater than 100mV/m.

Waves are said to be *polarised* in the direction of (parallel to) the electric lines of force. Normally the polarisation is parallel to the length of the antenna, ie a horizontal antenna produces horizontally polarised waves. In order to receive maximum signal strength, the receiving antenna must be orientated to the same polarisation. In practice, particularly at VHF and UHF, the polarisation may be modified by factors such as abnormal weather conditions and reflection from the ionosphere.

The electromagnetic wave is an alternating quantity. Its wavelength (λ) is the distance, in the direction of propagation, between points where the intensity of the field is similar in magnitude and sign, ie the distance travelled in space to complete one cycle. Therefore:

$$\text{velocity} = \text{frequency} \times \text{wavelength}$$
$$c = f \times \lambda$$

where c is the velocity of propagation which for electromagnetic waves in space is approximately 300,000,000m/s (186,000 miles/s). Therefore:

$$\lambda(\text{m}) = \frac{300,000,000}{f(\text{Hz})} = \frac{300}{f(\text{MHz})}$$

MODES OF PROPAGATION

The three main modes of propagation of electromagnetic waves are:

(a) ground (or surface) wave;
(b) ionospheric wave (sky wave);
(c) tropospheric wave.

Ground-wave propagation

In ground-wave propagation, the radiated wave follows the surface of the Earth. It is the major mode of propagation for frequencies up to 1MHz or 2MHz. Attenuation of the ground wave increases very rapidly above 2MHz and it may extend for only a few kilometres at frequencies of the order of 15–20MHz. At very low frequencies the attenuation decreases to such an extent that reliable world-wide communication is possible at all times. The ground wave is not affected as much by atmospheric conditions or time of day as other modes, particularly at frequencies below about 500kHz.

Ionospheric propagation

Ionospheric propagation is the *refraction* (ie bending), and therefore reflection, of radio waves back to the Earth by layers

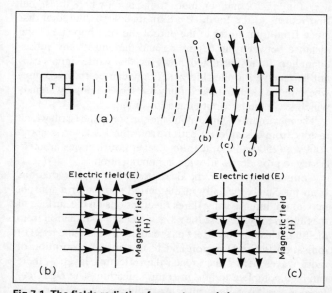

Fig 7.1. The fields radiating from a transmitting antenna. (a) The expanding spherical wavefront consists of alternate reversals of electric field, with which are associated simultaneous reversals of the magnetic field at right-angles to it, as shown in (b) and (c). The dotted arcs represent nulls. The lower diagrams should be interpreted as though they have been rotated through 90° of arc, so that the magnetic field lines are perpendicular to the page

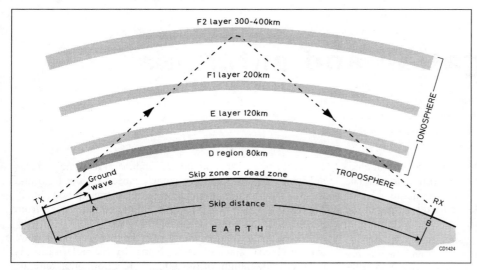

Fig 7.2. Reflections of radio waves by ionised layers

Mainly during the summer months, regions of intense ionisation may occur in the E layer which is therefore able to reflect much higher frequencies than normal, ie up to 100MHz and occasionally 150MHz. This ionospheric propagation can occur in the 50, 70 and 144MHz bands. This is known as *sporadic E* propagation; it often also causes extremely strong signals with deep fading, particularly on 28MHz.

▶The *critical frequency* is the highest frequency reflected when the radiation is vertical. This frequency is lower than the MUF and will be different for each layer. The forecasting of MUF from daily measurements of critical frequency made at radio observatories all over the world is of great importance in commercial communications. Forecasts are made for several years ahead and are continually refined as later measurements become available. ◀

of ionised gases as shown in Fig 7.2. It is the normal mode of propagation over the frequency range of about 1MHz to 30MHz.

These layers are the *F2 layer* (height 300–400km); *F1 layer* (about 200km) and the *E layer* (about 120km). At night and in midwinter, the F1 and F2 layers tend to combine into a single layer at a height of about 250km. At about 80km there is a much less distinct layer which is generally known as the *D region*.

The ionised layers are the result of ionisation of the molecules of air in the rarefied atmosphere at these heights by X-ray and ultra-violet radiation which comes from the Sun.

When these gases are ionised the molecules split up into ions and free electrons, and recombine after sunset. This whole region is therefore known as the *ionosphere*.

The solar radiation which causes the ionisation is continually changing and so the amount of ionisation varies considerably according to season and time of day. The degree of ionisation is affected by the number of sunspots.

The number of sunspots varies over a period of time, with maximum activity occurring at about 11-year intervals. The maximum ionisation occurs at the same intervals. As the frequency of the radio wave increases, a higher level of ionisation is needed to cause refraction (reflection). The F2 layer normally has the greatest ionisation and so it is the F2 layer which reflects the highest frequencies which have passed through the lower layers. It is seen from Fig 7.2 that it is this layer which reflects back to the ground at the greatest distance from the transmitter. Therefore it is the characteristics of the F2 layer which are of most interest and importance in long-distance communication. The D region is a problem simply because it absorbs some of the signals in abnormal circumstances.

The maximum frequency which is reflected in the ionosphere is known as the *maximum usable frequency* (MUF). This frequency depends on many factors, ie season, time of day, path latitude and state of the sunspot cycle. Signals above the MUF pass through the F2 layer and are lost in space or are re-transmitted to Earth be means of a satellite station. Around the sunspot maximum, the MUF may exceed 50MHz for short periods, but at the minimum it rarely exceeds 25MHz.

There is no simple explanation of the many anomalies in the behaviour of the F2 layer and most of what is known is based on experimental results and deduction. As far as amateur radio is concerned, it is convenient to accept the published variations of MUF in particular as being of most significance to communication on the amateur bands. The fact that the MUF is highest in the early winter months should be noted.

Fig 7.2 shows that there is a region between the transmitter and the point at which the reflected wave returns to the Earth (B) where no signal is received. This is the *skip zone* or *dead zone* – it starts where the ground wave has become very weak, ie (A) in Fig 7.2 and continues to the point where the signal first returns to the Earth (B). Skip distance is the total distance from transmitter to the end of the first hop (B) or the distance between the beginning and the end of any subsequent hop. It must be noted, however, that while signals cannot be received in the skip zone, they can be received anywhere in the skip distance of any subsequent hop by signals which leave the transmitter at a lower angle.

The maximum distance along the surface of the Earth which results from a single reflection from the F2 layer is about 4000km (2500 miles); therefore several reflections are necessary to provide world-wide communication.

Communication may be disrupted by unusual radiations from the Sun, especially in the period soon after a sunspot maximum. Intense solar flares (ie eruptions on the surface of the Sun) greatly increase the ultra-violet and X-radiation from the Sun. This has the effect of greatly increasing the level of ionisation in the D region and results in the absorption of radio waves before they reach the reflecting layers – there can be a complete failure in communication. The *Dellinger fade-out*, as it is called, can cause problems over all or part of the HF spectrum which may last for a few minutes to an hour or so. This is known as a *sudden ionospheric disturbance* (SID).

A SID may be followed about two days later by another form of fade-out or blackout, the *ionospheric storm*, and this can last from a few hours to several days. It is thought that ionospheric storms are caused by slower-moving particles, emitted at the same time as the solar flare, which cause increased ionisation in the D region but decreased ionisation in the F layer.

Fading of a signal propagated ionospherically, as opposed to the fade-out just described, is a common occurrence. The signal received at a given point is rarely constant because of the continually changing conditions in the ionosphere, ie layer height, ionisation level and possibly skip distance (if the frequency is close to the MUF).

It is also possible that the signal may arrive by two different paths; the two or more signals may change in their phase relationship, causing enhancement or cancellation of the signal arriving at the antenna. This effect will vary if the path lengths change.

The effects of fading may be minimised by really effective automatic gain control in the receiver.

Tropospheric propagation

This is the major mode of propagation over long distances (ie beyond the line-of-sight range) at frequencies above about 50MHz.

The troposphere is the name given to the lower part of the atmosphere. Its height varies from about 6km to about 17km and depends upon latitude and atmospheric pressure. Changes in temperature, pressure and humidity of the atmosphere (ie weather changes) cause large changes in its *refractive index* at increasing height above the Earth's surface (refractive index is a quantity which is a measure of how much a radio wave is bent as it passes through the atmosphere).

These changes in the refractive index (the ability to bend a radio wave) affect the propagation within the troposphere of waves of frequencies above approximately 40–50MHz in a number of ways.

1. Localised variations cause scattering of radio waves.
2. Sharp changes between horizontal layers cause reflection (ie ionospheric propagation).
3. A sharp decrease in refractive index with height can produce the phenomenon of *ducting*.

A duct is a region of indeterminate shape which may cover a very large area but only be 40–50m high. It has the property of propagating radio waves with extremely low attenuation, and such waves therefore tend to hug the Earth's surface. A duct may last for several days.

A wave which gets *trapped* in such a tropospheric duct can travel for very long distances (1500km or more) but can leak out at any point.

This is not a reliable mode of propagation; it can cause severe interference to distant services. However, it is of great interest in amateur radio as it enables long-distance contacts on the VHF and UHF bands to be made with very low power and simple antennas.

Periods of enhanced tropospheric propagation can often be forecast by observation of weather changes.

The mode of propagation depends on the frequency used, but there is no sharp transition from one mode to another as the frequency increases. This depends on many factors and at some frequencies significant propagation can occur by more than one mode. For example, long-distance propagation on

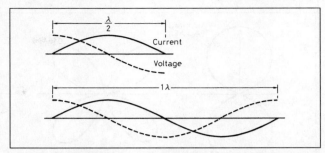

Fig 7.3 Standing waves on resonant antennas showing voltage and current variation. Upper antenna is half-wavelength long (fundamental antenna); lower is one wavelength (second harmonic) antenna

the medium-wave broadcast band and the 1.8MHz amateur band during the hours of darkness is by sky wave.

ANTENNAS

The fundamental antenna is a piece of wire which is one half of a wavelength ($\lambda/2$) long, corresponding to the frequency at which radiation is required. The voltage and current vary over the length of this antenna, as shown in Fig 7.3 (top).

If the piece of wire is made a whole wavelength (1λ) long, the current and voltage variations are as in Fig 7.3 (bottom). This is known as a *full-wave* or *second harmonic* antenna. Larger multiples of the basic half-wave antenna show similar voltage/current variations. These variations are known as *standing waves*, and this type of antenna is known as a *resonant* antenna.

It is seen that the ratio of voltage and current varies over the length of the antenna, and may be resistive, inductive or capacitive. This ratio is referred to in general terms as the antenna *impedance*.

The *radiation resistance* of an antenna is an imaginary resistance which would dissipate the power radiated by it.

Antenna length

The length of a half-wavelength ($\lambda/2$) in space is:

$$\frac{150}{f(\text{MHz})} \text{ metres}$$

The actual length of a half-wave antenna is somewhat less than this, owing to:

(a) the velocity of propagation in the wire being different from that in space;
(b) the presence of insulators at the end of the wire and of nearby objects (trees or buildings);
(c) the diameter of the wire or element.

The actual length is normally taken to be 5% less than (or 0.95 of) the electrical length. This constant, 0.95, is sometimes known as the *correction factor*. The actual length is

$$\frac{150 \times 0.95}{f(\text{MHz})} = \frac{143}{f(\text{MHz})} \text{ metres}$$

Radiation patterns

If a half-wave antenna is assumed to be parallel to and at least a wavelength high, and also remote from all other objects, the radiation is concentrated at right-angles to its length, as shown in Fig 7.4(a). This is the radiation pattern of a half-wave

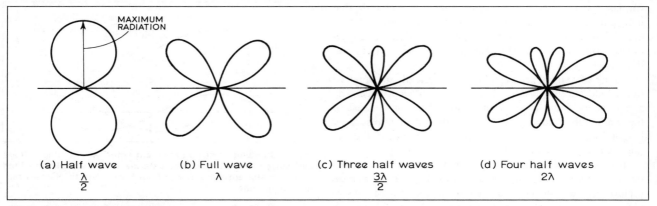

Fig 7.4. Theoretical radiation patterns of resonant antennas

antenna and, as the antenna radiates in directions all round the wire, the radiation pattern in space is the shape formed by imagining the pattern of Fig 7.4(a) to be rotated round the antenna with the antenna as the axis.

Radiation patterns of antennas working on higher harmonics are shown in Figs 7.4(b), (c) and (d), where it is seen that the effect is to produce more lobes; the four lobes of the full-wave case tend to swing towards the ends of the antenna, and subsidiary lobes appear. In the case of an extremely long antenna the radiation tends to be concentrated towards the ends.

If one end of the antenna is tilted, the lobes tend to move together and radiation tends to become concentrated off the lower end. Consideration of the half-wave pattern shows that radiation is all around (*omnidirectional*) when the antenna is vertical.

Angle of radiation

This is the angle with respect to the surface of the Earth (which is assumed to be horizontal) at which the maximum radiation occurs. Its value depends upon interaction between the direct ray from the antenna and the ray reflected in particular from the ground. Therefore it is determined by both the antenna height and the characteristics of the ground. A single lobe exists in the vertical plane at an antenna height of approximately a half-wave, and above this height the one lobe splits into two, one at a higher angle and the other at a lower angle. These two lobes could be felt to be of more use than a single lobe from the point of view of total coverage (see Fig 7.2). As the height increases the higher lobe increases in angle and magnitude. It is clear that the angle of radiation produced by a multiband antenna at an average height of 7–8m varies considerably between 3.5MHz and 28MHz.

Directional antennas

It is possible to modify the radiation pattern of an antenna in order to concentrate the radiation in a particular direction. In this way a *directional* or a *beam* antenna is created.

This is normally achieved by the addition of parasitic elements known as a *director* and a *reflector* parallel to the antenna, as shown in Fig 7.5(a), which also shows the approximate spacing in terms of the operating wavelength. This arrangement is known as the *Yagi array*.

The radiation pattern is shown in Fig 7.5(b). The addition of more directors produces a narrower beam. Because of the physical size more than one director is usually only possible

at VHF and UHF, where up to 20 or more directors may be used.

Means must be provided for rotating a beam antenna so that it can be turned to the required direction.

An additional feature of the directional antenna is the fact that when used for reception, signals to the back of the beam are attenuated, ie interfering signals from an unwanted direction may be significantly reduced in strength. When working *simplex* the use of a beam shows consideration for other amateurs operating on or near the transmission frequency if they are situated towards the back of the beam antenna. This is especially true when operating in the VHF and UHF bands. The characteristics of a beam antenna are the *forward gain* (compared with a dipole) and *front-to-back ratio*, these terms being self-explanatory; they are expressed in decibels.

Feeders and transmission lines

For obvious reasons, antennas should be as high and as far away from buildings etc as possible. Therefore it may be necessary to transfer power from the transmitter to the antenna over a fairly long distance, say 10 to 25m. The way in which this is done depends on the type of antenna used. The general name for this connection is *feeder*, which can be just a single wire or a transmission line which may be *balanced* or *unbalanced*, both types consisting of two conductors. In a balanced line, both conductors have equal potential to earth, ie neither is earthed. In the unbalanced line, one conductor is earthed.

Connections of this type are subdivided according to a

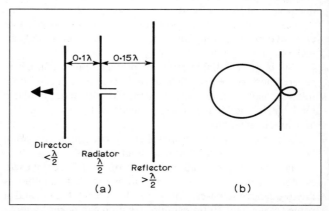

Fig 7.5. (a) Arrangement of Yagi directional beam antenna. (b) Radiation pattern of directional antenna

property known as the *characteristic impedance* (Z_0) which is measured in ohms. The characteristic impedance of a balanced line depends upon the diameter of the conductors and the spacing between them. Balanced or *twin feeder* is commercially available with impedances of 75 and 300Ω (300Ω ribbon). Open-wire feeders of 300 to 600Ω impedance can be made by spacing apart two lengths of wire of 14 SWG (2mm) or 16 SWG (1.6mm) by low-loss spacers tied to the wire at intervals of 30–40mm. The unbalanced line is the familiar coaxial cable, where the characteristic impedance now depends upon the diameter of the conductor (the *inner*) and the internal diameter of the screen (the *outer*) which is earthed. The common impedances are 50 and 75Ω.

The velocity of propagation of an electromagnetic wave in a transmission line is less than in free space. The ratio of the velocities is the *velocity ratio* or *velocity factor*. For most solid polythene-insulated coaxial cables the velocity factor is about 0.66; 300Ω twin feeder has a velocity factor of about 0.85.

For the optimum transmission of power, a transmission line must be *matched*, ie *terminated* at the load end by the correct impedance; this is equal to the characteristic impedance of the line.

Standing waves

In a transmission line which is not correctly terminated, ie the load impedance is not equal to its characteristic impedance, the energy from the transmitter cannot be completely converted to power in the load – the remainder is reflected back to the input end. The forward wave and the reflected wave cannot cancel each other but combine to create points of maximum (in-phase) and minimum (out-of-phase) voltage (and current).

These variations of voltage (and current) in a mismatched transmission line are known as *standing waves*. The ratio of maximum and minimum voltage (or current) is the *standing wave ratio*. Generally it is the voltage which is measured, leading to the term *voltage standing wave ratio* (VSWR) which is usually abbreviated to SWR. (The SWR meter described in Chapter 8 does not measure SWR but provides an indication of its value – this is explained fully in the chapter). In a correctly terminated line, there is no reflection of the forward power at all and the SWR is 1 to 1.

▶ Stubs

A line is completely mismatched when the far end is either a short-circuit or an open-circuit. There is then no load resistance to dissipate power, and 100% reflection of current and voltage occurs. It can be shown that a quarter-wave length of a line which is open-circuit is equivalent to a series-tuned circuit at the frequency corresponding to the wavelength and therefore presents a very low resistance at that particular frequency. In a complementary fashion a short-circuit is equivalent to a parallel-tuned circuit and so presents a very high resistance.

These lengths of line are known as *stubs*. The open-circuit stub is particularly useful as a means of creating a short-circuit at a particular frequency.

The velocity ratio must be taken into account when calculating the length of the line which is somewhat shorter then the free-space length. ◀

Coupling the transmitter to the antenna

Modern commercial transmitters and transceivers have output circuits which are designed to *look into* an unbalanced

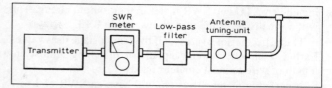

Fig 7.6. Preferred arrangement of antenna-to-antenna circuit

load of 50 to 70Ω. For optimum transfer of power to the antenna, impedances throughout the system must be matched. For example, if the antenna feed-point impedance is 50Ω, this should be connected to the transmitter output socket by an unbalanced line, ie coaxial cable of 50Ω impedance. The output power for which the transmitter is designed is then transferred to the antenna from which it is all radiated.

In practice the feed-point impedance of an antenna can vary widely from its nominal value. Two typical reasons are:

1. Siting conditions: the proximity of the antenna to local objects such as buildings and trees and, with HF antennas in particular, height above ground. For a given band, the lower the antenna, the lower the impedance.
2. For a given antenna, changing the operating frequency within a band, ie from one end to the other, will cause a change. Some types, in particular multiband antennas, will vary more than others and also from band to band.

As the mismatch increases, the reflected (reverse) power rises and the SWR increases. SWR is a measure of the effectiveness of the whole system.

Matching the feeder impedance to the antenna itself may not be a straightforward task, particularly in the case of multiband antennas which are themselves a compromise.

The solution to this problem, which has become virtually standard practice, is to match the transmitter to the feeder plus antenna as shown in Fig 7.6 and, in more detail, in Fig 6.6 in Chapter 6 (Electromagnetic compatibility).

Matching is achieved by means of an antenna tuning unit (ATU). This does not tune the antenna; it matches it to the transmitter output and hence should really be called an *antenna matching unit*, but it has been known as an 'ATU' by common usage for very many years. Other names now used are *antenna system tuning unit*, *transmatch* or *matching network*.

The transmitter-to-ATU connection is a very short matched transmission line at 50/70Ω. This has the advantage that it can include means of measuring the SWR and a low-pass or other filter if necessary. The ATU is basically a tuned circuit and so provides about 25dB attenuation of harmonics and other unwanted frequencies in the transmitter output. It has an unbalanced input socket and generally it can provide both balanced and unbalanced outputs.

A basic circuit of an SWR meter is shown in Fig 8.12 in Chapter 8 (Measurements). This is the simple reflectometer type which originated in the USA. An alternative type is shown in Fig 8.13. The SWR meter and the ATU exist in many home-made and commercial transceivers.

This arrangement has become more significant in recent years due to the use of transistors in the transmitter output stage. Such transmitters often incorporate automatic means of switch-off or power reduction (ALC) if the SWR rises above about 2.5 to 1. The more sophisticated transmitters now include an ATU and SWR meter in their output circuit. This will normally be of the type shown in Fig 8.13.

This aspect is not so critical if the output stage uses valves. Earlier transmitters were capable of matching almost any length of wire to most amateur bands.

A perfectly matched system will have an SWR of 1 to 1. There are many possible errors in SWR measurement and an SWR of 1 to 1 suggests that there are some errors in the method of measurement. A system which appears to have an SWR greater than about 5 to 1 should certainly be investigated, although the power loss then is only just less than 3dB and is almost entirely in the feeder due to increased current flow (out of phase). It is probably more important to reduce SWR to safeguard a solid-state transmitter output stage than for any other reason.

In practice the effects of a poor SWR are as follows:

1. Greater loss in the feeder. How much greater depends on feeder type and frequency. In general it can be said to be inconsequential at HF (up to 30MHz), but may be significant at VHF (144MHz) and will certainly be so at UHF (432MHz and upwards).

2. Use of very high power with an excessive SWR may cause breakdown of the feeder or units *in line*, such as filters or switches. Breakdown can be caused by flashover (due to high voltage) or melting of conductors or dielectric (due to high current).

3. Loss of output due to the built-in ALC.

Note that a high SWR does not cause a feeder to radiate or produce TVI or other interference.

The impedance matching of the transmitter/antenna system discussed above applies to the HF bands. At VHF and UHF, the transmitter and antenna are normally designed for single-band operation rather than for several bands. A much tighter control of impedance is therefore possible. Antenna length is much shorter compared with the height above ground, and there is less doubt about feed-point impedances. An SWR meter can be incorporated to check the integrity of the antenna system.

To summarise, current amateur technology is to match as closely as possible to the ATU input and to accept the SWR presented by the antenna to the ATU output.

▶It may be difficult to measure this. It depends on how the antenna is fed: single wire, coaxial cable or open-wire feeder for example.

The performance of an antenna can normally be assessed by visual inspection, ie is it in the clear and at a reasonable height compared with the longest wavelength used? If it is, then it is likely to have a good performance, propagation conditions permitting! If the antenna is low and hemmed in by buildings and trees, it is then likely to be less good, although sometimes antennas in this situation perform surprisingly well.◀

Practical antennas

Antennas for use in the amateur bands are usually based on the fundamental antenna, ie the half-wave dipole. Many different forms of antenna have been developed and details of these can be found in the usual textbooks on amateur radio. Basic information on the more common types only is within the scope of this manual.

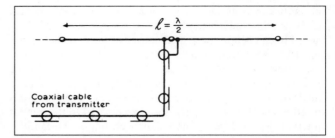

Fig 7.7. A half-wavelength dipole antenna fed by coaxial cable. Length is approximately equal to 143/f metres (f = frequency)

The dipole

The impedance of a half-wave antenna at the centre point is roughly 50–70Ω (resistive). This point could be coupled directly to the output of a transmitter by 50Ω coaxial cable, resulting in a good impedance match (Fig 7.7). This arrangement is known as a *half-wave dipole* or simply as a *dipole*. Lengths of half-wave dipoles are given in Table 7.1.

As mentioned earlier, the centre impedance of the dipole depends upon the height of the antenna and the proximity of buildings etc. The arrangement of Fig 7.6 may therefore be preferable.

However, if a 7MHz dipole was fed with power at 14MHz or 28MHz, there would be an impedance mismatch, as the impedance at the centre would no longer be 50Ω. It would be much higher than this and would not be resistive.

The exception to this is that the impedance at the third harmonic is around 90Ω. The only application of this in amateur radio is the use of a 7MHz dipole at its third harmonic, ie in the 21MHz band. The mismatch is then not excessive.

The dipole is a satisfactory antenna but, apart from the example quoted above, it is a single-band antenna. The common use of coaxial cable (unbalanced) to feed a dipole is convenient as the output of most transmitters is unbalanced, but consideration of the antenna itself shows that a dipole is balanced so that it should not be fed with an unbalanced cable.

Alternative arrangements are either the use of 75Ω twin cable between the antenna and the ATU, or a balance-unbalance transformer between the top end of the coaxial feeder and the antenna.

The balance-unbalance transformer, commonly called a *balun*, enables a balanced circuit to be coupled to an unbalanced circuit and vice versa. In one version, it consists of

Table 7.1. Approximate lengths of λ/2 dipoles		
Band (MHz)	**λ/2 (m)**	**λ/2 (ft)**
1.8	75.2	247
3.5	39.2	129
7	20.3	67
10	14.1	46
14	10.05	33
18	7.9	26
21	6.7	22
24	5.7	18.8
28	4.93	16.2
50	2.8	9.3
70	2.02	6.6
144	0.97	38.4in
430	0.32	12.8in

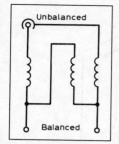

Fig 7.8. Arrangement of the windings in a balun transformer

three tightly coupled windings on a small ferrite core, as shown in Fig 7.8.

The trap dipole

The trap dipole is a dipole having a parallel-tuned circuit or *trap* inserted at a particular point in each leg as shown in Fig 7.9. At resonance, the trap presents high impedance and therefore at the resonant frequency the length beyond the trap is virtually isolated from the centre portion. Below the resonant frequency the trap provides an inductive reactance which reduces the length of antenna required for resonance.

Fig 7.9 gives the dimensions of the trap dipole; the traps are resonant at 7.1MHz. At 7MHz the system operates as a half-wave dipole, the traps isolating the outer sections. At 3.5MHz it again operates as a half-wave dipole, the traps electrically lengthening the top.

▶At frequencies above the resonance of the trap, the end sections are not isolated, but the traps do provide series capacitance. This enables the antenna top to resonate at odd harmonics of its fundamental and so at 14MHz, 21MHz and 28MHz the trap dipole functions as a 3λ/2, 5λ/2 and 7λ/2 antenna respectively. A reasonably satisfactory match to a 75Ω feeder is obtained on each band. At 1.8MHz the feeders may be joined together at the transmitter and the system will operate satisfactorily as a top-loaded Marconi antenna against ground or a counterpoise. ◀

The trap dipole has become very popular as a multiband antenna in recent years because of the commercial availability of suitable traps. It must be appreciated that, as with all multiband antennas, it is a compromise arrangement and will not give optimum results on every band.

The folded dipole

A folded dipole is shown in Fig 7.10(a). This is the simplest example of folding and it results in the centre impedance being multiplied by four.

This increase in impedance is the main advantage of folding. When a Yagi array is used for VHF or UHF the presence of a large number of directors reduces the centre impedance

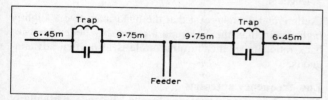

Fig 7.9. The trap dipole

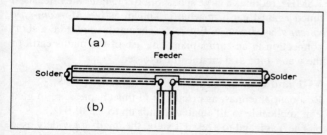

Fig 7.10. (a) Folded dipole. (b) Construction of a folded dipole from 300Ω ribbon feeder

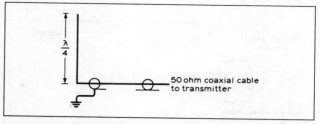

Fig 7.11. Quarter-wavelength vertical antenna

by a considerable amount, and folding the dipole can increase the impedance so that it is corrected to 50Ω. A folded dipole (with no directors) has an impedance of about 300Ω and so may be fed with 300Ω twin feeder.

▶The loss in 300Ω feeder is somewhat lower than that in 50Ω coaxial cable and so a folded dipole may be preferred if the feeder length is extremely long. In fact, as shown in Fig 7.10(b), it is possible to construct a folded dipole entirely of 300Ω feeder. ◀

The vertical antenna

A vertical antenna offers the attraction of low-angle, omnidirectional radiation and is popular where space does not allow a long horizontal antenna.

The simplest form is a vertical radiator one quarter of a wavelength long (see Fig 7.11); the impedance at the bottom is 30–40Ω and so it can be fed by 50Ω coaxial cable.

It is difficult to produce a satisfactory earth which is needed when a vertical antenna is to be used. A single earth rod, say 2m long, is unlikely to be satisfactory unless the soil has exceptional conductivity. Two or three rods bonded together close to the bottom of the radiator may reduce the earth resistance. If a really satisfactory earth is required a number of copper rods can be bonded together and buried in a series of deep trenches but this operation is often unpopular with other members of the household!

Earthing problems with a vertical antenna may be virtually eliminated by erecting it over a perfectly-conducting surface, eg a large sheet of copper. This is known as a *ground-plane antenna*, but is only realisable at VHF or UHF (eg a quarter-wave radiator mounted on a car roof).

In practice a satisfactory ground plane may be made by laying four to six radial wires about a quarter of a wavelength long on the surface of the ground (they can be buried a few centimetres below the surface if more convenient). Alternatively, the radiator may be mounted at the top of a mast which uses the ground-plane radials as guy wires, insulators being introduced at the appropriate points as shown in Fig 7.12. A

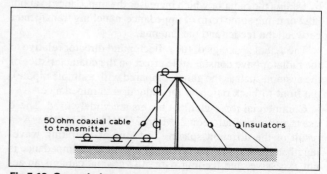

Fig 7.12. Ground-plane antenna mounted on a mast

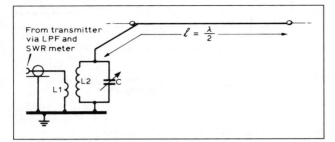

Fig 7.13. End-fed antenna

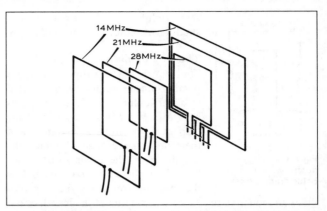

Fig 7.14. A three-band nest of two-element quads (radiator and reflector) maintaining optimum spacing for each band

ground plane erected in this manner does in fact present a better match to 50Ω coaxial cable than the conventional ground plane.

Traps may be inserted in a vertical antenna to enable it to be used on more than one band.

The end-fed antenna

This is probably the simplest antenna of all as it consists of a length of wire brought from the highest point available direct to the transmitter output. The wire can be straight but good results are often obtained with quite sharp bends in the run of the wire.

Optimum results are obtained with resonant lengths – a 40m long end-fed antenna operates on bands from 3.5MHz to 28MHz, while an 80m length enables 1.8MHz to be used. This arrangement, although often used, is liable to create breakthrough problems (Chapter 5) as the end of the antenna (ie a high-voltage point) is brought into the house; if the transmitter is not at ground level there may be significant unwanted radiation from the long earth lead. The use of an antenna tuning unit as shown in Fig 7.13 is advisable. The ATU should be preceded by a low-pass filter and SWR meter as shown in Fig 7.6.

The three-element beam

The Yagi antenna consisting of a radiator and two parasitic elements (a reflector and one director) mounted on a suitable tower with provision for rotating it is known as a *three-element beam*. The radiator is a dipole which must be about 10m in overall length for operation at 14MHz; the physical size normally dictates that 14MHz is the lowest frequency for which the rotating Yagi is used.

The addition of a director and a reflector to the normal dipole has the effect of reducing the centre impedance to the order of 20Ω. Therefore in order to feed it with 50Ω coaxial cable the impedance must be increased. This can be achieved by folding the radiator which increases the impedance to about 80Ω or using some form of impedance-matching transformer between the feeder and the antenna.

The actual spacings of the reflector and director relative to the radiator have considerable effect on the characteristics of the system, such as the gain (compared with a simple dipole), the front-to-back ratio and the reduction in impedance.

Commercial three-element beams are widely used. These use traps for operation on 28MHz, 21MHz and 14MHz. As a result of the different spacing in terms of operating wavelength at these three frequencies, the change in impedance is not excessive, and feeding with 50Ω coaxial cable is an acceptable compromise.

The quad antenna

The quad antenna consists of a square loop of wire as shown in Fig 7.14. The side of the loop is approximately a quarter-wavelength long and it is normally fed with 50Ω coaxial cable at the point shown. The loop can be mounted with a diagonal vertical and fed at the bottom corner; in either case the feed point is of low impedance and the performance is identical. In the configuration shown, the polarisation is horizontal.

Parasitic elements may be added to form a beam antenna. The most popular is a radiator plus reflector (the two-element quad), but one or more directors may be added, depending on the frequency. Spacings between the radiator and parasitic elements are similar to the Yagi. Commonly, quads for 28MHz, 21MHz and 14MHz are assembled on the same mounting and rotating system and fed by 50Ω cable. In order to maintain the optimum spacing between the elements, the radiators, reflectors and directors for each band cannot be in the same vertical plane (see Fig 7.14).

▶The quad is made up of wire supported on lightweight spreaders of bamboo or glass fibre.

Front-to-back ratio and SWR are optimised on each band by adjustment of the tuning stub on the reflectors, but alternatively a reasonable compromise is often obtained by eliminating the stub and making the reflector about 3% greater than the radiator in length.◀

Commercial data suggest that the quad may give a slightly higher gain than the Yagi and a noticeably better front-to-back ratio. Its smaller turning circle is also often advantageous.

Low-frequency antennas

An effective resonant antenna for the LF bands, particularly 1.8MHz, requires a large space. Shorter lengths are often used tuned against earth in what is known as the *Marconi-type antenna*, as shown in Fig 7.15. The earth should be a short connection to an earth spike. The use of the mains earth or the water-pipe system must be avoided.

VHF and UHF antennas

Resonant antennas, as discussed in this chapter, are in general applicable to all amateur bands up to 1300MHz.

The Yagi, and to a lesser extent, the quad, are widely used at VHF and UHF because the much shorter physical length of a half-wavelength means that more elements occupy less

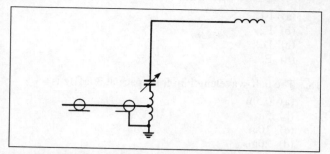

Fig 7.15. Marconi antenna for use at 1.8MHz; additional loading at outer end is useful if the length is less than a quarter-wavelength

space and so antennas of appreciably higher gain than at HF are possible.

▶Several such antennas may be stacked, provided they are correctly matched and phased, to provide even higher gain.

At even higher frequencies, parasitic elements are replaced by parabolic-shaped reflectors or *dishes*; however, these are beyond the scope of the RAE.◀

Loading of an antenna

Shortness in length of a resonant antenna may be compensated for to a certain extent by the addition of a small amount of inductance, for instance as shown in Fig 7.15. Another example is the effect of the trap inductance when the trap dipole (Fig 7.9) is used on the 3.5MHz band. This method is commonly used on whip antennas for mobile use and may allow a beam antenna to be made to fit into a smaller than normal space. The process of loading an antenna will almost certainly introduce losses in the loading coil in addition to the shortening of the effective radiator.

Power radiated from an antenna

Effective radiated power (ERP)

The ERP in a given direction is the product of the power supplied to the antenna and the gain of the antenna (relative to a half-wave dipole) in that direction.

▶**Effective isotropically radiated power (EIRP)**

The product of the power supplied to the antenna and its gain, in a given direction, relative to an *isotropic* (ie omnidirectional) antenna. By convention, ERP is used below 1GHz and EIRP above 1GHz.

In assessing the power supplied to the antenna, the loss in the feeder system must be taken into account. This is negligible in the lower-frequency bands but significant at UHF and above.

The calculation of the field strength produced at a point distant from the transmitting antenna under practical conditions is difficult. This is because the signal is reflected and absorbed by surrounding objects, particularly those close to the transmitting antenna and especially the ground and, of course, the ionosphere. This is not generally important in amateur radio, but from the aspect of EMC (see Chapter 6) it is often useful to obtain some indication of the likely field strength at quite short distances in order to assess the likelihood of breakthrough of your signal to other equipment in the immediate vicinity.◀

Receiving antennas

It is normal practice for the transmitting antenna to be used for reception. Should a separate receiving antenna be required, 12–18m of wire erected in the clear normally gives good results on all bands. An antenna tuning unit is often advantageous. Protection against overloading of the receiver during transmission is normally required. Two diodes connected in

parallel but 'back to back' across the receiver input will usually be satisfactory.

PRACTICE QUESTIONS FOR CHAPTER 7

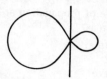

Fig Q7.1

1. The radiation pattern shown in Fig Q7.1 is typical of a
    (a) half-wave dipole
    (b) quarter-wave antenna
    (c) beam antenna
    (d) Marconi antenna.

2. The approximate velocity of propagation in free space is
    (a) 2×10^8 m/s
    (b) 2.5×10^8 m/s
    (c) 3×10^8 m/s
    (d) 3.5×10^8 m/s.

3. In daylight hours, which one of the following bands below would be suitable for working between Lands End and John O'Groats?
    (a) 160m.
    (b) 80m.
    (c) 40m.
    (d) 15m.

4. A sunspot cycle lasts about
    (a) 3 years
    (b) 5 years
    (c) 11 years
    (d) 20 years.

5. The ionospheric layer mainly responsible for long-distance communication at HF is
    (a) D
    (b) E
    (c) F2
    (d) F1.

6. When two out-of-phase signals arrive at a point
    (a) fading will occur
    (b) signal enhancement occurs
    (c) cross-polarisation is produced
    (d) the antenna impedance varies.

7. A vertical antenna will produce
    (a) circular polarisation
    (b) high-angle radiation
    (c) low-angle radiation
    (d) elliptical polarisation.

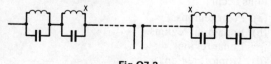

Fig Q7.2

8. Fig Q7.2 represents a trap dipole for three bands: 20, 15 and 10 metres. The traps marked 'X' will tune to

    (a) 12.4MHz

    (b) 14.2MHz

    (c) 21.2MHz

    (d) 29.0MHz.

9. The main mode of propagation at VHF over long distances is known as

    (a) tropospheric

    (b) ionospheric

    (c) ground wave

    (d) surface wave.

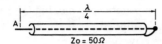

Fig Q7.3

10. In Fig Q7.3 what is the impedance seen at A?

    (a) Zero.

    (b) 50Ω.

    (c) 150Ω.

    (d) Infinite.

11. The dielectric of open-wire feeder is usually

    (a) air

    (b) polythene

    (c) rubber

    (d) water.

12. The wavelength of a signal in free space with a frequency of 100MHz is

    (a) 30mm

    (b) 0.3m

    (c) 3m

    (d) 30m.

13. The beamwidth of an antenna is normally measured at the

    (a) −1dB point

    (b) −3dB point

    (c) −6dB point

    (d) −9dB point.

14. The side of a practical quad antenna is

    (a) a quarter-wavelength

    (b) a half-wavelength

    (c) three-quarters of a wavelength

    (d) a full wavelength.

15. The polarisation of an electromagnetic wave is defined by the direction of

    (a) the H field

    (b) propagation

    (c) the E field

    (d) the receiving antenna.

16. In which one of the following areas do auroral reflections occur?

    (a) Polar regions.

    (b) Equatorial regions.

    (c) Lunar regions.

    (d) Tropical regions.

17. Which one of the following is the lowest ionospheric region?

    (a) F1.

    (b) F2.

    (c) D.

    (d) E.

18. The half-wavelength in free space at 30MHz is

    (a) 0.5m

    (b) 5m

    (c) 10m

    (d) 20m.

19. The relationship between velocity of propagation, frequency and wavelength is

    (a) $v = f \times \lambda$

    (b) $\lambda = f \times v$

    (c) $f = v \times \lambda$

    (d) $v \times f \times \lambda = 1$.

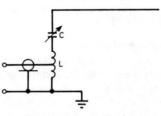

Fig Q7.4

20. The antenna shown in Fig Q7.4 is known as a

    (a) Marconi

    (b) Yagi

    (c) cubical quad

    (d) W3DZZ dipole.

21. In Fig Q7.4, L and C are used for

    (a) the earth connection

    (b) increasing the radiation resistance

    (c) decreasing the radiation resistance

    (d) matching the antenna to the transmitter.

22. When signals return to the ground after being reflected from charged layers above the Earth they are known as

    (a) ground waves

    (b) ionospheric waves

    (c) tropospheric waves

    (d) direct waves.

23. The order of the ionospheric layers starting at the Earth's surface is

    (a) D, E, F2, F1

    (b) D, E, F1, F2

    (c) E, D, F1, F2

    (d) F1, D, E, F2.

24. At a sunspot minimum which one of the following bands would be used for consistent long-distance communications?

    (a) 3.5MHz.

    (b) 7MHz.

    (c) 14MHz.

    (d) 28MHz.

25. What is the frequency corresponding to a wavelength of 300mm in a vacuum?
   (a) 100kHz.
   (b) 1MHz.
   (c) 100MHz.
   (d) 1GHz.

26. The angle between the E and H fields in an electromagnetic wave is
   (a) 45 degrees
   (b) 90 degrees
   (c) 180 degrees
   (d) 360 degrees.

27. Which one of the following cables has the lowest loss at HF?
   (a) Twisted flex.
   (b) Coaxial cable.
   (c) Open wire feeder.
   (d) Mains cable.

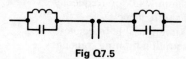

Fig Q7.5

28. Fig Q7.5 shows
   (a) an end-fed wire
   (b) a simple dipole
   (c) a cubical quad
   (d) a trap dipole.

29. The radiation resistance of a half-wave dipole at least one wavelength above ground is about
   (a) 50Ω
   (b) 75Ω
   (c) 100Ω
   (d) 300Ω.

30. The velocity factor of open-wire feeder is about
   (a) 0.1
   (b) 0.4
   (c) 0.6
   (d) unity.

31. Approximately how high is the F1 layer above ground?
   (a) 80km
   (b) 120km
   (c) 200km
   (d) 300km.

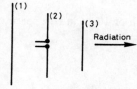

Fig Q7.6

32. Fig Q7.6 shows a simple beam antenna. The names of the elements in numerical order are
   (a) radiator, director, reflector
   (b) director, radiator, reflector
   (c) director, reflector, radiator
   (d) reflector, radiator, director.

33. A balun is a
   (a) balanced-to-unbalanced transformer
   (b) mains transformer
   (c) single winding inductor
   (d) semiconductor device.

34. The critical frequency is the
   (a) highest frequency reflected when the radiation is vertical
   (b) lowest frequency reflected when the radiation is vertical
   (c) highest frequency reflected when the radiation is horizontal
   (d) lowest frequency reflected when the radiation is horizontal.

35. The major mode of propagation up to about 2MHz is by
   (a) direct wave
   (b) tropospheric wave
   (c) ionospheric wave
   (d) ground wave.

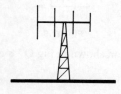

Fig Q7.7

36. Fig Q7.7 shows a beam antenna. The polarisation of the transmitted signal will be
   (a) vertical
   (b) horizontal
   (c) elliptical
   (d) left-handed.

37. In respect of electromagnetic radiation, which one of the following is true?
   (a) E and H are at 180 degrees to each other.
   (b) E, H and the direction of propagation are all at right-angles to each other.
   (c) The angle between E and H is zero.
   (d) The direction of propagation is at 180 degrees to the E field but in line with the H field.

38. When reflectors and directors are added to a folded dipole
   (a) the radiation resistance is raised
   (b) there is no effect on its radiation resistance
   (c) the radiation resistance is lowered
   (d) it will not provide any directivity.

39. The impedance at the centre of the radiator of a beam antenna is dependent on the
   (a) radiation resistance of the dipole
   (b) spacing of directors and reflectors
   (c) feed cable impedance
   (d) propagation conditions.

40. The velocity factor of a coaxial cable with solid poly-thene dielectric is about
    (a) 0.66
    (b) 0.1
    (c) 0.8
    (d) 1.0.

41. When an electromagnetic wave is refracted it is
    (a) the same as being absorbed
    (b) the bending of its path
    (c) absorption by the ionosphere
    (d) bouncing from a stellar object.

42. A half-wavelength transmission line is terminated with 68Ω. The input to the line is
    (a) 34Ω
    (b) 68Ω
    (c) 136Ω
    (d) 204Ω.

Fig Q7.8

43. The polarisation shown in Fig Q7.8 is
    (a) vertical
    (b) horizontal
    (c) forwards
    (d) backwards.

44. To match a 300Ω antenna to a 75Ω transmission line, a transformer can be used that has a ratio of
    (a) 2:1
    (b) 4:1
    (c) 8:1
    (d) 16:1.

45. The unit of Z_0 is
    (a) ohms
    (b) farads
    (c) siemens
    (d) henrys.

46. A half-wave dipole will also resonate at
    (a) a sub-harmonic
    (b) the second harmonic
    (c) the third harmonic
    (d) the fourth harmonic.

47. Ionospheric fading can be caused by
    (a) a poor antenna
    (b) horizontal polarisation
    (c) interaction of the sky and ground wave
    (d) poor coaxial cable.

48. Inserting traps into each leg of a dipole
    (a) allows it to operate only on one band
    (b) cuts out harmonics
    (c) gives broad-band matching
    (d) allows it to resonate on more than one band.

49. When the F2 layer is more highly ionised than usual, it will cause
    (a) poorer reflections at higher frequencies
    (b) a lower MUF
    (c) a higher MUF
    (d) poor HF conditions.

50. Which one of the following should be connected in series with an antenna wire 15m long so that it is resonant on the 3.5MHz band?
    (a) A capacitor.
    (b) An inductor.
    (c) A capacitor and inductor in series.
    (d) A capacitor and inductor in parallel.

51. The highest frequency that can be used between two stations for satisfactory communications on HF is called the
    (a) optimum working frequency
    (b) critical frequency
    (c) maximum usable frequency
    (d) penetration limiting frequency.

52. A transmission on 14.18MHz can be received by station A 3000 miles away but not by station B only 40 miles away. This is because
    (a) station B is in the skip zone
    (b) the ground and ionospheric wave cancel out at station B
    (c) two reflected waves arrive at B with opposite phase
    (d) there is a Dellinger fadeout in progress.

53. Increased ionisation in the D layer preventing radio waves from reaching the normal reflecting layers is known as
    (a) an aurora
    (b) sporadic E
    (c) a critical fade-out
    (d) a Dellinger fade-out.

54. Z_0 for a transmission line is normally called the
    (a) velocity factor
    (b) characteristic impedance
    (c) characteristic factor
    (d) copper resistance.

55. A wavelength of 10cm in free space corresponds to a frequency of
    (a) 3MHz
    (b) 300MHz
    (c) 3GHz
    (d) 30GHz.

56. Typical characteristic impedances for coaxial cables are
    (a) 50 and 300Ω
    (b) 50 and 75Ω
    (c) 75 and 300Ω
    (d) 300 and 600Ω.

57. A half-wave dipole resonates at
    (a) a sub-harmonic
    (b) the fundamental
    (c) the third harmonic
    (d) the fourth harmonic.

58. As frequency increases, the ionisation which reflects a signal back to earth must
    (a) decrease
    (b) go to zero
    (c) not change
    (d) increase.

59. The velocity of propagation in coaxial cable is
    (a) greater than in free space
    (b) the same as free space
    (c) less than in free space
    (d) zero.

60. The typical dielectric found in present-day coaxial cable is
    (a) rubber
    (b) porcelain
    (c) ceramic
    (d) polythene.

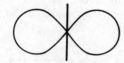

Fig Q7.9

61. Refer to Fig Q7.9. The radiation pattern is typical of a
    (a) half-wave dipole
    (b) four-element beam
    (c) full-wave antenna
    (d) three-half-wavelength antenna.

62. A half-wave dipole has an impedance of 70Ω at the centre. It is fed with a half-wavelength of 300Ω ribbon cable. The impedance at the input to the feeder is
    (a) 70Ω
    (b) 185Ω
    (c) 300Ω
    (d) 370Ω.

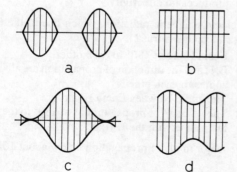

Fig Q7.10

63. Refer to Fig Q7.10. Which one of the following oscilloscope patterns represents 100% amplitude modulation?

64. A quarter-wave transmission line is open-circuit at one end. The impedance looking in at the other is
    (a) almost zero
    (b) the characteristic impedance
    (c) three times the characteristic impedance
    (d) infinity.

65. The length of wire used to make a folded dipole equates to
    (a) one half-wavelength
    (b) one wavelength
    (c) two wavelengths
    (d) four wavelengths.

66. Which one of the following represents the correction factor normally used in calculating the length of a wire antenna?
    (a) 65%.
    (b) 75%.
    (c) 80%.
    (d) 95%.

67. The addition of more directors on a beam antenna will
    (a) broaden the beamwidth
    (b) raise the radiation resistance
    (c) narrow the beamwidth
    (d) give a lower front-to-back ratio.

68. The skip zone is where the ground wave
    (a) is enhanced
    (b) is reflected
    (c) has decayed to zero and the reflected wave has not returned to Earth
    (d) and reflected wave combine to form a continuous wave.

69. The MUF for a given radio path is the
    (a) mean of the maximum and minimum usable frequencies
    (b) maximum usable frequency
    (c) minimum usable frequency
    (d) mandatory usable frequency.

70. A folded dipole has a radiation resistance of about
    (a) 50Ω
    (b) 75Ω
    (c) 300Ω
    (d) 1000Ω.

71. The polarisation of a transmitted electromagnetic wave is determined by the
    (a) position of the transceiver
    (b) direction of propagation
    (c) the transmission path over the North Pole
    (d) the orientation of the transmitting antenna.

72. What is the length of a piece of coaxial cable cut for a full wavelength at 100MHz if the velocity factor is 0.6?
    (a) 0.18m.
    (b) 1.8m.
    (c) 3m.
    (d) 60m.

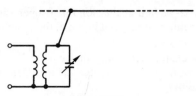

Fig Q7.11

73. Fig Q7.11 shows a
    (a) Yagi antenna
    (b) dipole
    (c) long wire antenna
    (d) monopole.

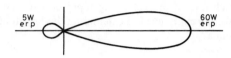

Fig Q7.12

74. Refer to Fig Q7.12. The front-to-back ratio of the antenna is
    (a) 10.8dB
    (b) 12dB
    (c) 21.6dB
    (d) 60dB.

75. A transformer can be used to match a 75Ω transmission line to a 300Ω antenna. The transformer should have a turns ratio of
    (a) 1:1
    (b) 1:2
    (c) 1:4
    (d) 1:6.

76. A transmission line is said to be perfectly matched when it is terminated by an impedance equal to
    (a) half the characteristic impedance
    (b) twice the characteristic impedance
    (c) an open-circuit
    (d) the characteristic impedance.

77. A balanced transmission line has
    (a) one side connected to earth
    (b) both sides connected to earth
    (c) a coaxial construction
    (d) equal impedance of each line to earth.

78. The term 'dBi' is often used when considering the gain of various antennas. This corresponds to dB with respect to
    (a) an isotropic radiator
    (b) a dipole balanced indicator
    (c) an input
    (d) an impedance.

79. The wavelength of a signal of 100MHz in free space is
    (a) 30mm
    (b) 0.3m
    (c) 3.0m
    (d) 30m.

80. In order to radiate, an electromagnetic wave must have
    (a) E field only
    (b) H field only
    (c) E and H field
    (d) air to travel in.

81. Polarisation of an electromagnetic wave is determined by
    (a) the direction of the H field
    (b) the direction of propagation
    (c) by an anti-phase signal
    (d) the orientation of the transmitting antenna.

82. Fading can be caused by
    (a) a poor antenna system
    (b) horizontal polarisation
    (c) interaction of the sky and ground wave
    (d) poor coaxial cable.

83. Skip distance is the
    (a) space from the transmitter to the point where the wave first returns to earth
    (b) space from the end of the ground wave to the point where the wave first returns to earth
    (c) maximum distance from the transmitter over which a signal can be received
    (d) space in which no signal can be received from the transmitter.

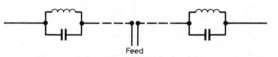

Fig Q7.13

84. The antenna shown in Fig Q7.13 represents a
    (a) single-band dipole
    (b) simple dipole
    (c) cubical quad
    (d) trap dipole.

85. The addition of reflectors and a director to a folded dipole
    (a) raises its impedance
    (b) has no effect on its impedance
    (c) lowers its impedance
    (d) produces no directivity.

86. In electromagnetic radiation, which one of the following statements is true?
    (a) E and H are at 180° to each other.
    (b) E, H and the direction of propagation are all at right-angles to each other.
    (c) The angle between E and H is 0°.
    (d) The velocity of propagation is at 180° to the E field but in line with the H field.

87. The major mode of propagation below about 10MHz is by
    (a) direct wave
    (b) tropospheric wave
    (c) ionospheric wave
    (d) ground wave.

88. Which one of the following will not affect skip distance?
    (a) Change in frequency of the signal radiated.
    (b) Change in power radiated.
    (c) The time of day.
    (d) The state of the sun-spot cycle.

89. The MUF for a given radio path is the
    (a) mean of the maximum and minimum usable frequencies
    (b) maximum usable frequency
    (c) measured usable frequency
    (d) most usable frequency.

90. A 1m wavelength in air corresponds to
    (a) 30MHz
    (b) 300MHz
    (c) 3GHz
    (d) 30GHz.

91. A trap in each leg of a dipole
    (a) improves the efficiency of the one band in use
    (b) helps to increase compatibility
    (c) increases the effective radiated power (ERP)
    (d) enables it to be correctly matched on at least two bands.

Check your answers using the key in Appendix 4.

8 Measurements

ANY operator of amateur radio equipment must be able to make simple measurements to ensure that the equipment is working correctly.

There are three basic quantities which need to be measured: voltage, current and frequency. Occasionally there will be a need to make measurements of other quantities which will be described later.

For example, in even the simplest transmitter it is necessary to know the drive to the various stages (current measurements), the input power to the PA (current and voltage measurements) and the frequency of the radiated signal.

DC MEASUREMENTS

The basic instrument used for the measurement of voltage and current is the *moving-coil meter*. This comprises a coil of wire, generally wound on a rectangular former, which is mounted on pivots in the field of a permanent magnet (Fig 8.1). The coil develops a torque (turning force) proportional to:

(a) the current flowing through it;
(b) the strength of the field of the permanent magnet.

Current is fed to the coil through two hair springs mounted near to each pivot. These springs also serve to return the pointer to the zero position (on the left-hand side of its travel in standard meters) when the current ceases to flow. Provision for adjusting the position of the pointer is made by a *zero adjuster*, accessible from the front of the instrument.

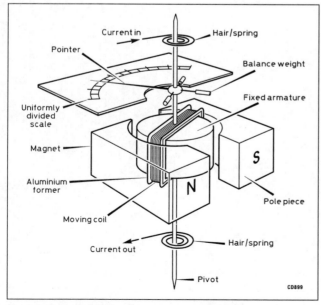

Fig 8.1. The construction of a moving-coil meter

Fig 8.2. Extending the range of an MC meter (a) to read higher current with a parallel shunt, (b) to measure voltage with a series resistor or multiplier

It is usual to *damp* the coil system (ie prevent it swinging freely after a change of current). A common method is to wind the coil on an aluminium former, which then acts as a short-circuited, single-turn coil in which the eddy currents serve to oppose the movement. The degree of eddy current damping also depends on the external resistance across the terminals of the moving coil and is greatest when the resistance is low. It is always wise to protect sensitive instruments not in use by short-circuiting the terminals.

The scale of the moving-coil instrument is linear unlike some other types. It can only be used on DC, but can be adapted to measure AC.

Milliammeters

Milliammeters and microammeters are commonly manufactured with full-scale deflections (FSDs) between about 25µA and 10mA. For higher current ranges, a *shunt resistor* is connected across the meter (see Fig 8.2(a)). For example, if a milliammeter with an FSD of 10mA is required to measure up to 1A, the value of the shunt resistor must be such that it passes 990mA when 1A is being 'measured', the other 10mA flowing through the meter. The value of the shunt will normally be low compared with the resistance of the milliammeter.

Voltmeters

A milliammeter may be used to read DC voltages by connecting a resistor, termed a *multiplier*, in series with it (see Fig 8.2(b)). The value of this multiplier must be such that the maximum voltage will cause the FSD current to flow through the meter. For example, to enable a milliammeter having an FSD of 100µA to measure up to 10V the multiplier must have a value of $100,000\Omega = 100k\Omega$ (less the resistance of the meter which will be very small – 50Ω approximately).

The accuracy of a meter depends on many factors, eg size, quality, accuracy of shunt or multiplier resistor, the scale deflection (ie full-scale reading). Usually, the size of meter most likely to be used in amateur radio would be 60–75mm in diameter and the accuracy would be of the order of 3%. In other words, if the meter is used to measure an exact value of 100V, the reading may be as high as 103V or as low as 97V.

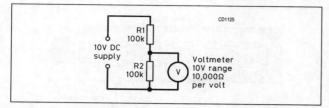

Fig 8.3. An error is caused by the meter resistance – 100kΩ

If the resistance of a voltmeter is too low, it is likely that the current drawn by the meter will cause an error; the voltage measured will therefore be lower than it was before the meter was connected.

Fig 8.3 shows an example of this. The resistance of the voltmeter is placed in parallel with R2. In the example above, the meter resistance was 100kΩ which when connected in parallel with R2 produces an effective resistance of 50kΩ so that the voltage across R2 (and the meter will be only 3.33V instead of the 5V which existed before the meter was connected.

The sensitivity of a voltmeter is usually defined in *ohms per volt* (Ω/V). For example if a voltmeter has a resistance of 20,000Ω (ie meter and multiplier) and a full-scale reading of 100V, its sensitivity is 20,000Ω/100V or 200Ω/V. This value is much too low for use on radio circuits. A satisfactory value is 20,000Ω/V which corresponds to a basic meter full-scale deflection of 50µA.

AC MEASUREMENTS

A moving-coil meter modified to respond to AC will normally be calibrated in RMS values but the movement actually responds to the average value of the current flowing through it. Errors will occur if the waveform of alternating voltages or currents to be measured is not sinusoidal.

The moving-coil meter can be adapted to measure AC by the addition of a bridge rectifier known as an *instrument rectifier*. The meter indicates the average value, ie 0.636 of the peak value of a sine wave, but it is normally calibrated in RMS. Rectifier meters may be used at frequencies up to about 10kHz, but are only accurate when the waveform is sinusoidal. Multiplier resistors can be added to a rectifier instrument but current measurement requires a special transformer known as a *current transformer*. A diagram and description of such a transformer appears later in this chapter in the section relating to VSWR measurement.

Thermocouple meters

The thermocouple is a junction of two dissimilar metals which when heated generates a DC voltage. The junction is heated by the current to be measured passing through a heater wire to which it is attached. In conjunction with a thermocouple, a moving-coil instrument can be used to read alternating currents of up to radio frequencies. A disadvantage is that low current readings (on the scale) are rather severely compressed. Thermocouple instruments read RMS values irrespective of waveform. Unless specially designed, they become less accurate as frequency increases, owing to the effect of the shunt capacitance.

These meters must be used with great care as the thermocouple itself can be burnt out by a current not much greater than the maximum reading of the meter.

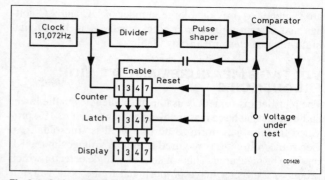

Fig 8.4. A simplified diagram of a digital voltmeter

DIGITAL METERS

Measuring and test equipment is now available with digital read-out. The basic accuracy of these depends upon the standard of the internal electronic circuits used but the overall accuracy is very high because the read-out is much easier to read accurately than a pointer instrument (or mechanical dial). The meter compares the voltage under test with an internally generated *linear ramp*. This is simply a sawtooth waveform in which the voltage rises from zero to a maximum value in an accurate, linear manner. Clock pulses from a crystal oscillator are fed to a counter at the beginning of the ramp and are stopped when the ramp voltage and the test voltage become equal. By dividing the output of the clock, a square wave of one per second is generated for the pulse shaper which produces the sawtooth waveform. The output of the counter is passed to the digital display. Fig 8.4 shows the simplified arrangement and Fig 8.5 the waveforms which are generated within the meter.

A disadvantage of a digital instrument is its inability to follow slowly-changing voltages because the value indicated can change only once every second (or whatever sampling period is used). Also the delay in displaying the voltage under test can be quite annoying when fault finding is being carried out.

MULTI-RANGE METERS

Many commercial multi-range meters are available. These consist of a number of voltage multipliers and current shunts, an instrument rectifier and current transformer, all of which

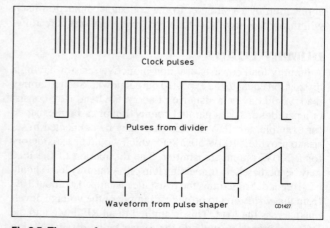

Fig 8.5. The waveforms used in the digital voltmeter shown in Fig 8.4

are switched to provide a large number of DC and AC voltage and current ranges on a high-sensitivity meter. Digital multi-range meters are also available.

VOLTAGE MEASUREMENT AT HIGH FREQUENCIES

The rectifier instrument is usable at frequencies in the lower audio range and has a reasonable accuracy (order of 4%) provided that the waveform to be measured is sinusoidal. An electronic voltmeter is required to enable voltages in the RF range to be measured. This consists of a diode detector which produces a direct voltage proportional to the peak value of the alternating voltage. This is followed by amplifier circuits feeding a meter calibrated in volts. The electronic voltmeter can give accurate readings up to a frequency of several hundreds of megahertz and may have a sensitivity in the order of 10MΩ/V. The load it places on the circuit is therefore so small that it can be ignored, but the capacitance of the diode circuit becomes important at very high frequencies.

Measurement of voltage and current in the transmitter

The tuning or setting up of a transmitter is the resonating of the various tuned circuits in the transmitter at the required frequencies.

The low-power, fixed-frequency oscillators, mixers or frequency multiplier circuits are often pre-set, particularly in commercially built equipment when they are set up during manufacture.

▶Low-power semiconductor stages may be resonated by tuning the input for maximum collector current and then resonating the collector tuned circuit for minimum collector current. Facilities for measuring collector current must be provided. This is most conveniently arranged by a *test point* in each stage to which a current meter of the appropriate range may be switched or connected.◀

A meter of a suitable range can be wired permanently into the PA collector circuit. This circuit may require to be retuned whenever the frequency band is changed. The PA current must be checked to ensure that the DC input power does not exceed the required value, for of course DC input equals voltage times current. It is satisfactory to measure the PA collector voltage at the DC input terminal of the PA, otherwise the application of a voltmeter to the collector connection itself will throw the circuit off-tune and give an incorrect reading.

DUMMY LOADS

A dummy load consists of a non-inductive resistor having a dissipation equal to the expected output power. Such a dummy load would have a resistance of about 50Ω and may consist of a parallel or series/parallel connection of carbon resistors; for example, ten 10W 5Ω resistors may be connected in series to provide a 100W 50Ω load which would be satisfactory for a 100W output transmitter. The dissipation of the load may be increased by immersing it in oil. A dummy load should be screened. Sometimes the resistance is tapped at about 10Ω from the *earthy* end to provide a sample of the voltage developed across the load. This is applied to an RF diode and the DC output used to *indicate* the power being dissipated. Fig 8.6 shows a typical dummy load.

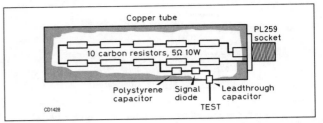

Fig 8.6. The general layout of a dummy load. The copper tube has been shown cut away to allow the components to be seen

FREQUENCY MEASUREMENT

The reasons for measuring frequency in the amateur station are to ensure that the:

(a) tuned circuits in the receiver or transmitter cover the required frequency range;
(b) frequency calibration of the receiver is correct;
(c) transmissions from the station are within the licensed bands.

Assuming that a receiver having a reasonably accurate frequency calibration is available, the calibration can be checked against short-wave broadcast stations of known frequency or against standard frequency transmissions, for example WWV (2.5, 5, 10, 15, 20 and 25MHz).

An accurate calibration may also be made by listening to the *pips* produced in the receiver by harmonics of a crystal oscillator (a crystal calibrator). When used in conjunction with a general-coverage receiver, a 100kHz crystal is usually adequate for checking frequencies up to about 4MHz. For higher frequencies, the spacing between 100kHz marker points may be too small to resolve, and a crystal of 500kHz or preferably 1MHz should be used in addition. If the receiver covers only the amateur bands, the bandspread is normally adequate to resolve the harmonics from the 100kHz crystal.

▶100kHz crystals for use in frequency standards are available with frequency accuracies of 0.002%. One of these should be considered as the prime frequency standard.

A calibration graph or table can now be drawn up for each range of the receiver. It must be kept in mind that the accuracy of this depends on the precision of the receiver dial mechanism, its logging arrangement and the presence of bandspread. The frequency of operation of a transmitter may then be measured using the receiver, calibrated as above.

Obviously the receiver cannot be tuned to even a low-power transmitter in the immediate vicinity, but it can *listen to* the output of the VFO, the frequency of which may then be determined and the final output frequency of the transmitter found. Although the VFO is screened, it will be found necessary to considerably reduce the receiver RF gain. The tuning range of a VFO can be quite easily adjusted to the required value in this manner.◀

The absorption frequency meter

The absorption frequency meter (absorption wavemeter) consists of a coil tuned by a variable capacitor, with a scale calibrated in frequency. It operates by absorbing power from a tuned circuit when tuned to the same frequency as that circuit. The tuned circuit under test must therefore be activated. The absorption of energy is indicated by a meter which is connected to the tuned circuit via a signal diode.

An absorption frequency meter has the advantages of:

(a) rugged construction and simplicity;

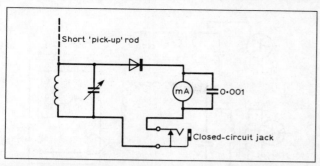

Fig 8.7. An absorption wavemeter with a microammeter as an indicator of resonance

(b) low cost;

(c) no power supply required;

(d) direct reading calibration with no confusing production of beat notes or harmonics.

The disadvantages are as follows.

(a) Only the *order* of the frequency being checked is indicated. An absorption frequency meter will show whether a transmitter frequency is nearer one end or the other of the amateur band, but not whether the frequency is just inside or just outside the limit of the band. The accuracy is about 5–10%.

(b) It lacks sensitivity. To obtain an indication in low-power transmitters, or in receiver tuned circuits, the absorption frequency meter must be held close to the coil being checked. Screening or other components may make this difficult, if not impossible.

(c) The presence of the frequency meter may cause an appreciable de-tuning of the circuit under test.

An absorption frequency meter is useful for checking that frequency-multiplying stages are tuned to the correct harmonics, for example, in checking whether a particular stage being driven by a 7MHz oscillator is tuned to 21MHz (third harmonic) or to 28MHz (fourth harmonic). Checking of harmonics is necessary in the initial tuning up of VHF equipment, which may operate on the 18th harmonic or higher of a given crystal frequency.

A rectifier and a microammeter are normally added to the absorption frequency meter so that a visual indication is obtained. This is shown in Fig 8.7. With the addition of a short antenna coupled to the coil, this arrangement becomes the so-called *field strength meter* which may also be used for searching for parasitic oscillations in the transmitter. If a close-circuit jack for headphones is connected in series with the meter, the circuit can be used for monitoring an amplitude-modulated transmission.

A much more effective way of detecting harmonics is by the use of a general-coverage receiver. This will often have a digital read-out of frequency which will give an accurate assessment of any harmonics. Because of the high sensitivity of this type of receiver it must be used at some distance from the oscillator/transmitter under test otherwise the very small output from intermediate circuits may give confusing results.

The dip meter

This is more flexible than the absorption meter in that the tuned circuit under test does not have to be energised.

It consists of an oscillator using a FET. When the oscillator is tuned to the frequency of the tuned circuit under test, energy is absorbed from the oscillator. This is indicated by a dip in the gate current of the FET. The dip oscillator has the same accuracy as the absorption meter but, if used in conjunction with a digital frequency meter, has the same accuracy as that instrument. There is a minor disadvantage that a power source is needed.

The digital frequency meter

This type of frequency meter uses integrated circuits to count electronically the number of complete sine waves in a given period. Although these digital integrated circuits are themselves complex, the principle of operation of the digital frequency meter (DFM) is quite simple; it consists of four major circuits: the *clock*, the *gate*, the *counter* and the *display*. Fig 8.8 is a simple block diagram of a DFM.

The clock produces a series of pulses of length 1s, 100ms, 10ms, 1ms etc, selected by a switch. These pulses are derived from a crystal-controlled 1MHz (or 5MHz) oscillator and their duration is controlled to a very high degree of accuracy. The pulses are applied to the gate which may be considered as an electronic on/off switch operated by the clock.

The input sine-wave signal whose frequency is to be measured is converted to a train of square pulses and when the clock pulse opens the gate, these pulses are allowed to pass to the counting circuits. These count the number of pulses (cycles) which arrive while the gate is open and then pass the answer to the display circuits which present the answer in the form of normal decimal digits.

The accuracy of the DFM depends upon the accuracy of the clock. If this produces pulses which are longer than they should be, the gate remains open for a longer period and more pulses are counted. If the clock pulse is too short, fewer pulses are counted. Accuracy can be increased if the clock oscillator crystal is housed in a crystal oven (thermostatically controlled) to hold the crystal temperature more or less constant.

▶The counting circuits will only respond to complete pulses and this may give rise to errors in measurement. For example, consider a signal of frequency of, say, 5671Hz. If the gate is open for only 0.1s, 567 whole pulses will be counted and it appears that the frequency is 5670Hz. If the gate is opened by the clock pulse for 0.01s, only 56 complete pulses are counted, suggesting that the frequency is 5600Hz and so on. The duration of the clock pulse plays an important point in determining the accuracy of measurement.◀

In practice, the clock pulse duration or resolution of a DFM can be set by a switch on the front panel of the instrument.

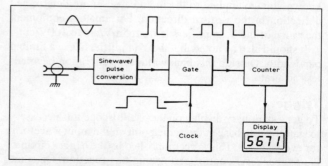

Fig 8.8. A simplified block diagram of a digital frequency meter

With careful use, an accuracy of ±5Hz can be achieved. This is more than adequate for most amateur applications.

Many types of IC may be used in digital frequency meters. The more common (and cheaper) types will permit measurement of frequencies up to 100MHz or so, and this may be extended by the latest ICs to well over 1000MHz.

The digital frequency meter is the most accurate type of frequency meter available.

THE CATHODE-RAY OSCILLOSCOPE

The cathode-ray oscilloscope is probably the most valuable tool used in electronics. The heart of the oscilloscope is the cathode-ray tube. In this device, electrons emitted from an indirectly heated cathode are focused into a beam of small diameter which, when it strikes the front of the tube or screen, causes a special coating on the internal surface of the screen to fluoresce (glow), creating a spot of light which may be blue or green according to the coating material used. On its way to the screen, the electron beam passes between one pair of parallel plates and then another pair at right-angles to the first. These are called the *X and Y deflector plates*. If a voltage is applied between the deflector plates, the beam is deflected one way or the other according to the polarity of the voltage applied, and so the spot on the screen moves. If a voltage proportional to time (in the form of a sawtooth waveform) is applied to one pair of plates, the horizontal-deflector (X) plates, and an alternating voltage is applied to the vertical-deflector (Y) plates, the spot traces out the waveform of this alternating voltage.

Timebase

The sawtooth voltage applied to the X plates (ie horizontal motion) is generated inside the oscilloscope by a circuit called the *timebase*. The speed of the timebase can be varied over a large range to accommodate signals of widely differing frequencies.

For the less-expensive oscilloscope as used by the amateur, the range of the timebase is from 1ms/cm to 1s/cm.

Y amplifiers

The signals to be displayed are usually very small. If they are applied directly to the Y plates, little, if any, movement in the vertical direction would be observed. It is necessary, therefore, to amplify the signals before applying them to the Y plates. This amplifier is called the *Y amplifier* and is built into the oscilloscope – it is normally a DC (directly coupled) amplifier so that DC voltages can be used. Several ranges of amplification are available, and each is calibrated so that a known voltage applied to the input causes a pre-determined deflection in the vertical direction. For amateur equipment the range of the Y amplifiers is from 5mV/cm to 100V/cm.

It should also be noted that the Y amplifiers have a limited bandwidth. Outside this bandwidth the calibration becomes less accurate.

Trigger

To get a stationary display on the oscilloscope it is necessary to start the timebase at the same point on the input waveform for every sweep. This is accomplished by the *trigger* circuits, the *trigger level* control performing this function. On some older oscilloscopes stabilisation is accomplished by altering

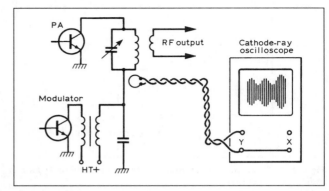

Fig 8.9. The arrangement for measuring modulation depth in which the waveform of a modulated carrier is displayed. The waveform of the oscilloscope must be linear

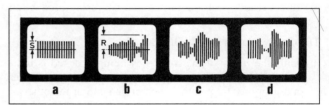

Fig 8.10. Typical patterns obtained by the method shown in Fig 8.9. (a) An unmodulated carrier, (b) a modulation depth of 50%, (c) depth 100%, (d) over-modulation. A period of zero carrier shows that over-modulation is occurring

the frequency of the timebase until it synchronises with the input waveform.

▶**Measurement of modulation depth**
It is important to ensure that, when amplitude modulation is used, the modulation depth on peaks does not exceed 100% as over-modulation creates serious interference (see Chapter 5).

The actual depth of modulation may be measured by displaying the waveform of the modulated output of the transmitter on an oscilloscope.

The circuit arrangement is shown in Fig 8.9 which is largely self-explanatory. Typical patterns produced are shown in Fig 8.10. By measuring the height R corresponding to a modulation peak and the height of the unmodulated carrier (S), the depth of modulation can be calculated directly:

$$M = \frac{R - S}{S} \times 100\%$$ ◀

SWR MEASUREMENT

As a result of the almost inevitable mismatch of an RF transmission line or feeder, neither the voltage nor the current is constant along the length of the line, that is, the voltage and current will vary according to the point along the line at which they are measured.

The performance of an RF transmission line can therefore be judged only by the measurement of its standing wave ratio (SWR) as defined in Chapter 7.

SWR is measured by means of a circuit known as a *reflectometer*. A basic reflectometer circuit is shown in Fig 8.11. An insulated wire is threaded down between the outer shield and the insulation of a coaxial cable. When an RF signal passes down the coaxial cable, part of it is coupled into the wire. This RF signal is rectified and the resulting DC is displayed on a milliammeter. When an RF transmission line is terminated in an impedance other than the characteristic

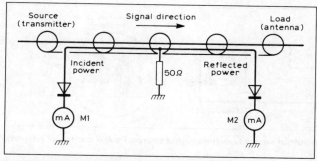

Fig 8.11. A simple reflectometer for indication of VSWR

impedance, ie when the line is not properly matched, the meter marked M1 in Fig 8.11 gives an indication of the incident (forward) power and M2 indicates the reflected power and therefore the SWR. The ratio of the power reflected to the power incident on the termination is directly related to VSWR. Unfortunately the device is *frequency conscious* and gives different readings at various frequencies.

A more satisfactory type of SWR meter is shown in Fig 8.12. This type is used in many modern transceivers when the SWR meter is often built-in. It is an excellent example of a simple analogue computer system which will display the value of some quantity without actually measuring it! Learning the way in which it works is well worth the effort.

When an AC source is connected to a load of unknown impedance, the current flowing through it and the voltage across it can be measured – the impedance can now be calculated by using the Ohm's Law expression $Z = V/I$. In addition, it is necessary to determine the phase relationship between the current and the voltage. From these data the SWR can be calculated. It follows that the circuit in Fig 8.12 must be able to assess the current flowing through the load and the voltage across it. Also it must have some means of determining the phase relationship between the two values.

The RF to the load flows through the primary of the current transformer (CT). This is a single turn consisting of the inner of the short piece of coaxial cable passing through the centre of a ferrite ring. The secondary is formed by the 20 turns of wire wound around the ring. Fig 8.13 shows the general arrangement. The current induces a voltage in the secondary L which is proportional to the value of the current through the primary. This voltage is divided into two equal portions by the potential divider comprising the two *equal* resistors R1 and R2. (Coaxial cable is used as the primary to

prevent the secondary being affected by the electric field around the primary.)

A small proportion of the voltage across the load is provided by the capacitive potential divider C3 and VC1. The voltage across VC1 is applied to R3. With a purely resistive load of 50Ω the current and voltage will be in phase so that the voltage applied to M1 (via D1 and RV1) will be the simple sum of the voltages across R1 and R3, while the voltage similarly applied to M2 will be the difference between the voltages across R2 and R3. If VC1 is adjusted, the reading given by M2 will fall to zero as the two voltages become equal (but opposite) and the voltage indicated by M1 will be double the voltage across R3 because the two values add up. Normally RV1/M1 will also be RV2/M2 when the combinations are switched.

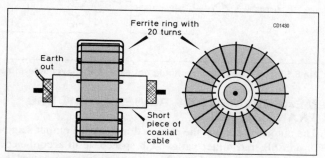

Fig 8.13. The construction of an RF current transformer

If, while the 50Ω resistive load is still connected, either the output of the transmitter is varied or the sensitivity control RV1/RV2 is adjusted, the reading on M1 can be set to full-scale. M2 will still display zero. In order to have consistent results this is used as a reference (M1 reading full-scale).

Suppose the dummy load is replaced by a non-inductive resistor of 150Ω and the drive from the transmitter (or the sensitivity control) adjusted to give full-scale on M1. The voltages across R1/R2 and R3 will no longer be equal, the current will be reduced to one third of the original value and the voltage across R1/R2 will also be reduced to one third. However, the voltage across VC1 remains as it was so that the sum of the voltages will be twice as big as the difference between them. M2 will now register half scale. The SWR scale on M2 will be marked '1' at the zero point and '3' at the *half scale* point. If the load is disconnected (dangerous for the transmitter output stage) there will be no current through the CT primary and both meters will record the voltage across R3. With M1 set to the reference of full scale deflection, M2 will also indicate FSD. The SWR scale at this point will be marked infinity (∞).

The meter will now give an indication of the SWR for any resistive load but what happens when the load is inductive or capacitive? The voltage across L (the current reading) will no longer be in phase with the voltage across VC1 (the voltage reading) and will never be able to cancel the voltage across R2 so that M2 will register some value between 1 and infinity on the SWR scale.

A final thought – as the dummy load is often connected directly to the output of the SWR meter (bridge) how can there be a standing wave when there is nowhere for it to stand? As stated at the beginning, the meter does not measure anything other than voltages.

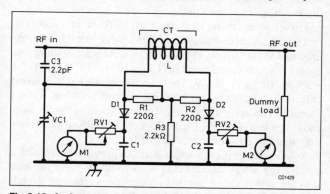

Fig 8.12. An improved type of SWR meter using a current transformer

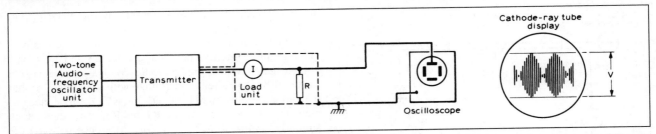

Fig 8.14. The method of measuring PEP output in relation to the mean output with a two-tone signal source. Power output = I^2/R, peak envelope power = 2 x mean power represented by V

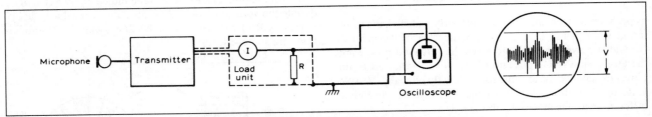

Fig 8.15. The speech peaks should not exceed the level determined by V in the two-tone test

MEASUREMENT OF POWER OF AN SSB TRANSMITTER

The output power and the current drawn by the output stage of an SSB transmitter varies with speech, ie in accordance with the speech waveform. Measurement of input power is therefore not possible because the conventional meter is much too slow in operation to follow the rapid variation of the input current.

The power rating of an SSB transmitter is therefore expressed as peak envelope power (PEP) as derived in Chapter 4. This is the power which exists at the peaks of the speech waveform. The maximum permitted PEP is 400W (26dBW).

The meter described in Fig 8.12 can also be used to measure power output and M1 will normally be calibrated in watts (or dBW) as well as in SWR. So that the peak power can be measured with reasonable accuracy the voltage across C1 is passed through a simple *buffer amplifier* to a filter which allows a capacitor to charge rapidly and to discharge very slowly. The voltage across this capacitor is applied to the meter which will display the peaks of the power long enough for it to be read. The buffer amplifier is necessary to prevent the *long time constant* filter affecting the operation of the SWR circuit.

▶One recommended method of measuring PEP is to monitor the output of the transmitter on a dummy load, by means of a cathode-ray oscilloscope, when the transmitter is modulated by the output of a *two-tone generator* as shown in Fig 8.14. This device contains two AF oscillators which produce non-harmonically related sinusoidal tones of equal amplitude which are combined.

The transmitter operating level is set to produce a mean power output in the dummy load of 200W as measured by the current flowing through it. The pattern produced on the oscilloscope will be as in Fig 8.14 and the limits of the deflection V should now be marked by two thin lines drawn by a Chinagraph pencil. The mean power as just measured (200W) is equivalent to a PEP of twice this value, ie 400W. Thus the two lines on the CRO face represent the deflection which corresponds to an output of 400W PEP. It is not essential to set the transmitter output to 200W mean, any power will do, but 200W is a convenient level because it causes a deflection which corresponds to the maximum PEP permitted.

To avoid waveform errors, the current in the load resistor is measured by a thermocouple meter. If an RF voltmeter is used to measure the voltage across the load, waveform errors in the voltmeter must be taken into account in calculating the power output.

When high-power equipment is used, the overall accuracy of the power measurement must be known and taken into account in calculating the power in order to avoid exceeding the licensed power.

When the two-tone generator is replaced by the microphone, the oscilloscope now shows the extremely peaky speech waveform (see Fig 8.15). The maximum deflection must not be allowed to exceed that deflection which corresponds to 400W PEP.

It will be appreciated that the majority of SSB transmitters and transceivers have outputs of 200W or less. The need for PEP measurement only really arises when a high-power transmitter is in use, or where a transceiver is followed by a linear amplifier, many of which are rated at power levels greater than that permitted by the UK licence.

The procedure described above and illustrated in Fig 8.15 can be used to measure the power output of a transmitter operating in any mode. A single tone of a convenient frequency (say 1000Hz) should be used to modulate an AM transmitter. The modulation depth should be adjusted to 100% by variation of the tone input to the modulator when the transmitter is operating at the input intended. If CW or FM is in use, the transmitter should be in the *key down* or *transmit* state respectively.◀

ERRORS IN MEASUREMENT

When taking any measurements, the effect of inaccuracies in the meter used, ie the tolerances (which may be positive or negative) on the meter readings must be taken into account.

To take a simple case, suppose the input to a PA is measured as 15V at 10A, ie 150W. If both meters are reading low by say 5%, the actual input is (15V + 5%) = 15.75V at (10A + 5%) = 10.5A or 165W. This can be considered as a worst case as it is unlikely that both meters will read low by this amount. The error in reasonably new good-quality meters should be less than 5%, while old meters of unknown history may have an error of more than 10%.

Tolerances are usually expressed as a percentage (eg ±2%), a value (eg ±0.3V or ±200Hz) or as so many *parts per million* (eg ±100ppm). A number of tolerances affecting a reading may be added together, although this is likely to give a pessimistic total.

Statistical methods are preferable. The effect of the likely tolerances on components and transistors etc are taken into account in complex equipment.

As an example, consider the following sample examination question:

A transmitter operating in the band 21MHz to 21.450MHz has a frequency tolerance of 100 parts in one million and a radiated bandwidth of 6kHz when using emissions of type A3E. If the frequency checking equipment at the station has a frequency tolerance of 10 parts in one million, what is the highest frequency a licensee can use that ensures no emission above 21.450MHz?

(a) 21,474.14kHz
(b) 21,444.63kHz
(c) 21,442.72kHz
(d) 21,440.03kHz

The tolerance build-up is as follows:

Band edge 21,450.0kHz

Frequency tolerance is 100ppm, ie
  100Hz per megahertz 2.15kHz

Frequency meter tolerance 10ppm 0.22kHz

A3E bandwidth is 6kHz, ie carrier must
  be in centre of this band 3.0kHz

The sum of these is 5.37kHz.

Subtract this figure from 21,450.00 to give   21,444.63kHz

which is the highest frequency which can be used.

PRACTICE QUESTIONS FOR CHAPTER 8

1. Which one of the following types of ammeter should be used to measure RF current in a dummy load?

   (a) A moving-coil meter.
   (b) A moving-iron meter calibrated to 50Hz.
   (c) A thermocouple instrument.
   (d) An eddy current instrument.

2. An ammeter placed in series with a 50Ω load reads 2 amps. The power in the load is

   (a) 0.04W
   (b) 25W
   (c) 100W
   (d) 200W.

3. The typical accuracy of a moving-coil meter is

   (a) 0.03%
   (b) 0.3%
   (c) 3%
   (d) 10%.

4. A meter is quoted as 10kΩ per volt. For full-scale deflection the current taken is

   (a) 10µA
   (b) 50µA
   (c) 100µA
   (d) 200µA.

5. A 'standing wave ratio meter' physically measures the

   (a) forward and reverse impedances
   (b) actual forward and reverse power

(c) forward and reverse voltages
(d) cable characteristic impedance.

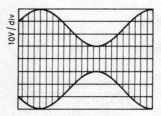

Fig Q8.1

6. Fig Q8.1 represents a trace from an oscilloscope monitoring an AM transmission. The depth of modulation is

   (a) 40%
   (b) 50%
   (c) 60%
   (d) 70%.

7. The resonant frequency of an RF tuned circuit can be checked by

   (a) a DC voltmeter
   (b) a dip oscillator
   (c) a digital frequency meter
   (d) an ohmmeter.

8. A thermocouple instrument responds to a rise in

   (a) resistance
   (b) temperature
   (c) electric field
   (d) magnetic field.

9. Peak envelope power is defined as the

   (a) average power of an SSB transmission
   (b) average power at the peak of the envelope
   (c) peak-to-peak power at the crest of the modulation envelope
   (d) minimum power at the peak of modulation.

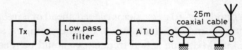

Fig Q8.2

10. Fig Q8.2 shows a typical equipment arrangement. At which point should the SWR meter be placed?

    (a) A.
    (b) B.
    (c) C.
    (d) D.

11. A moving-coil meter by itself should only be used to measure

    (a) AC
    (b) DC
    (c) AC and DC
    (d) frequency.

12. An SWR meter is used to check transmitter

    (a) efficiency
    (b) harmonic output
    (c) bandwidth
    (d) to antenna matching.

13. If the connecting cable at the output of an SWR meter in an HF system goes open circuit the VSWR will be

   (a) 0:0
   (b) very low
   (c) 1:1
   (d) very high.

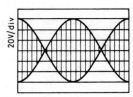

Fig Q8.3

14. Fig Q8.3 shows a trace which is typical of

   (a) an FM waveform
   (b) a two-tone SSB test
   (c) a 100% AM signal
   (d) a CW signal.

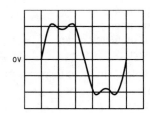

Fig Q8.4

15. A pure sine wave is applied to the input of an AF amplifier. The oscilloscope trace at the output is shown in Fig Q8.4. This represents

   (a) second harmonic distortion
   (b) third harmonic distortion
   (c) fourth harmonic distortion
   (d) fifth harmonic distortion.

16. If a divide-by-10 prescaler is placed ahead of a frequency counter and the frequency on the counter shows 43.3350MHz, the actual frequency should be read as

   (a) 0.433350MHz
   (b) 4.33350MHz
   (c) 433.350MHz
   (d) 4333.50MHz.

17. The horizontal X axis on an oscilloscope displays

   (a) voltage
   (b) capacitance
   (c) reactance
   (d) time.

18. Which one of the following components could be attached to a moving coil meter in an attempt to measure power?

   (a) Resistor.
   (b) Thermistor.
   (c) Thermocouple.
   (d) Therm.

19. Which one of the following could best be used to construct an RF dummy load?

   (a) Light bulbs.
   (b) A column of water.
   (c) Wirewound resistors.
   (d) Non-reactive resistors.

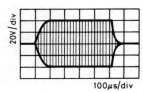

Fig Q8.5

20. The duration of the pulse shown in Fig Q8.5 is

   (a) 5μs
   (b) 50μs
   (c) 350μs
   (d) 500μs.

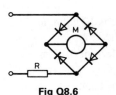

Fig Q8.6

21. Fig Q8.6 shows a moving-coil meter which allows measurement of

   (a) AC and DC
   (b) AC only
   (c) DC only
   (d) frequency.

22. Which one of the following is most suitable for accurate frequency measurements?

   (a) An absorption wavemeter.
   (b) An oscilloscope.
   (c) A multimeter.
   (d) A digital frequency counter.

23. The movement in a typical multimeter is

   (a) a moving permanent magnet
   (b) electrostatic
   (c) non-magnetic
   (d) a moving coil.

24. The control used on an oscilloscope to obtain a stable display is the

   (a) Y sensitivity
   (b) X sensitivity
   (c) trigger
   (d) calibrator.

25. When monitoring the frequency of an unmodulated carrier, the readout of the digital frequency counter should show

   (a) the carrier frequency plus harmonics
   (b) the number of sidebands
   (c) nothing at all
   (d) the carrier frequency.

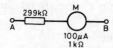

Fig Q8.7

26. In Fig Q8.7, to obtain full-scale deflection on the meter, the DC voltage across AB must be

    (a) 1V
    (b) 3V
    (c) 10V
    (d) 30V.

27. A 50Ω dummy load is made from eleven 560Ω carbon resistors, each of 5W rating. Total safe power that can be dissipated is

    (a) 0.5W
    (b) 5W
    (c) 27.5W
    (d) 55W.

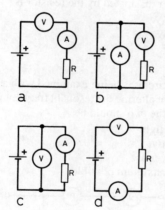

Fig Q8.8

28. In Fig Q8.8, which one of the circuits could be used to estimate the value of a resistor by Ohm's Law ?

29. An SWR meter is inserted into a perfectly matched transmitter/antenna system. The value shown should indicate

    (a) 10W reflected power
    (b) 1:1 VSWR
    (c) 1:0 VSWR
    (d) 0:1 VSWR.

30. For a moving-coil meter to respond to AC it must be combined with a

    (a) DC blocking capacitor
    (b) transformer
    (c) resistor
    (d) rectifier.

31. An oscilloscope shows a peak-to-peak reading of 25V across a 1000Ω resistor. The RMS current through the resistor is

    (a) 8.8mA
    (b) 12.5mA
    (c) 25mA
    (d) 50mA.

32. When first testing a transmitter it should be fed into

    (a) an antenna
    (b) a capacitor of reactance 50Ω
    (c) a 50Ω wire-wound resistor
    (d) a non-reactive 50Ω dummy load.

33. A frequency counter has a quoted accuracy of one part in a million. If it is set to the 100MHz range, then the accuracy at the top of the range will be plus or minus

    (a) 10Hz
    (b) 20Hz
    (c) 100Hz
    (d) 200Hz.

34. The RMS calibration of a rectifier instrument is

    (a) only true for a sine wave
    (b) true for all waveforms
    (c) true for a square wave and a sine wave only
    (d) only true for harmonics.

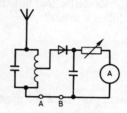

Fig Q8.9

35. Fig Q8.9 shows the circuit of

    (a) an absorption wavemeter
    (b) a dip oscillator
    (c) an SWR meter
    (d) heterodyne wavemeter.

36. Refer to Fig Q8.9. If headphones are inserted between A and B, monitoring is possible of

    (a) AM signals
    (b) FM signals
    (c) harmonics
    (d) parasitic oscillations.

37. An SWR meter should be placed between

    (a) coaxial cable and antenna
    (b) ATU and antenna feeder
    (c) transmitter and ATU
    (d) the mains and the transmitter.

38. Which one of the following would be used to examine the shape of a waveform?

    (a) An oscilloscope.
    (b) An absorption wavemeter.
    (c) A digital frequency counter.
    (d) A grid-dip meter.

39. The simplest piece of equipment necessary to check that a crystal is working on its correct overtone is

    (a) a voltmeter
    (b) an ammeter
    (c) an absorption wavemeter
    (d) a dip oscillator.

40. For best accuracy a digital frequency meter should be based on

(a) an R-C timebase
(b) an L-C timebase
(c) a crystal timebase
(d) a television timebase.

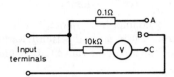

Fig Q8.10

41. In Fig Q8.10, which connection should be made so that the circuit acts as a voltmeter?

(a) A to B.
(b) A to C.
(c) B to C.
(d) A to B to C.

42. To obtain full-scale deflection, how much current will be taken by a 20kΩ/V meter?

(a) 50μA.
(b) 100μA.
(c) 200μA.
(d) 500μA.

43. A digital frequency meter can be used to measure

(a) harmonic content accurately
(b) sideband content
(c) frequency deviation
(d) frequency accurately.

44. An RTTY signal requires a bandwidth of ±3kHz. A frequency counter with an accuracy of 1 part per million is used to check the frequency readout of a 145MHz transmitter. How close can the signal be transmitted to the upper band edge in order to ensure that the transmission is within the licence conditions?

(a) 1.55kHz.
(b) 2.855kHz.
(c) 3.145kHz.
(d) 4.45kHz.

Fig Q8.11

45. Refer to Fig Q8.11. If 1A causes full-scale deflection, what is the current I?

(a) 0.9A.
(b) 0.99A.
(c) 0.999A.
(d) 1.1A.

46. Refer to Fig Q8.11. If the resistance of the meter is 500Ω, the value of the shunt must be

(a) 0.05Ω
(b) 0.5Ω
(c) 5Ω
(d) 50Ω.

47. If water gets into a correctly matched antenna feeder, the VSWR will

(a) tend to reduce
(b) go below 11
(c) stay constant
(d) tend to rise.

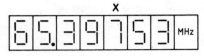

Fig Q8.12

48. Fig Q8.12 shows the output of a digital frequency counter. What does the digit at X give?

(a) Hertz.
(b) Tens of hertz.
(c) Hundreds of hertz.
(d) Thousands of hertz.

49. An ammeter in series with a 10kΩ resistor shows 5mA. The power dissipated by the resistor is

(a) 0.025W
(b) 0.25W
(c) 2.5W
(d) 25W.

50. A tuned circuit is being examined with a dip oscillator. To prevent altering the resonant frequency, the coupling between the two should be

(a) very tight
(b) resistive
(c) fairly loose
(d) the maximum possible.

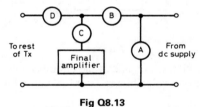

Fig Q8.13

51. In Fig Q8.13 which combination of meters should be used to measure DC input power to a final amplifier?

(a) Voltmeter at A, ammeter at B.
(b) Voltmeter at A, ammeter at C.
(c) Voltmeter at C, ammeter at A.
(d) Voltmeter at C, ammeter at D.

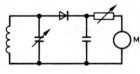

Fig Q8.14

52. Fig Q8.14 shows

(a) a dip meter
(b) an absorption wavemeter
(c) a heterodyne wavemeter
(d) an oscillator.

53. A dummy load for use at VHF should be made from

(a) wire-wound resistors

(b) carbon resistors

(c) ceramic capacitors

(d) electric fire heating elements.

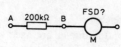

Fig Q8.15

54. For full-scale deflection on the meter in Fig Q8.15, with 10V across AB, the current should be

(a) 10µA

(b) 50µA

(c) 100µA

(d) 200µA.

55. Which one of the following CANNOT be used to check for harmonics?

(a) A heterodyne wavemeter.

(b) An absorption wavemeter.

(c) A digital frequency counter.

(d) A spectrum analyser.

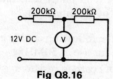

Fig Q8.16

56. In Fig Q8.16, a meter with a sensitivity of 20kΩ/V is set to the 10V range. What value of voltage will be shown?

(a) 0V.

(b) 4V.

(c) 6V.

(d) 8V.

57. The typical accuracy of an absorption wavemeter might be

(a) 0.001%

(b) 0.05%

(c) 1.0%

(d) 5%.

58. Which one of the following instruments can be used to indicate the matching between a transmitter and a feeder cable?

(a) Multimeter with resistance scale.

(b) Reflectometer.

(c) DC resistance bridge.

(d) Transformer.

59. Which one of the following is most suitable to determine the resonant frequency of a trap to be used for a trap dipole?

(a) A frequency meter.

(b) A dip meter.

(c) An SWR bridge.

(d) An absorption wavemeter.

60. A dummy load is made from twelve 600Ω wire-wound resistors in parallel. This is suitable for

(a) radio frequencies up to 30MHz

(b) audio frequencies up to 15kHz

(c) VHF use

(d) UHF use.

61. As well as crystal-controlled counters, receivers can be checked against

(a) the 50Hz mains

(b) an L-C oscillator

(c) WWV

(d) an R-C oscillator.

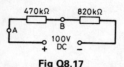

Fig Q8.17

62. Refer to Fig Q8.17. Which one of the following is most suitable to measure the voltage between A and B accurately?

(a) Moving-coil meter of 2kΩ/V.

(b) Moving-coil meter of 10kΩ/V.

(c) Moving-iron meter.

(d) Digital voltmeter.

63. A digital frequency counter has a tolerance of 1 in 100,000 and is used to measure a 144MHz transmission. Which one of the following has the most suitable number of decimal places for the given accuracy?

(a) 144.375MHz.

(b) 144.3752MHz.

(c) 144.37522MHz.

(d) 144.375221MHz.

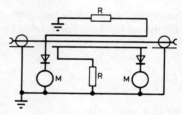

Fig Q8.18

64. The circuit in Fig Q8.18 shows a simple

(a) reflectometer

(b) oscilloscope

(c) absolute power meter

(d) absorption wavemeter.

65. An oscilloscope can be used to measure

(a) approximate amplitude

(b) harmonic content accurately

(c) distortion accurately

(d) frequency to 0.001% accuracy.

66. An ammeter reads 2A when placed in series with a 50Ω dummy load. The power in the load is

(a) 25W

(b) 100W

(c) 200W

(d) 250W.

67. A 12.5V DC power supply is connected to an amplifier. When the RF output from the amplifier is 90W the ammeter on the power supply reads 16A. The efficiency of the amplifier is

(a) 45%
(b) 55%
(c) 100%
(d) 222%.

68. The RF output of a transmitter is 100W into a matched transmission line. At the antenna end of the line the power is only 50W but still at 1:1 VSWR. Therefore the line attenuation is
(a) −6dB
(b) 0dB
(c) 3dB
(d) 10dB

69. Which one of the instruments below can measure the exact frequency of a harmonic in a complex waveform?
(a) A heterodyne wavemeter.
(b) A digital frequency counter.
(c) An absorption wavemeter.
(d) An oscilloscope.

70. Resolution of an instrument is
(a) the smallest division to which a reading can be made
(b) how close the instrument is to the true reading
(c) the same as the accuracy of the instrument
(d) the same as the full-scale reading of the instrument.

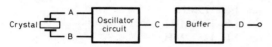

Fig Q8.19

71. When measuring frequency in the equipment shown in Fig Q8.19, the probe should preferably be placed at
(a) A
(b) B
(c) C
(d) D.

72. A moving-coil meter relies on
(a) the interaction of a magnetic and an electric field
(b) the interaction of two permanent magnetic fields
(c) only one magnetic field
(d) the interaction of a permanent magnetic and an electromagnetic field.

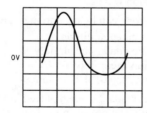

Fig Q8.20

73. A CRO connected to the output of an AF amplifier gives a trace as shown in Fig Q8.20. If the input to the amplifier is a pure sine wave the distortion introduced is
(a) none
(b) second harmonic
(c) third harmonic
(d) fourth harmonic.

74. An accuracy of one part in a million is equivalent to
(a) 0.1%
(b) 0.01%
(c) 0.001%
(d) 0.0001%.

75. A voltmeter and ammeter are used to measure the DC power to a circuit. The voltmeter reads 10V and the ammeter 1A. If both read low by 5%, the true power taken is
(a) 9.025W
(b) 10W
(c) 10.5W
(d) 11.025W.

76. The action of the so-called dip oscillator depends on
(a) the extraction of energy from the tuned circuit under test
(b) the extraction of energy from the dip oscillator by the circuit under test
(c) radiation from a nearby transmitter
(d) the tuned circuit under test changing the oscillator frequency of the dip meter.

77. Which one of the following could be used when making a dummy load for use at 50MHz?
(a) 10 off 500Ω carbon resistors
(b) 1 off 50Ω wire-wound resistor
(c) 10 off 500Ω wire-wound resistors
(d) 30 turns of heating element wound on a brass former.

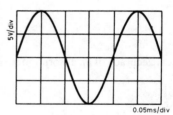

Fig Q8.21

78. The diagram shown in Fig Q8.21 represents a trace on an oscilloscope. What is the frequency of the displayed waveform?
(a) 1kHz.
(b) 5kHz.
(c) 10kHz.
(d) 100kHz.

79. In the diagram shown in Fig Q8.21, what is the peak-to-peak value of the waveform?
(a) 1V.
(b) 2V.
(c) 10V.
(d) 20V.

80. A dummy load for use at VHF should be made from
(a) wire-wound resistors
(b) carbon resistors
(c) metal oxide resistors
(d) electric-fire heating elements.

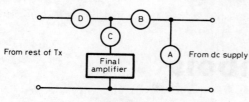

Fig Q8.22

81. To measure DC input power to a final amplifier, various meters are used. In the circuit shown in Fig Q8.22, three of the meters are ammeters. They are
    (a) A, B and C
    (b) B, C and D
    (c) A, C and D
    (d) A, B and D.

82. The action of the so-called 'dip oscillator' depends on
    (a) extraction of energy from the tuned circuit on test
    (b) extraction of energy from the dip oscillator by circuit under test
    (c) radiation from a nearby transmitter
    (d) the tuned circuit on test changing the dip oscillator frequency.

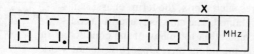

Fig Q8.23

83. The diagram in Fig Q8.23 represents the output of a digital frequency counter. What does the digit at X signify?
    (a) Hertz.
    (b) Tens of hertz.
    (c) Hundreds of hertz.
    (d) Thousands of hertz.

84. Which of the following would be used to examine the shape of a waveform?
    (a) An oscilloscope.
    (b) An absorption wavemeter.
    (c) A digital frequency counter.
    (d) A dip meter.

85. Which one of the following instruments would be used to indicate AF distortion?
    (a) An absorption wavemeter.
    (b) An oscilloscope.
    (c) A moving-coil multimeter.
    (d) A digital frequency counter.

86. While making a test with an SWR meter on a transmitter with an output impedance of 50Ω, a dummy load having a value of 150Ω is inadvertently connected. The indicated SWR will be
    (a) 1:1
    (b) 2:1
    (c) 3:1
    (d) 4:1.

87. Which one of the instruments below has the highest accuracy?
    (a) A heterodyne wavemeter.
    (b) A digital voltmeter.
    (c) An analogue electronic voltmeter.
    (d) An oscilloscope.

88. A good dummy load may have a tapping at about 10Ω from the earthy end. This enables
    (a) the band of operation to be changed
    (b) the efficiency of the load to be improved
    (c) the SWR bridge to be set to 'zero'
    (d) a calibrated meter to indicate power output.

89. The typical accuracy of a dip oscillator is in the region of
    (a) 0.001%
    (b) 0.05%
    (c) 1.0%
    (d) 10%.

Check your answers against the key in Appendix 4.

1 Radio circuit symbols

SCHEMATIC or circuit diagrams are theoretical pictures used to show how the various components of an electronic circuit are connected together. The following information is intended to help those who have little idea of such diagrams.

Most of the diagrams will be self-explanatory and only the more unusual details will be discussed. Straight lines represent the conductors which connect individual components together. In practice these may be wires (usually insulated) or strips of copper on a printed circuit board.

To illustrate some of the features described, a slightly modified diagram from Chapter 3 (Fig 3.44) is used (Fig A1.1).

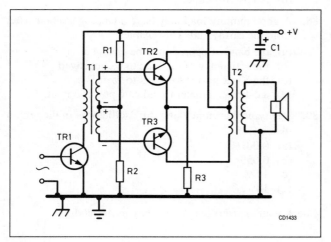

Fig A1.1

If two lines representing conductors meet, a dot is placed at the junction indicating that the conductors are connected together. If two lines are shown crossing but with no dot at the junction, the conductors are not connected. In some diagrams non-connecting lines may be shown by means of breaks or as a bridge as shown in Figs A1.2(a) and A1.2(b).

In order to avoid any confusion, lines that cross should NEVER be shown connected but should be shown offset as indicated in Fig A1.3.

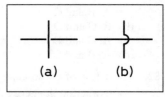

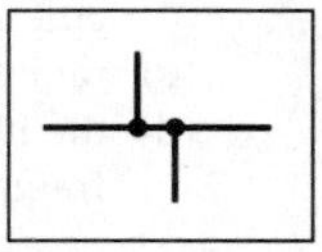

Fig A1.2

Fig A1.3

In the early days of electronics the circuits were built up on an aluminium or steel inverted box which was called the *chassis* and, although modern practice no longer requires such a box, the term 'chassis' has been retained. The chassis is used as a common connection for many of the conductors in circuits including any supporting metal work which will normally (but not always) connected to earth and is indicated by the symbol shown in Fig A1.4.

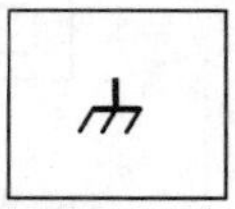

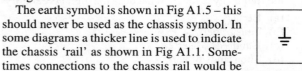

Fig A1.4

The earth symbol is shown in Fig A1.5 – this should never be used as the chassis symbol. In some diagrams a thicker line is used to indicate the chassis 'rail' as shown in Fig A1.1. Sometimes connections to the chassis rail would be long and would unnecessarily complicate the diagram – in this case the connection to chassis is shown by the use of the chassis symbol as is the case with C1 in Fig A1.1. In large circuit diagrams there may be many such 'short cuts' and it is important mentally to connect these points to the chassis rail.

Fig A1.5

The standard for symbols is being updated almost continually and therefore it is important to know some of the 'outdated' diagrams. In spite of the changes there should be little difficulty in following a diagram which was drawn 50 years ago. The old symbols are different but still recognisable.

All the circuit symbols you will need for the examination are given on the following page.

RADIO CIRCUIT SYMBOLS

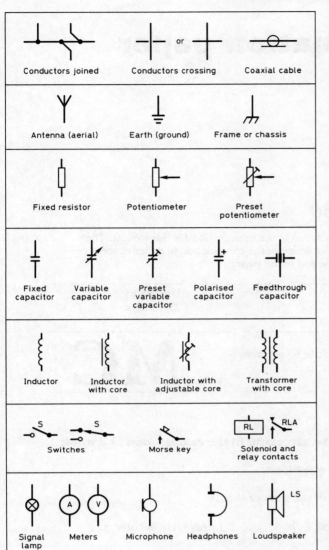

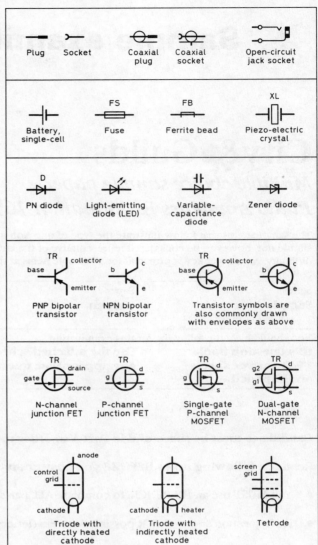

2 Sample examination paper

City&Guilds

Multiple choice sample paper
Radio Amateurs Examination 7650

The sample items that follow illustrate the type of question included in the examination for this subject. They should not, however, be considered representative of the entire scope of the examination in either content or difficulty. An answer key is provided for all sample items at the end of the paper.

Series	Paper	Duration
Sample	**Written**	**2¼ hours**

You should have the following for this examination
this question book   **Use the attached schedule to answer**
TWO answer sheets   **any appropriate questions**
an HB pencil

MC

Candidates must be successful in Part A in order to be successful in the examination as a whole.

Read the following notes BEFORE you answer any questions.

- You MUST use an HB PENCIL to complete ALL parts of the answer sheets.

- Each question shows FOUR possible answers (lettered 'a', 'b', 'c', and 'd'), only ONE is correct.

  Decide which one is correct and mark your answer on the ANSWER SHEETS with your HB pencil.

  For example if you decide 'c' is correct, mark your answer like this

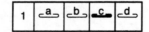

If you want to change your answer, cancel your first choice by filling in the lower half of the box like this

Then mark the answer which you have now decided is correct.

- Any calculations or rough work can be done in this question book.

- Attempt all questions; if you find a question difficult, leave it and return to it later.

This sample paper contains 80 questions; answer them using the 'boxes' numbered 1 to 25 and 26 to 80 on <u>separate</u> answer sheets.

Part A
Licensing Conditions and Operating Procedures

1   ONE of the qualifications required for an Amateur Radio Licence (A) is that the applicant must

   a   be over 16 years of age
   b   have paid the fees for the Radio Amateurs Examination
   c   have passed the Morse Test
   d   have applied to take the Morse Test.

2   The holder of an Amateur Radio Licence may transmit telephony to

   a   relay the signals of another station in order to increase the range
   b   transmit news provided it is of amateur radio interest
   c   give traffic information to amateur stations in general when operating the station from a vehicle on a motorway
   d   exchange messages when requested by the police during an emergency exercise.

3   The Station established and used by the holder of an Amateur Radio Licence MUST be equipped for reception on

   a   the frequency bands listed in the Schedule to the Licence
   b   the same frequencies and with the same classes of emission in use for transmission
   c   frequencies used in disaster relief operations by the Red Cross, St John Ambulance Brigade and Police Force
   d   at least one band in the frequency range 3 MHz to 300 MHz.

4   A CEPT Class 2 licence corresponds to the UK

   a   Amateur Radio Licence (A)
   b   Amateur Radio Licence (B)
   c   Amateur Radio (Novice) Licence (A)
   d   Amateur Radio (Novice) Licence (B).

5   Certain amateur h.f. bands may be used for communication in times of

   a   breakdown of the international public correspondence services
   b   international disaster communications
   c   propagation difficulties with the maritime mobile service
   d   propagation difficulties with the aeronautical service.

6   If a licence is held on behalf of a club, greetings messages may be sent by non-licensed persons provided that

   a   they are over 14 years of age
   b   they are members of the club
   c   each greetings message does not exceed two minutes
   d   greetings messages are exchanged only with stations in non-CEPT countries.

7   An English Licence holder, G2XYZ, is operating from a hotel room in Scotland. Which ONE of the following call signs must the station use?

   a   G2XYZ/P.
   b   GM2XYZ/P.
   c   GW2XYZ/M.
   d   GW2XYZ.

8   Which ONE of the following is classified as J3E emission?

   a   One sideband with a reduced carrier.
   b   Two sidebands with a vestigial carrier.
   c   One sideband with a full carrier.
   d   One sideband with a suppressed carrier.

9   The period of validity of an amateur transmitting licence is

   a   six months
   b   one year
   c   five years
   d   ten years.

10   The Amateur Radio Licence (A) permits the Licensee to

   a   use the Station for business, advertisement or propaganda purposes
   b   send or receive news or messages on behalf of, or for the benefit or information of, any social, political, religious or commercial organisation
   c   use copyright material in messages transmitted by the Station
   d   record messages addressed to the Licensee by any licensed amateur with whom he is in direct communication.

11 In order to ensure that no undue or harmful interference is being caused to any wireless telegraphy the Amateur Radio Licence (A) requires that

a   the apparatus comprised in the Station shall be monitored during operation on telegraphy to ensure the key clicks are not present

b   adequate protection against overmodulation shall be incorporated in the transmitter

c   tests shall be carried out from time to time

d   harmonic suppression devices shall be incorporated in the power amplifier stage of the transmitter.

12 The operator of an amateur station is normally permitted to transmit

a   messages or visual images on behalf of a third party

b   messages of a technical nature relating to the Station

c   music or other form of entertainment

d   news on behalf of a political organisation.

13 The essential requirement for a Log Book is that it must

a   have no fewer than 20 pages

b   be obtained from the RSGB

c   be loose-leaf

d   not be loose-leaf.

14 The times shown in the Log must be given in

a   CET (Central European Time)

b   BST (British Summer Time)

c   EST (Eastern Standard Time)

d   UTC (Coordinated Universal Time).

15 Radiation of harmonics and other spurious emissions shall be suppressed to a level that causes no undue or harmful interference with

a   any other amateur radio transmission

b   any other wireless telegraphy

c   any local electronic apparatus

d   TV transmissions only.

16 The conditions of the Amateur Radio Licence (A) as regards frequency control and measurement and non interference, require that the Station shall have

a   a satisfactory method of ensuring that the emitted frequency is as stable and as free from unwanted emissions as the state of technical development permits

b   equipment capable of continuously monitoring that the sending apparatus is operating with emissions within the authorised frequency bands

c   apparatus so designed and used that harmonics are attenuated to at least 40 dB below the fundamental frequency output

d   frequency measuring equipment capable of measuring frequency to an accuracy of ±0.05%.

17 Which ONE of the following frequencies is outside an authorised amateur band?

a   51.69 MHz.

b   70.57 MHz.

c   144.35 MHz.

d   435.55 MHz.

18 Which is the lowest frequency amateur band that has secondary status?

a   1.810 – 1.830 MHz.

b   3.500 – 3.800 MHz.

c   10.100 – 10.150 MHz.

d   51.00 – 52.00 MHz.

19 When making a call in Morse, the call sign of the calling station should be sent at the speed

a   at which the sender is prepared to receive a reply

b   of 20 words per minute

c   at which the sender is prepared to receive a reply but not more than 25 words per minute

d   of 15 words per minute.

20 Which ONE of the following is NOT acceptable for a Log?

a   Magnetic tape.

b   Disc.

c   Book.

d   Sheets of paper.

21 Repeaters are mainly

a   for contacting overseas countries

b   for extending the range of mobile stations

c   to stop fading

d   to indicate radio conditions.

22 The main purpose of Q codes is to

a save time on telephony
b save time on telegraphy
c use in the station log
d use on contact confirmation cards.

23 Observance by amateur radio stations of the h.f. band plan recommended by the International Amateur Radio Union (IARU)

a assists in ensuring the best possible use of the frequency bands available to amateurs
b is required by member countries of the International Telecommunication Union
c is recommended by the Radiocommunications Agency
d is only intended to assist in long distance h.f. contests.

24 The recommended phonetic spelling for the word SQUELCH is

a Sierra Quebec Uniform Echo Lima Cuba How
b Sugar Queenie United Easy Love Cuba Havana
c Sierra Quebec Uniform Echo Lima Charlie Hotel
d Sugar Queenie Uncle Easy Love Charlie Hotel.

25 When working on the equipment in an amateur radio station, the operator should

a be isolated from earth by a rubber mat or other insulation
b maintain a good earth connection to his or her body
c maintain a headphone watch to ensure that no interference is being caused to other stations
d use a wandering earth lead held firmly in the hand.

Part B
Principles and Practice

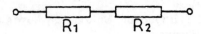

FIG. 1414

26 In Fig. 1414, the resistors R_1 and R_2 are coded 200 Ω and 150 Ω respectively at ±10%. The maximum effective resistance could be

    a   350 Ω
    b   385 Ω
    c   390 Ω
    d   420 Ω.

27 A transmitter has an output power of 50 W. This is equivalent to

    a   0 dBW
    b   7 dBW
    c   17 dBW
    d   20 dBW.

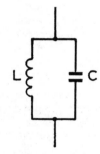

FIG. 2179

28 Refer to Fig. 2179. At resonance the

    a   impedance of the circuit is low
    b   reactance of C equals the reactance of L
    c   capacitance of C equals the inductance of L
    d   capacitance of C is much greater than the inductance of L.

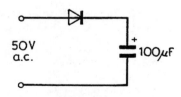

FIG. 0277

29 In Fig. 0277 the peak inverse voltage across the rectifier will be approximately

    a   141 V
    b   100 V
    c   70.7 V
    d   35.4 V.

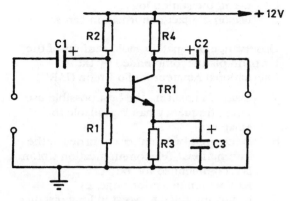

FIG. 0150

30 In Fig. 0150, if C1 = 2.2 μF, C2 = 6.8 μF and C3 = 47 μF, the circuit would function as

    a   an audio amplifier
    b   a selective r.f. amplifier in a receiver
    c   a frequency multiplier in a transmitter
    d   a mixer in a superheterodyne receiver.

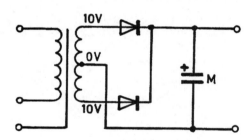

FIG. 1850

31 Fig. 1850 shows part of the circuit of a power supply unit. What type of capacitor is shown at M?

    a   Electrolytic.
    b   Non-polarised.
    c   Paper.
    d   Tantalum.

32 In a receiver, the r.f. amplifier stage

    a   operates at the intermediate frequency
    b   increases radiation from the local oscillator
    c   decreases the selectivity of the receiver
    d   increases the signal to noise ratio.

33 A receiver is tuned to 7050 kHz. Image frequency interference occurs due to a strong signal on 10 250 kHz. The intermediate frequency of the receiver is

    a   12.5 kHz.
    b   150 kHz.
    c   1.6 MHz.
    d   3.2 MHz.

34 Which ONE of the following enables a multi-mode receiver to receive s.s.b?

a Carrier insertion oscillator.
b Heterodyne oscillator.
c Local oscillator.
d R.F. oscillator.

35 To which stage in a receiver is a.g.c. normally applied?

a Beat frequency oscillator.
b Carrier insertion oscillator.
c Intermediate frequency amplifier.
d Mixer.

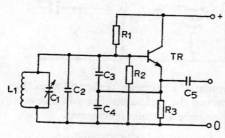

FIG. 1791

36 Fig. 1791 shows a Colpitts oscillator. The function of C_5 is to

a block d.c. and allow the r.f. signal to pass
b act as an emitter by-pass capacitor
c provide decoupling
d smooth the output.

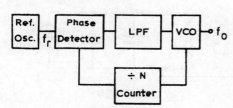

FIG. 1805

37 Fig. 1805 shows the block diagram of a phase locked loop oscillator as used in a frequency synthesiser. f_r is the reference frequency and f_o the output frequency. For a dividing factor of N the output frequency is equal to

a f_r
b $\dfrac{f_r}{N}$
c $f_r \times N$
d $\dfrac{N}{f_r}$.

38 The heater supply to a valve power amplifier stage of a transmitter

a can be decreased in order to increase the power output
b should always be a d.c. voltage
c may be derived from the r.f. power output of the stage
d should be by-passed to earth with capacitors.

39 The function of a dummy load is to

a measure the direct current to a transmitter
b check transmitter output without radiating
c load up the power supply to the receiver
d reduce the radio frequency to the antenna.

40 If the variable frequency oscillator of a transmitter is fed from an unregulated power supply, one of the most noticeable effects would be

a self oscillation of the power amplifier stage
b an unstable carrier frequency
c excessive harmonic radiation
d excessive mains borne interference.

41 Key clicks producing long range interference are caused by

a a steep rise and decay of carrier amplitude
b sparking at the key contacts
c keying the power amplifier
d shift of oscillator frequency when keying.

42 Parasitic oscillations are caused by

a r.f. being induced in the mains supply to the transmitter and being fed back to domestic radio, television or audio equipment connected to the same supply
b self-oscillation of a stage of a transmitter due to the high total amplification between the oscillator and the power amplifier stage
c fluctuations of the power supply to the oscillator stage of a transmitter resulting in oscillation on two frequencies
d the inductance and capacitance of the wiring to the connections of an amplifier stage resulting in self-oscillation.

43 Increasing the deviation level of a frequency modulated transmitter will

a improve the speech quality
b increase the speech compression ratio
c overcome f.m. noise
d widen the r.f. bandwidth.

44 Frequency chirp in a c.w. transmitter is often due to

a fast rise time of the carrier envelope
b poor power supply regulation
c radio frequency feedback
d thermal expansion.

45 Which ONE of the following types of spurious signals which can be heard on a receiver, arises in the receiver itself?

a   Parasitic oscillation.
b   Chirps.
c   Harmonic radiation.
d   Second channel interference.

46 Audio bandwidth of a transmitter should be limited in order to

a   reduce transmitter power requirement
b   prevent over modulation
c   prevent wasteful use of the r.f. spectrum
d   improve readability.

47 The SUREST way of detecting the presence of parasitic oscillations is by

a   tuning through the bands on a television receiver
b   using a general coverage receiver
c   tuning a receiver through the amateur band to which the transmitter is tuned
d   tuning an f.m. receiver through the 80–100 MHz band.

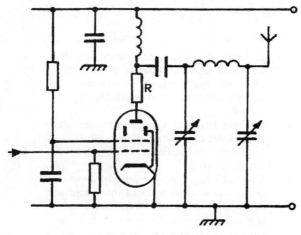

FIG. 2158

48 Refer to Fig. 2158. The purpose of the resistor R is to

a   reduce the voltage to the anode
b   prevent parasitic oscillations
c   act as an anode load
d   increase the efficiency of the stage.

49 Splatter from a single sideband transmitter can be reduced by

a   better screening
b   fitting ferrite beads in the power amplifier
c   reducing the microphone gain
d   using a low pass filter.

50 On keying, it is found that severe local r.f. interference is being caused by sparking at the key contacts. Which ONE of the following circuits would be most effective in curing this condition?

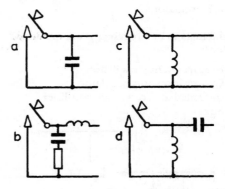

51 The use of a properly designed π-section between the final amplifier and a low impedance antenna feeder will

a   prevent parasitic oscillators
b   improve the power output of the stage
c   considerably reduce harmonic content in the output
d   avoid the need to neutralise the amplifier.

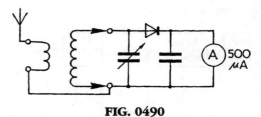

FIG. 0490

52 The circuit shown in Fig. 0490 may be used to

a   check on which band a transmitter is operating
b   ensure that an amateur transmission is free from frequency instability
c   check that the transmission is not unnecessarily broad
d   measure accurately the percentage depth of modulation.

53 A convenient means of measuring the frequency of a received signal would be to use a

a   beat frequency oscillator
b   receiver whose calibration can be checked against a crystal calibrator
c   digital frequency meter coupled to the receiver antenna
d   local transmitter to zero beat the incoming signal.

54 If one of the items of equipment in an amateur station is a computer, which part of the computer is likely to cause narrow band interference?

a   Visual display unit.
b   Computer power supply.
c   Internal clock oscillator.
d   Disk drive.

55 Which ONE of the following devices causes narrow band interference?

a   A thermostat.
b   A thyristor.
c   A radio transmitter.
d   A commutator motor.

56 When transmitting on 433.000 MHz a neighbour complains of interference on a television receiver. What is the most likely cause of the interference?

a   3rd harmonic radiation.
b   5th harmonic radiation.
c   Saturation of r.f. into the TV antenna.
d   2nd sub-harmonic radiation.

57 An amateur receiver tuned to 144.55 MHz receives aircraft signals transmitted on 123.15 MHz. The receiver intermediate frequency is 10.7 MHz. The reason for the interference is

a   image (second channel) reception
b   reception of the second harmonic
c   the different modulation modes used by aircraft and radio amateurs
d   the failure to fit a low-pass filter to the receiver antenna input.

58 Mains borne interference is most likely to be caused by

a   a highly inductive mains supply
b   an antenna which is too close to an overhead power supply cable
c   harmonics generated in the power amplifier stage
d   the choice of power amplifier transistors.

59 Which ONE of the following modes of emission is least likely to cause audio breakthrough to nearby audio equipment?

a   Single sideband reduced carrier.
b   Double sideband full carrier.
c   Continuous wave telegraphy.
d   Narrow band frequency modulation.

60 S.S.B. transmissions are picked up on a nearby domestic audio system when it is being used to play CDs and tapes. A likely cure would be to fit a

a   ferrite ring in the speaker leads as close to the audio unit as possible
b   ferrite ring in the speaker leads as close to the speakers as possible
c   ferrite ring in the centre of the speaker leads
d   low value by-pass capacitor directly across the speaker terminal.

61 Which ONE of the following circuits could be used as a filter to suppress mains borne interference?

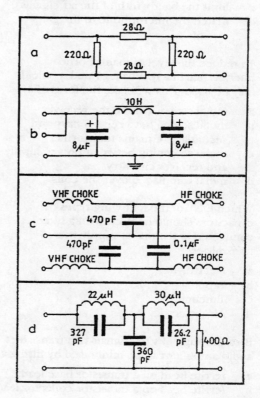

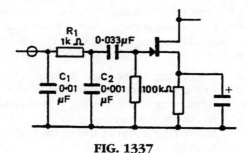

FIG. 1337

62 The purpose of the components R_1, C_1 and C_2, in the microphone amplifier shown in Fig. 1337, is to

a reduce the level of mains hum
b filter out any r.f. feedback
c limit the bandwidth of the a.f. signals
d match the microphone to the gate circuit.

63 To reduce the level of mains borne interference in a receiver, a Faraday shield may be used. This will take the form of a

a metal screen around the receiver
b metal screen between primary and secondary of mains transformer
c metal screening between power supply and receiver circuitry
d metal can placed over the coils.

64 Which ONE of the following types of capacitors should be used with a filter connected in the mains supply to a transmitter?

a Electrolytic.
b Paper.
c Tantalum.
d Air dielectric.

65 Breakthrough of v.h.f. signals to a transistor audio amplifier can be minimised by fitting a

a ferrite bead on a transistor base lead
b ferrite bead on a transistor collector lead
c 1 nF capacitor between a transistor base and collector
d 1 nF capacitor between a transistor emitter and collector.

66 A neighbour has complained and logged the interference to a television receiver. What should be the first action taken by the amateur to establish the likely cause?

a Compare the amateur log with that of the neighbour for any likely correlation.
b Ask the DTI RIS to investigate.
c Reduce transmitter power on all amateur bands.
d Fit filters to neighbour's equipment.

67 When installing an amateur radio transceiver in a car the 12 V supply should be

a connected directly to the battery with fuses in positive and negative wires
b plugged into the cigar lighter socket on the dashboard
c connected to the interior light circuit
d supplied from the engine management system.

68 In high frequency sky wave transmission, the length of the skip distance is dependent on the

a frequency of operation of the transmitter
b type of ground over which the wave is passing
c plane of polarisation of the radio wave
d effective radiated power.

69 On which ONE of the following amateur bands can long distance communication take place as a result of sporadic E propagation?

a 1.8 MHz.
b 18.1 MHz.
c 144 MHz.
d 1.2 GHz.

70 The effect of a sudden burst of ultra-violet radiation from the sun on high frequency propagation can be

a a fade out
b fading
c selective fading
d unusually strong signals.

71 A radio wave of frequency 50 MHz has a wavelength of

a 5 m
b 6 m
c 50 m
d 60 m.

72 Radials are normally used with a

a quad antenna
b trap dipole antenna
c vertical antenna
d Yagi antenna.

FIG. 1742

73 Fig. 1742 shows a half-wave dipole antenna. The feeder used to connect the antenna to the transmitter coupling unit should be

a 75 Ω coaxial
b 75 Ω balanced twin
c 300 Ω ribbon
d 600 Ω open wire line.

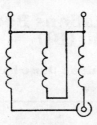

FIG. 1870

74   Fig. 1870 represents

    a   an antenna tuning unit
    b   a balun
    c   a π network
    d   a trap.

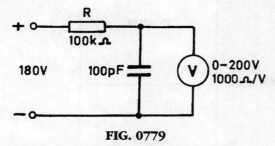

FIG. 0779

75   Refer to Fig. 0779. The voltmeter has a resistance of 200 kΩ. Its reading will be

    a   60 V
    b   90 V
    c   120 V
    d   180 V.

76   The advantage of expressing radio frequency power in dBW is that

    a   it is required by the Radiocommunications Agency (RA)
    b   it is mandatory by international agreement
    c   it allows the gains and losses in the transmitter and antenna system to be added and subtracted
    d   power measuring devices are always calibrated in dBW.

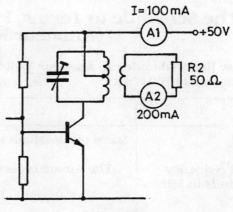

FIG. 0122

77   Refer to Fig. 0122. The overall efficiency of the stage is

    a   80%
    b   50%
    c   40%
    d   20%.

78   To ensure that a transmitter operates within the amateur frequency bands, its emission can most readily be checked with

    a   an oscilloscope
    b   a digital frequency counter
    c   reception of standard frequency signals
    d   a multi-meter with r.f. probe.

79   A standing wave meter is used to check the

    a   stability of the oscillator
    b   efficiency of a transmitter
    c   resonant frequency of an antenna
    d   matching of the transmitter to the antenna system.

80   The main component in a dummy load is

    a   a non-inductive resistor
    b   a wire wound resistor
    c   an inductor
    d   a variable capacitor.

NOW GO BACK AND CHECK YOUR WORK BEFORE HANDING IN <u>BOTH</u> ANSWER SHEETS TO THE INVIGILATOR

● IMPORTANT —

Have you filled in your candidate number in PENCIL in the appropriate boxes on the answer sheets?

Have you filled in your answers in PENCIL in the appropriate boxes on the answer sheets?

Note: answers to this sample paper are in given in Appendix 4.

The Schedule to Terms, Provisions and Limitations Booklet BR68 (Amateur Radio Licence (A) and (B))

Those licensed under an Amateur Radio Licence (B) may not transmit on those bands between 1.810 and 29.700 MHz.

1	2	3	4	5
	Status of allocations in the United Kingdom to:			
Frequency bands in MHz	The Amateur Service	The Amateur Satellite Service	Maximum Power level (in dB relative to one watt) PEP	Permitted Types of Transmissio
1.810-1.830	Primary. Available on the basis of non-interference to other services (outside the United Kingdom)	(Not allocated)	26 dBW	Morse Telephony RTTY Data Facsimile SSTV
1.830-1.850	Primary			
1.850-2.000	Available on the basis of non-interference to other services (inside or outside the United Kingdom)		15 dBW	
3.500-3.800	Primary. Shared with other services			
7.000-7.100	Primary	Primary		
10.100-10.150	Secondary	(Not allocated)		
14.000-14.250	Primary	Primary	26 dBW	
14.250-14.350		(Not allocated)		
18.068-18.168		Primary		
21.000-21.450		Primary		
24.890-24.990				
28.000-29.700				

1	2	3	4	5
	Status of allocations in the United Kingdom to:			
Frequency bands in MHz	The Amateur Service	The Amateur Satellite Service	Maximum Power level (in dB relative to one watt) PEP	Permitted Types of Transmission
50.00-51.00	Primary. Available on the basis of non-interference to other services outside the United Kingdom	(Not allocated)	26 dBW	Morse Telephony RTTY Data Facsimile SSTV
51.00-52.00	Secondary. Available on the basis of non-interference to other services inside or outside the United Kingdom		20 dBW	
70.00-70.50	Secondary. Available on the basis of non-interference to other services outside the United Kingdom		22 dBW	
144.0-146.0	Primary	Primary	26 dBW	
430.0-431.0	Secondary	(Not allocated)	16 dBW erp	Morse Telephony RTTY Data Facsimile SSTV FSTV
431.0-432.0	Secondary. Not available for use; within a 100 km radius of Charing Cross, London (51°30'30"N, 00°07'24"W)			
432.0-435.0	Secondary		26 dBW	
435.0-438.0		Secondary		
438.0-440.0		(Not allocated)		

1	2	3	4	5
	Status of allocations in the United Kingdom to:			
Frequency bands in MHz	The Amateur Service	The Amateur Satellite Service	Maximum Power level (in dB relative to one watt) PEP	Permitted Types of Transmission
1240-1260	Secondary	(Not allocated)		
1260-1270		Secondary. Earth to Space only		
1270-1325		(Not allocated)		
2310-2400				
2400-2450	Secondary. Users must accept interference from ISM users	Secondary. Users must accept interference from ISM users		
3400-3475	Secondary	(Not allocated)		
5650-5670		Secondary. Earth to Space only		
5670-5680				Morse Telephony RTTY Data Facsimile SSTV FSTV
5755-5765		(Not allocated)		
5820-5830	Secondary. Users must accept interference from ISM users			
5830-5850		Secondary. Users must accept interference from ISM users. Space to Earth only	26 dBW	
10000-10150	Secondary	(Not allocated)		
10300-10500		Secondary		
24000-24050	Primary. Users must accept interference from ISM users	Primary. Users must accept interference from ISM users		
24050-24150	Secondary. May only be used with the written consent of the Secretary of State. Users must accept interference from ISM users	(Not allocated)		
24150-24250	Secondary			
47000-47200	Primary	Primary		
75500-76000				
142000-144000				
248000-250000				

ISM (Industrial, Scientific and Medical)

3 Mathematics for the RAE

THE basic mathematical processes are: addition, subtraction, multiplication and division. As long as only 'whole numbers' are involved, such sums are simple.

However, very often we must consider quantities which are less than one (unity), for instance $1/2$, $1/3$, $1/8$ etc. Here $1/8$ means one-eighth part of the whole and so on.

$1/8$ is called a vulgar fraction and has two parts: the '8' (the bottom part) is called the *denominator* and the '1' (the top part) is called the *numerator*. The magnitude of a fraction is not changed if we multiply top and bottom by the same number, ie:

$$\frac{3}{16} \times \frac{2}{2}$$

As the '2' is on the top and bottom we can *cancel* it thus:

$$\frac{3}{16} \times \frac{\cancel{2}}{\cancel{2}} = \frac{3}{16}$$

A fraction should always be cancelled down to its simplest form:

$$\frac{12}{16} = \frac{3 \times \cancel{4}}{4 \times \cancel{4}} = \frac{3}{4}$$

Here top and bottom have been divided by 4.

Fractions can be:

(a) Multiplied

$$\frac{1}{2} \times \frac{3}{4} \times \frac{5}{8} = \frac{1 \times 3 \times 5}{2 \times 4 \times 8} = \frac{15}{64}$$

(b) Divided

$$\frac{3}{4} \div \frac{1}{2}$$

Dividing by $1/2$ is the same as multiplying by $2/1$, ie:

$$\frac{3}{4} \div \frac{1}{2} = \frac{3}{4} \times \frac{2}{1} = \frac{6}{4} = 1\frac{2}{4} = 1\frac{1}{2}$$

In other words, dividing by a fraction is the same as multiplying by that fraction 'upside down'. Another example is:

$$\frac{7}{8} \div \frac{3}{4} = \frac{7}{8} \times \frac{4}{3} = \frac{7}{2} \times \frac{1}{3} = \frac{7}{6} = 1\frac{1}{6}$$

Here we divide top and bottom by 4.

(c) Added

$$\frac{2}{3} + \frac{2}{3} = \frac{2 + 2}{3} = \frac{4}{3}$$

If the denominators are different, we must make them the same, ie *bring them to a common denominator* and normally the lowest common denominator is used. For example:

$$\frac{2}{3} + \frac{5}{6} = \frac{4}{6} + \frac{5}{6} = \frac{9}{6} = \frac{3}{2} = 1\frac{1}{2}$$

Here we have multiplied top and bottom of $2/3$ by 2, making it $4/6$. Now we can add it to $5/6$, making $9/6$, which is then simplified to $1\frac{1}{2}$. Another example is:

$$\frac{1}{3} + \frac{5}{6} + \frac{7}{8} = \frac{8}{24} + \frac{20}{24} + \frac{21}{24} = \frac{8 + 20 + 21}{24}$$

$$= \frac{49}{24} = 2\frac{1}{24}$$

It is generally preferable to divide out fractions greater than one, as we have done above.

(d) Subtracted

Exactly the same rules apply to the subtraction of fractions.

We can also express parts of the whole as *decimals* or $1/10$ parts, written as 0.1, 0.2, 0.3 etc (these are equivalent to $1/10$, $2/10$, $3/10$ etc). The 'full stop' is known as the *decimal point*. In a decimal, the 'nought' before the decimal point should never be omitted.

The denominator of any fraction can be divided into the numerator to give a decimal, eg:

$$1/8 = 0.125$$
$$3/8 = 0.375$$

The more common fractions and decimal equivalents should be memorised, eg:

$1/10 = 0.1$	$1/8 = 0.125$
$2/10 = 1/5 = 0.2$	$2/8 = 1/4 = 0.25$
$3/10 = 0.3$	$3/8 = 0.375$
$4/10 = 2/5 = 0.4$ etc	$4/8 = 1/2 = 0.5$ etc

Numbers can be expressed to *so many significant figures* or *so many decimal places*.

12345 is a number to five significant figures
1234 is a number to four significant figures
123 is a number to three significant figures

Note also that 1.23 is a number to three significant figures (the decimal point is ignored).

12.345	is a number to three decimal places
12.34	is a number to two decimal places
12.3	is a number to one decimal place

Decimals may be *rounded off*; that means:

3.3267	to three decimal places is 3.327
	(the 7 is greater than 5, so 6 becomes 7)
3.327	to two decimal places is 3.33
	(the 7 is greater than 5, so 2 becomes 3)
3.33	to one decimal place is 3.3
	(the 3 is less than 5, so is ignored)

Powers of numbers

When, say, two of a certain number are multiplied together, that number is said to be *raised to the power 2*. Thus $2 \times 2 = 4$ means that 2 raised to the power 2 is 4. In this case we would say 2 *squared* is 4 and write it as $2^2 = 4$. The 'little 2 up in the air' is called an *index*. Similarly, $2 \times 2 \times 2 = 8$ means that 2 raised to the power 3 is 8, or 2 *cubed* is 8, written as $2^3 = 8$. Also $2 \times 2 \times 2 \times 2 = 16$. Here we have no alternative but to say 2 *to the power 4* = 16, or $2^4 = 16$.

The use of indices or the index notation is a very convenient way of expressing the large numbers which often occur in radio calculations, eg:

$$100 = 10 \times 10 = 10^2$$

$$10,000 = 10 \times 10 \times 10 \times 10 = 10^4$$

$$1,000,000 = 10 \times 10 \times 10 \times 10 \times 10 \times 10 = 10^6$$

Note that $10 = 10^1$ (the index here is taken for granted). Similarly:

$$\frac{1}{100} = \frac{1}{10 \times 10} = \frac{1}{10^2} \quad \text{(written as } 10^{-2})$$

$$\frac{1}{10,000} = \frac{1}{10 \times 10 \times 10 \times 10} = \frac{1}{10^4} \quad \text{(written as } 10^{-4})$$

$$\frac{1}{1,000,000} = \frac{1}{10 \times 10 \times 10 \times 10 \times 10 \times 10} = \frac{1}{10^6}$$

$$\text{(written as } 10^{-6})$$

Numbers expressed in the index notation are multiplied and divided by adding and subtracting respectively the indices.

$$10^2 \times 10^3 = 10^{2+3} = 10^5$$

$$10^4 \div 10^2 = 10^{4-2} = 10^2$$

$$\frac{10^5 \times 10^7 \times 10^{-2}}{10^3 \times 10 \times 10^{-3}} = \frac{10^{5+7-2}}{10^{3+1-3}} = \frac{10^{10}}{10^1} = 10^9$$

We can do this as long as the *base* is the same in each case. In the above examples, the base is 10. For example, $10^2 \times 2^2 = 100 \times 4 = 400$, which is neither 10^4 or 2^4!

Roots of numbers

The *root* of a number is that number which, when multiplied by itself so many times, equals the given number; the *square root* of 4 is 2, ie $2 \times 2 = 4$, and this is written $^2\sqrt{4} = 2$.

Similarly the *cube root* of 8 is 2, ie $2 \times 2 \times 2 = 8$, and $^4\sqrt{16} = 2$ etc. Note the little 2 in the sign for square root is normally omitted so that $\sqrt{}$ signifies the square root.

Numbers like 4, 16 and 25 are called *perfect squares* because their square roots are whole numbers, for example:

$$\sqrt{49} = 7 \qquad \sqrt{121} = 11 \quad \text{etc}$$

The following should be memorised as they can often be very useful.

$$\sqrt{2} = 1.41 \quad \sqrt{3} = 1.73 \quad \sqrt{5} = 2.24 \quad \sqrt{10} = 3.162$$

For example:

$$\sqrt{200} = \sqrt{2 \times 100} = \sqrt{2} \times \sqrt{100} = 1.41 \times 10 = 14.1$$

$$\sqrt{192} = \sqrt{3 \times 64} = \sqrt{3} \times \sqrt{64} = 1.73 \times 8 = 13.8$$

It is always worth checking to see if the number left after dividing by 2, 3 or 5 is a perfect square.

The square root of a number expressed in the index notation is found by dividing the index by 2, thus $\sqrt{10^6} = 10^3$ and $\sqrt{10^{12}} = 10^6$, and so on. Similarly $\sqrt{10^{-6}} = 10^{-3}$ etc. Should the index be an odd number, it must be made into an even number as follows.

$$\sqrt{10^{-15}} = \sqrt{10 \times 10^{-16}}$$

$$= \sqrt{10} \times 10^{-8}$$

$$= 3.162 \times 10^{-8}$$

The constant term 'π' occurs in many calculations; π has great significance in mathematics and is the ratio of the circumference to the diameter of a circle. π can be taken to be 3.14 or $^{22}/_7$. The error in taking π^2 as 10 is less than 1.5 per cent and is acceptable here. $1/\pi$ can be taken as 0.32 and $1/2\pi$ as 0.16 (the error in calling this $^1/_6$ is really somewhat too high). $1/2\pi = 0.16$ is particularly useful.

Typical calculations

We will now apply these rules to the solution of problems likely to be met in radio work as a lead-in to some typical numerical multiple-choice questions.

The most important aspect is to remember that the units met with are most likely to be the practical ones such as microfarads, picofarads, milliamperes, millihenrys etc. These must be converted into the basic units of farads, amperes and henrys before substituting them into the appropriate formula. This involves multiplying or dividing by 1000 (10^3), 1,000,000 (10^6) and so on. Therefore the important thing is to get the decimal point in the right place or the right number of noughts in the answer. The commonest conversions are as follows:

There are 10^6 microfarads in 1 farad
hence $8\mu F = 8 \times 10^{-6}$ farads

There are 10^{12} picofarads in one farad
hence $22pF = 22 \times 10^{-12}$ farads

(The use of *nano* or 10^{-9} is now fairly common; there are 10^9 nanofarads in 1 farad so $1nF = 1 \times 10^{-9}$ farads, but such a capacitor may well be marked '1000pF'.) Similarly other conversions are:

$50\mu H = 50 \times 10^{-6}$ henrys
$3mH = 3 \times 10^{-3}$ henrys
$45mA = 45 \times 10^{-3}$ amperes
$10\mu A = 10 \times 10^{-6}$ amperes

Problem 1

What value of resistor is required to drop 150V when the current flowing through it is 25mA?

This involves Ohm's Law which can be expressed in symbols in three ways:

$$R = \frac{V}{I} \qquad I = \frac{V}{R} \qquad V = I \times R$$

where R is in ohms, V in volts and I in amperes. Clearly the first, $R = V/I$, is needed. First of all, we must express the current (25mA) in amperes.

$$25mA = \frac{25}{1000} \text{ A} \quad (\text{or } 25 \times 10^{-3}A)$$

Substituting values for V and I:

$$R = \frac{V}{I}$$

$$= 150 \times \frac{1000}{25}$$

(we are dividing by $^{25}/_{1000}$, ie multiplying by $^{1000}/_{25}$)

hence $\quad R = \dfrac{150 \times 1000}{25}$

25 'goes into' 150 six times, so:

$$R = 6 \times 1000$$

$$= 6000\Omega$$

Problem 2

What power is being dissipated by the resistor in Problem 1?

The power dissipated in the resistor is power (watts) = V (volts) $\times I$ (amps). By Ohm's Law, power can be expressed in two other forms.

$$W = \frac{V^2}{R} \quad \text{and} \quad W = I^2R$$

Because we know V, I and R we can use any of the above relationships, say:

$$W = \frac{V^2}{R}$$

$$W = \frac{150 \times 150}{6000}$$

Two 'noughts' on the top and bottom can be cancelled, leaving:

$$= \frac{15 \times 15}{60}$$

Cancelling 15 into 60 leaves:

$$= \frac{15}{4} = 3\,\tfrac{3}{4}\ \text{W}$$

The other two forms will, of course, give the same answer – try them!

Problem 3

Resistors of 12Ω, 15Ω and 20Ω are in parallel. What is the effective resistance?

$$\frac{1}{R} = \frac{1}{R_1} + \frac{1}{R_2} + \frac{1}{R_3}$$

$$= \frac{1}{12} + \frac{1}{15} + \frac{1}{20}$$

60 is the lowest common denominator of 12, 15 and 20, so:

$$\frac{1}{R} = \frac{5}{60} + \frac{4}{60} + \frac{3}{60}$$

$$= \frac{5 + 4 + 3}{60}$$

$$= \frac{12}{60}$$

This is a simple equation in R, and the first step in solving it is to *cross-multiply*. It may be shown that the denominator of one side multiplied by the numerator of the other side is equal to the numerator of the first side multiplied by the denominator of the other side, thus:

$$R \times 12 = 1 \times 60$$

Hence, dividing each side by 12:

$$R = \frac{60}{12}$$

$$R = 5\Omega$$

Problem 4

Capacitors of 330pF, 680pF and 0.001µF are in parallel. What is the effective capacitance?

The first step is to express all the capacitors in the *same* units which can be either picofarads or microfarads.

$$0.001\mu F = 0.001 \times 1{,}000{,}000 pF$$

(there are 1,000,000pF in 1µF) and hence:

$$0.001\mu F = 1000 pF$$

Effective capacitance is therefore:

$$330pF + 680pF + 1000pF = 2010pF$$

Problem 5

What is the reactance of a 30H smoothing choke at a frequency of 100Hz?

$$X_L = 2\pi f L$$
$$X_L = 2\pi \times 100 \times 30 \ \text{ohms}$$
$$= 6000\pi \ \text{ohms}$$

We take π to be 3.14 so:

$$X_L = 6000 \times 3.14$$
$$= 18{,}840\Omega$$

Problem 6

What is the reactance of a 100pF capacitor at a frequency of 20MHz?

$$X_C = \frac{1}{2\pi f C}$$

(X_C is in ohms when f is in hertz, L in henrys and C in farads.)

$$f = 20\text{MHz} = 20 \times 10^6\text{Hz} = 2 \times 10^7\text{Hz}$$
$$C = 100\text{pF} = 100 \times 10^{-12}\text{F} = 10^{-10}\text{F}$$

(It is much more convenient here to use the index notation.) Hence:

$$X_C = \frac{1}{2\pi \times 2 \times 10^7 \times 10^{-10}} \text{ ohms}$$

$$= \frac{1}{2\pi} \times \frac{1}{2 \times 10^{-3}}$$

Note that we have kept $^1/_{2\pi}$ intact because $^1/_{2\pi} = 0.16$, thus

$$X_C = 0.16 \times \frac{1}{2 \times 10^{-3}}$$

$$= \frac{0.16 \times 1000}{2}$$

$$= 80\Omega$$

Problem 7

What is the impedance (Z) of an inductance which has a resistance (R) of 4Ω and a reactance (X) of 3Ω?

$$\begin{aligned} Z &= \sqrt{(R^2 + X^2)} \\ &= \sqrt{(4^2 + 3^2)} \\ &= \sqrt{16 + 9} \\ &= \sqrt{25} \\ &= 5\Omega \end{aligned}$$

Problem 8

At what frequency do a capacitor of 100pF and an inductance of 100μF resonate?

At resonance:

$$2\pi f L = \frac{1}{2\pi f C}$$

hence $\quad f = \dfrac{1}{2\pi\sqrt{LC}}$

(f is in hertz, L is in henrys, C is in farads.)

$$100\mu\text{H} = 100 \times 10^{-6}\text{H}$$
$$100\text{pF} = 100 \times 10^{-12}\text{F}$$

$$f = \frac{1}{2\pi\sqrt{LC}}$$

$$= \frac{1}{2\pi\sqrt{100 \times 10^{-6} \times 100 \times 10^{-12}}}$$

$$= \frac{1}{2\pi\sqrt{10^2 \times 10^{-6} \times 10^2 \times 10^{-12}}}$$

$$= \frac{1}{2\pi\sqrt{10^{-14}}}$$

$$= \frac{1}{2\pi \times 10^{-7}}$$

$$= \frac{1}{2\pi} \times 10^7$$

$$= 0.16 \times 10^7$$

$$= 1.6 \times 10^6\text{Hz}$$

$$= 1.6\text{MHz}$$

Numerical multiple-choice questions in the RAE

The numerical multiple-choice questions set in the RAE involve quite simple calculations in order to decide which of the four answers given is correct. The questions are likely to be similar to the problems just worked through and generally the answer comes out without the need for any aid to calculation. As in solving the previous problems, the most important thing is to 'get the units right'. The way to solve these questions should be clear from the following worked examples.

Question 1

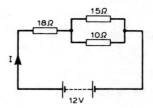

The current I is
(a) 0.25A
(b) 0.43A
(c) 0.5A
(d) 0.67A.

The effective resistance of the two resistors in parallel is:

$$R_{\text{eff}} = \frac{15 \times 10}{25} = 6\Omega$$

The effective resistance of the whole circuit is:

$$R_{\text{eff}} = 18 + 6 = 24\Omega$$
$$I = \frac{12}{24} = 0.5\text{A}$$

Answer (c) is therefore correct.

Question 2

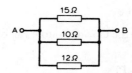

The effective resistance between points A and B is
(a) 4Ω
(b) 6Ω
(c) 17Ω
(d) 37Ω.

The effective resistance must have a value less than the value of the smallest resistor, so neither answers (c) nor (d) are correct. Take the top two resistors and apply the formula:

$$R_{eff} = \frac{R_1 \times R_2}{R_1 + R_2} = \frac{15 \times 10}{25} = 6\Omega$$

Again apply the formula to include the 12Ω resistor.

$$R_{eff} = \frac{6 \times 12}{18} = \frac{72}{18} = 4\Omega$$

Answer (a) is therefore correct.

Question 3

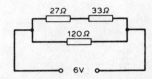

The current flowing through the 27Ω resistor has a value of
(a) 27mA.
(b) 33mA.
(c) 60mA.
(d) 100mA.

The current flowing through the 120Ω resistor has no bearing on the answer. The current through the 27Ω resistor will be the same as that through the 33Ω resistor. The current through the two resistors in series is:

$$= \frac{6}{27 + 33} = \frac{6}{60} = \frac{1}{10} \text{ A}$$

The correct answer is (d).

Question 4
The voltage across the 33Ω resistor in the previous question is
(a) 0.6V.
(b) 1.2V.
(c) 3.3V.
(d) 4.5V.

$$V = I \times R = \frac{1}{10} \times 33 = 3.3V$$

The correct answer is (c).

Question 5
A λ/2 dipole has a length of just under 7.5m. It will be resonant at a frequency of approximately
(a) 15MHz.
(b) 20MHz.
(c) 25MHz.
(d) 30MHz.

$$\lambda = 15m \quad f = \frac{c}{\lambda} = \frac{300 \times 10^6}{15} = 20 \times 10^6 Hz = 20MHz$$

Therefore (b) is the correct answer.

Question 6
An oscilloscope shows the peak-to-peak voltage of a sine wave to be 100V. The RMS value is

(a) 27.28V.
(b) 35.35V.
(c) 50V.
(d) 70.7V.

$$V_{rms} = V_{peak} \times 0.707$$
$$= 50 \times 0.707 = 35.35V$$

The correct answer is (b).

Question 7
The internal capacitance between the base and emitter of a transistor is 2pF. The reactance at a frequency of 500MHz will be approximately
(a) 16Ω.
(b) 160Ω.
(c) 1.6kΩ.
(d) 16kΩ.

$$X_C = \frac{1}{\omega C} = \frac{1}{2\pi \times 500 \times 10^6 \times 2 \times 10^{-12}} = \frac{1}{2\pi \times 10^{-3}}$$
$$= 0.16 \times 10^3 = 160\Omega$$

The correct answer is (b).

Question 8
A loudspeaker speech coil has a resistance of 3Ω. If the voltage across it is 3V, then the power in the speech coil is
(a) 1W
(b) 3W.
(c) 6W.
(d) 9W.

$$P = \frac{V^2}{R} \text{ watts} \qquad P = \frac{3^2}{3} = 3W$$

Answer (b) is therefore correct.

Question 9
A smoothing choke has an inductance of 0.2H. Its reactance at a frequency of 100Hz is approximately
(a) 40Ω.
(b) 125Ω.
(c) 400Ω.
(d) 1250Ω.

$X_L = 2\pi f L = 2\pi \times 100 \times 0.2 = 40\pi$ or about 125Ω. Hence (b) is the correct answer.

Question 10
A coil has a reactance of 1000Ω and a resistance of 10Ω. Its approximate impedance is
(a) 990Ω.
(b) 1000Ω.
(c) 1100Ω.
(d) 10kΩ.

$$Z = \sqrt{R^2 + X_L^2} = \sqrt{100 + 10^6} = \sqrt{1,000,100} \approx 1000\Omega$$

The effect of the resistance is so small that it can be neglected, so (b) is the correct answer.

Question 11

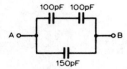

The capacitance measured between terminals A and B will be
(a) 37.5pF.
(b) 50pF.
(c) 200pF.
(d) 350pF.

The capacitance must be greater than 150pF. The two 100pF capacitors in series have an effective capacitance of 50pF. Therefore the answer is 150 + 50 = 200pF, ie answer (c).

Question 12

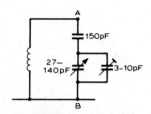

When the variable capacitor and the trimmer capacitor of a local oscillator tuned circuit are adjusted to their maximum values, the effective capacitance between points A and B will be
(a) 50pF.
(b) 75pF.
(c) 200pF.
(d) 300pF.

The tuning and trimmer capacitors will have an effective capacitance of 140 + 10 = 150pF. Therefore the capacitance between A and B will be 75pF, and (b) is the correct answer.

Question 13

When the variable capacitor and the trimmer are set at minimum, the effective capacitance between points A and B will be
(a) 25pF.
(b) 75pF.
(c) 120pF.
(d) 180pF.

Using the same calculations, (a) is the correct answer.

Question 14

The peak-to-peak value of a sine wave having an RMS value of 14.1V is approximately
(a) 20V.
(b) 28.2V.
(c) 40V.
(d) 56.4V.

The peak value of the positive half-cycle is $14.1 \times \sqrt{2} = 20$V. Therefore the peak-to-peak voltage = $2 \times 20 = 40$V.

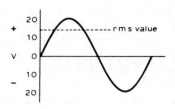

(c) is the correct answer.

Question 15

A quarter-wave antenna is resonant at 10MHz. Its approximate length will be
(a) 7.5m.
(b) 15m.
(c) 20m.
(d) 30m.

$$\lambda = \frac{C}{f} = \frac{300 \times 10^6}{10 \times 10^6} = 30\text{m}$$

$$\lambda/4 = 7.5\text{m}$$

(a) is the correct answer.

Summary of formulae

Ohm's Law $\quad R = \dfrac{V}{I} \quad V = IR \quad I = \dfrac{V}{R}$

Power $\quad W = V \times I \quad W = I^2R \quad W = \dfrac{V^2}{R}$

Reactance $\quad X_L = 2\pi fL$

$$X_C = \frac{1}{2\pi fC}$$

Resonance $\quad f_r = \dfrac{1}{2\pi\sqrt{LC}}$

Resistors (series) $\quad R = R_1 + R_2 + R_3 + \ldots$

Resistors (parallel) $\quad \dfrac{1}{R} = \dfrac{1}{R_1} + \dfrac{1}{R_2} + \dfrac{1}{R_3} + \ldots$

Capacitors (series) $\quad \dfrac{1}{C} = \dfrac{1}{C_1} + \dfrac{1}{C_2} + \dfrac{1}{C_3} + \ldots$

Capacitors (parallel) $\quad C = C_1 + C_2 + C_3 + \ldots$

Wavelength (metres) $\quad \lambda = \dfrac{300}{f(\text{MHz})}$

For a sine wave, RMS value = $0.707 \times$ peak value

$$Q = \frac{\omega L}{R}$$

$$R_D = \frac{L}{CR} \quad \text{and since} \quad Q = \frac{\omega L}{R}$$

$$R_D = \frac{Q}{\omega C}$$

$$e = \frac{7.02 \sqrt{\text{ERP}}}{d}$$

where e is the field strength (peak) in volts per metre, d is the distance in metres from the transmitter, and the ERP is measured in watts.

4 Answers to the practice questions

Chapter 1 – Licensing conditions

1	b	23	c	45	b	67	b
2	d	24	c	46	b	68	d
3	d	25	d	47	a	69	a
4	c	26	d	48	b	70	c
5	d	27	a	49	a	71	b
6	d	28	c	50	c	72	d
7	a	29	c	51	a	73	c
8	b	30	d	52	a	74	b
9	c	31	d	53	d	75	a
10	a	32	a	54	a	76	a
11	c	33	c	55	b	77	b
12	d	34	d	56	c	78	b
13	c	35	b	57	b	79	b
14	b	36	a	58	d	80	a
15	c	37	d	59	d	81	b
16	a	38	d	60	d	82	d
17	a	39	c	61	b	83	b
18	d	40	a	62	c	84	d
19	a	41	d	63	a	85	a
20	b	42	d	64	b	86	b
21	d	43	d	65	d	87	d
22	b	44	c	66	d		

Chapter 3 – Electronic principles and practice

1	a	26	c	51	b	76	c
2	c	27	b	52	d	77	c
3	b	28	d	53	c	78	b
4	b	29	b	54	b	79	b
5	d	30	d	55	c	80	d
6	b	31	c	56	b	81	a
7	b	32	a	57	c	82	b
8	c	33	c	58	c	83	c
9	b	34	a	59	c	84	d
10	b	35	d	60	d	85	a
11	b	36	b	61	b	86	d
12	b	37	c	62	c	87	d
13	b	38	c	63	c	88	c
14	d	39	a	64	d	89	a
15	a	40	a	65	b	90	c
16	b	41	c	66	b	91	c
17	a	42	c	67	c	92	c
18	c	43	d	68	d	93	d
19	a	44	a	69	a	94	d
20	c	45	d	70	b	95	a
21	a	46	d	71	c	96	c
22	d	47	c	72	a	97	b
23	d	48	c	73	c	98	c
24	a	49	b	74	a	99	a
25	a	50	a	75	a	100	a

Chapter 2 – Operating procedures and practices

1	c	18	c	35	a	52	d
2	b	19	d	36	d	53	c
3	c	20	d	37	b	54	a
4	b	21	d	38	c	55	b
5	b	22	b	39	a	56	b
6	d	23	d	40	a	57	b
7	c	24	a	41	c	58	d
8	a	25	c	42	c	59	c
9	b	26	b	43	a	60	c
10	d	27	b	44	c	61	b
11	a	28	b	45	c	62	a
12	b	29	a	46	b	63	b
13	a	30	c	47	d	64	d
14	a	31	b	48	d	65	b
15	b	32	b	49	d	66	b
16	d	33	d	50	d	67	c
17	b	34	c	51	a	68	b

Chapter 4 – Receivers, transmitters and transceivers

1	d	23	c	45	a	67	b
2	a	24	d	46	a	68	c
3	c	25	d	47	a	69	a
4	d	26	d	48	a	70	a
5	b	27	c	49	b	71	a
6	c	28	b	50	b	72	b
7	a	29	c	51	d	73	a
8	c	30	b	52	c	74	c
9	c	31	d	53	b	75	b
10	d	32	d	54	c	76	c
11	b	33	a	55	c	77	b
12	d	34	a	56	a	78	a
13	a	35	d	57	a	79	b
14	a	36	a	58	a	80	b
15	d	37	b	59	d	81	a
16	b	38	c	60	a	82	b
17	d	39	d	61	c	83	a
18	b	40	c	62	b	84	d
19	d	41	a	63	d	85	c
20	c	42	b	64	b	86	a
21	b	43	a	65	a	87	d
22	a	44	d	66	d	88	b

Chapter 5 – Transmitter interference

1	b	28	a	55	c	82	d
2	c	29	c	56	a	83	d
3	d	30	b	57	b	84	c
4	b	31	a	58	c	85	c
5	a	32	d	59	c	86	a
6	d	33	b	60	d	87	a
7	b	34	b	61	b	88	d
8	a	35	a	62	a	89	a
9	d	36	c	63	a	90	b
10	a	37	d	64	c	91	b
11	b	38	a	65	c	92	c
12	a	39	b	66	d	93	d
13	c	40	b	67	b	94	c
14	c	41	c	68	c	95	c
15	b	42	b	69	b	96	d
16	a	43	d	70	a	97	b
17	b	44	b	71	c	98	a
18	a	45	c	72	b	99	c
19	c	46	b	73	c	100	b
20	c	47	b	74	a	101	b
21	c	48	a	75	d	102	c
22	c	49	a	76	a	103	d
23	b	50	b	77	c	104	d
24	d	51	a	78	a	105	b
25	d	52	b	79	b	106	b
26	c	53	c	80	c		
27	c	54	a	81	b		

Chapter 7 – Propagation and antennas

1	c	24	c	47	c	70	c
2	c	25	d	48	d	71	d
3	c	26	b	49	c	72	b
4	c	27	c	50	b	73	c
5	c	28	d	51	c	74	a
6	a	29	b	52	a	75	b
7	c	30	d	53	d	76	d
8	d	31	c	54	b	77	d
9	a	32	d	55	b	78	b
10	d	33	a	56	b	79	c
11	a	34	a	57	b	80	c
12	c	35	d	58	d	81	d
13	b	36	a	59	c	82	c
14	a	37	d	60	d	83	a
15	c	38	c	61	a	84	d
16	a	39	b	62	a	85	c
17	c	40	a	63	c	86	b
18	b	41	b	64	a	87	d
19	a	42	b	65	b	88	b
20	a	43	b	66	d	89	b
21	d	44	a	67	c	90	b
22	b	45	a	68	c	91	d
23	b	46	c	69	b		

Chapter 6 – Electromagnetic compatibility

1	c	21	a	41	b	61	a
2	d	22	c	42	c	62	a
3	a	23	d	43	b	63	a
4	b	24	b	44	c	64	c
5	c	25	d	45	c	65	b
6	b	26	c	46	c	66	a
7	c	27	c	47	d	67	b
8	c	28	c	48	b	68	d
9	d	29	c	49	a	69	b
10	b	30	c	50	d	70	b
11	a	31	c	51	b	71	a
12	a	32	a	52	d	72	c
13	c	33	c	53	a	73	a
14	c	34	d	54	d	74	b
15	c	35	c	55	a	75	c
16	c	36	a	56	a	76	d
17	b	37	b	57	b	77	b
18	d	38	c	58	b	78	c
19	a	39	a	59	d		
20	c	40	d	60	c		

Chapter 8 – Measurements

1	c	24	c	47	d	70	a
2	d	25	d	48	d	71	d
3	c	26	d	49	b	72	d
4	c	27	d	50	c	73	b
5	c	28	d	51	b	74	d
6	c	29	b	52	b	75	d
7	b	30	d	53	b	76	b
8	b	31	a	54	b	77	a
9	b	32	d	55	c	78	b
10	a	33	c	56	b	79	d
11	b	34	a	57	d	80	b
12	d	35	a	58	b	81	b
13	d	36	a	59	b	82	b
14	b	37	c	60	b	83	b
15	b	38	a	61	c	84	a
16	c	39	c	62	d	85	b
17	d	40	c	63	a	86	c
18	c	41	c	64	a	87	c
19	d	42	a	65	a	88	d
20	d	43	d	66	c	89	d
21	a	44	c	67	a		
22	a	45	c	68	c		
23	d	46	b	69	a		

Appendix 2 – Sample examination paper

1	c	11	c	21	b	31	a	41	a	51	c	61	c	71	b
2	d	12	b	22	b	32	d	42	d	52	a	62	c	72	c
3	b	13	d	23	a	33	c	43	d	53	b	63	b	73	b
4	b	14	d	24	c	34	a	44	b	54	c	64	b	74	b
5	b	15	b	25	a	35	c	45	d	55	c	65	a	75	c
6	c	16	a	26	b	36	a	46	c	56	c	66	a	76	c
7	b	17	b	27	c	37	c	47	b	57	a	67	a	77	c
8	d	18	c	28	b	38	d	48	b	58	b	68	a	78	b
9	b	19	a	29	a	39	b	49	c	59	d	69	c	79	d
10	d	20	d	30	a	40	b	50	b	60	a	70	a	80	a

Index